The Origins of Garden P

Camellia, from *Chinese Drawings*, collected by John Reeves (1832) (overleaf)

The Origins of Garden Plants

John Fisher

Constable · London

First published in Great Britain 1982
by Constable and Company Limited
10 Orange Street London WC2H 7EG

Revised edition 1989
Filmset in 12pt Monophoto Garamond by
Servis Filmsetting Limited, Manchester
Printed in Great Britain by
BAS Printers Ltd
Over Wallop, Hampshire

ISBN 0 09 469510 5

La Nature semble vouloir dérober aux yeux des hommes ses vrais attraits, auxquels ils sont trop peu sensibles et qu'ils défigurent quand ils sont à leur portée.

Elle fuit les lieux fréquentés. C'est au sommet des montagnes, au fond des forêts, dans les isles désertes qu'elle étale ses charmes les plus touchants.

Ceux qui l'aiment et ne peuvent l'aller chercher si loins sont réduits à lui faire violence, à la forcer en quelque sorte à venir habiter avec eux, et tout cela ne peut se faire sans un peu d'illusion.

Nature seems to wish to shield her real attractions from the eyes of those who have too little feeling for them and who disfigure them when they are within reach.

She shuns frequented places. It is on the tops of mountains, in the depths of forests and on desert islands that she displays her most telling charms.

Those who love her, but cannot travel so far to find her, are reduced to doing violence to her, to force her, in some degree, to come and live with them, and all this cannot be accomplished without an element of unreality.

from J.-J. Rousseau, *La Nouvelle Héloïse*

Contents

Illustrations

Colour

Black and white

Drawings marked EP are by E. Powell

Acknowledgements

When first I was invited to prepare a book on the origins of garden plants I knew I could look forward to a fascinating botanical excursion – one which would inspire reverence for the copious researches to which gardeners, botanists and historians had devoted themselves in the past. But I have been overwhelmed, too, by the kindness and good nature of the experts of today.

I am deeply indebted to the staff of the Royal Horticultural Society's Lindley Library, and to Mr P. Stageman the Librarian and to Dr Brent Elliott, the Assistant Librarian, for allowing me to look at a number of the priceless and irreplaceable treasures under their care (and for obtaining permission to use some of the drawings from the Reeves Collection). The colour plates of *Paphiopedalum victoria-regina*, *Primula littoniana* and *Allium ostrowskianum* are taken from volumes of *Curtis's Botanical Magazine* stored in the Lindley Library and I would like to thank the library for permission to reproduce these illustrations.

Many of the historical works listed in the Select Bibliography – including Robert Edmeades' plant catalogue of 1776, were provided by the London Library, whose staff, as ever, have been unfailingly helpful.

I am also beholden to the staff of the British Museum (Natural History) for permitting me to examine the original drawings by Sydney Parkinson of the plants seen during Captain Cook's round-the-world voyage in HMS *Endeavour*, and to Mr Allen Paterson of the Chelsea Physic Garden for allowing me to consult Philip Miller's famous *Gardener's Dictionary* of 1752. The Librarian of the Linnean Society was kind enough to produce Peter Collinson's *Commonplace Book* in which were recorded many of his introductions of American and other eighteenth-century plants, and further information on this devout Quaker came from the Library of the Society of Religious Friends. I have also received help from the Information Department of the Society of Jesus, Farm Street, London, in tracing the movements of early Jesuit botanists.

The Librarian of the Royal College of Physicians made it possible to identify the Doctor Mounsey who served at the Court of the Empress Catherine the Great and sent home plants when he could.

Mr L.P. Townsend, Assistant Librarian to the Royal Society, allowed me to see relevant volumes of their *Philosophical Transactions* and their copy of John Ray's *Historia Plantarum* and the Appendix thereto, and His Grace, the Duke of Beaufort arranged for me to be shown the 'Flower Book' with original paintings of the plants growing at Badminton in the first years of the eighteenth century.

My thanks go to the Curator of the Roman Palace, at Fishbourne, West Sussex, for guidance on the garden plants which might or might not have been cultivated there in Roman times; to Dr John Harvey whose knowledge of early nurserymen and their catalogues is unrivalled, and to Ms S.A. Robertson of the Academic Relations Section of Imperial Chemical Industries for arranging for me to see an article by Professor W.T. Stearn on the voyage of the *Endeavour* published in *Endeavour* magazine. I am also most grateful to the Late Mr Edward Green for the loan of books from his personal library.

I have found *The Garden*, the Journal of the Royal Horticultural Society, as useful in relation to newly introduced plants, as *Garden History*, the Journal of the Garden History Society, is in relation to earlier trends. Specialised plant societies have been generous with their material, and I found an article by F.H. Fisher (no relation) entitled 'The Alpine Garden Society: Pages from the Society's History' of particular value.

At the same time I feel I owe an apology to botanists of the past and to scholars of the present for not using capital letters at the beginning of the latin names of species where these refer to personalities, or proper nouns.

In my own case this does not imply a lack of deference towards famous botanists – Banks *et al.* after whom species were named, but rather a desire to maintain a distinction between Genera (spelt with initial capitals) and species (without capitals) and also to encourage descriptions rather than dedications in the future.

My thanks are also due to Miss Ann Hoffman for research and to Mrs Jane Conway-Gordon for exemplary typing of involved and technical copy.

Finally I am particularly grateful to Mr Patrick M. Synge for his kindness in looking over the typescript, making a number of very helpful suggestions, and weeding out some errors. Any that remain are those of the author.

SECOND EDITION

I must also express by deepest gratitude to Dr. John Harvey, president of the Garden History Society for his kindness in making a number of important corrections and providing the background to them.

Introduction

Unlimited pleasure has been granted to gardeners, great and small, by new plants introduced to them over the centuries. Fortunes have been gained and squandered – and lives lost – in efforts to procure new species from jungles, near-deserts and cliff-sides.

The story reflects the great movements of world history.

The fall of the Roman empire, for example, cut off the flow of new garden plants from the Mediterranean to Britain, and eventually raised doubts in Anglo-Saxon and Norman minds as to the very existence of the plants so lovingly described by the great classical writers of Greece and Rome.

For several centuries, flowering plants survived only behind high monastery walls, and were cultivated for their supposed medical virtues, rather than for beauty's sake.

It took the Moorish occupation of Spain, the Crusades, and the arrival of the Turks in Constantinople to inspire Europeans with a desire to grow in their own gardens, the plants which the invaders already possessed. Then, with the Renaissance, the study of botany reached the stage where species could be validly distinguished from one another and, in time, systematically named.

The invention of printing made it possible, for the first time, to circulate not only descriptions of plants, but direct reproductions of artists' original drawings in place of indifferent and unreliable hand-copies. From then on explorers knew in advance at least some of the plants that had already been found.

The colonisation, of 'Virginia' by the English, of Canada by the French in the seventeenth century, and of Australia and New Zealand in the eighteenth, offered plantsmen and amateurs alike new challenges. The nineteenth century saw swarms of army men, together with merchants, memsahibs and civil servants, some of them amateur botanists, travelling to India and the Far East. South Africa went British; China and Japan reluctantly admitted a few more foreign devils.

An early illustration of the Passion Flower, shown in John Parkinson's *Paradisi in Sole*, 1629

The first quarter of the century also witnessed the liberation of Mexico, Argentina and Chile – among other Latin-American states – from the Spanish control which had, for so long, obstructed explorers and botanists. Brazil, the home of so many orchids, was freed from Portuguese rule.

In Britain, within the framework of political, military, economic and climatic restraints, the style of the pleasure garden, and therefore the range of plants introduced to it, varied considerably with the fashion of the day, and some attention has therefore to be devoted here to the notions held by landowners and garden designers as to what constituted the ideal garden. At one time there was even a danger of the flower-bed dying out altogether.

Technical advances also influenced what plants were grown. The invention of the lawnmower encouraged not only the extension of the lawn but the island flower beds in the middle of it, just as improved glazing in the greenhouse meant longer life expectancy for lilies and other pot plants. Faster and more dependable transport increased the chances that plants gathered at such risk by explorers and collectors would survive the journey home across the equator. Experience taught nurserymen and others the safest way to grow seedlings from seed sent from overseas.

But there is almost too much material to choose from.

The number of species in general cultivation in Britain today (excluding hybrids, cultivated varieties – and vegetables) has been put at not less than three thousand (and by some experts at a very much larger figure). And at least five times as many species appear to have been introduced at one time or another, though often with no more than marginal success.

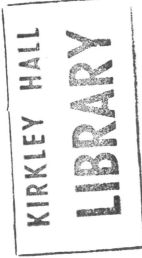

To refer to them all in an average size book would be to allot but a few words to each, and the task of describing them has been far more ably accomplished in the Royal Horticultural Society's *Dictionary of Gardening* which runs to four large volumes and a supplement. Here, therefore, we need to be selective, and to apologise to all those whose favourites have not found a place in these pages.

Even so, the problem of choosing which plants to write about and which to ignore is not so simple as it might at first appear. For what is a garden plant? How should we see that handsome rover *Impatiens glandulifera*, variously known as the Policeman's Helmet or Himalayan Balsam? The original seed came to England a century and a half ago from the East India Company's Botanic Garden in Calcutta; today there is scarcely any need for any to be grown by the garden pool because so many are to be seen wild along the fringes of country streams. One day, perhaps this species will share the fate of the Winter Heliotrope (*Petasites fragrans*) whose paint-brush flowers of pale mauve now bedeck an increasing number of hedgerows from as early as November. This plant was seen growing on Mount Pilat, 30 miles south of Lyon, and was brought here as a pot plant in 1806. When thrown out after flowering, it established itself first on the rubbish heap, then in the border. It is still as decorative as ever, but few gardening books mention it – except to say that it is hard to get rid of.

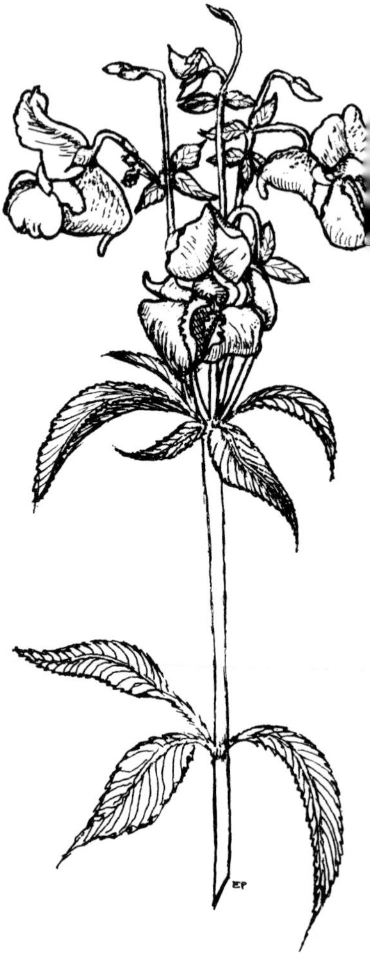

Himalayan Balsam (*Impatiens glandulifera*), a 19th-century importation from India

Again, tracing the origins of garden plants would be greatly simplified if we never had to set foot inside a greenhouse. But the greenhouse, like the balsam, cannot be ignored. Some plants which have to be grown inside it in exposed areas of the country will flourish outdoors in the milder climate of Cornwall or south-west Scotland. The hedgerows of fuchsias to be seen outside Cornish cottages are just one example. Many other plants spend the early part of the year under glass and appear later in the flower bed, and this practice of 'bedding out' has had a considerable influence on the character of the garden as a whole.

Even orchids, which appear seldom enough outdoors cannot be omitted, for some of the collectors we shall meet sent back orchids along with the other species they secured. And besides, the Royal Horticultural Society's Gardens at Wisley and the Royal Botanic Gardens at Kew each include an orchid house, and no one has suggested that the plants in it are illegal immigrants.

Most garden plants have had a sponsor – or sponsors; but which of them deserves the credit?

Is the collector the real originator; or the syndicate that pays his travelling expenses? Is it the expert with a lens who examines a specimen, certifies that it is new, and proposes an acceptable name for it? Is it the amateur who first gets the plant to flower – or seed – who is originator; or the nurseryman who makes it available to a wider public? And what about the explorer, or water-colour artist who first saw the plant and drew attention to it, although the season of the year or the individual's programme may have made it impossible to bring home seed or plant?

Some blurring occurs, too, over the date at which a plant can be said to have been successfully established in the garden, for while annuals reach maturity in a season, a tree may take many years to flower. More than a quarter of a century passed from the day when the Veitch nursery planted the seeds of *Cordia decandra*, a handsome hothouse shrub, until the appearance of the white flowers. Even a narcissus may take five years to flower from seed.

Apart from this, a plant may have been introduced in a certain year but may have failed to survive. The precious seed may have been left in its wrapping, unplanted; for nurserymen, before investing time and space, have to consider whether a plant is likely to be sufficiently attractive, fast growing and hardy to be worth cultivating at all. Or the specimen may have been a weakling taken in the first instance from an unsuitable locality or it may have flowered but not produced seed. Later, perhaps, another collector finds a healthier specimen growing in a more favourable habitat, or one that survives because more skill has been used in its cultivation. It is debatable which of the two dates should be seen as the more significant.

Only a broadly sketched outline of mainstream hybridisation and its limitations can be attempted here, while the origination of new mutation species with the help of colchicine, radiation or other kinds of genetic engineering will, for some time, remain a matter for the specialists.

Meanwhile it may seem strange that, in a land of gardeners such as ours, so few garden plants, whether species or hybrids, have been developed from those to be found growing wild. The explanation, however, is disappointingly simple. Britain, in comparison with other European countries, is poorly endowed with native species with show-garden potential, and has had to rely heavily on importations to remedy the deficiency.

Our first concern will be to discover why this should be so.

1 *How we lost the Alpine Poppy*

Even the experts hesitate to be precise. They cannot be sure of the circumstances in which the earth, from which all plants have originated, was itself formed. But scientists appear to have accepted a working hypothesis according to which the earth could be three to five thousand million years old.

Life on earth in its earliest stages existed on or under water, not necessarily very salt water, because the oceans have derived their salt from the continual flow of water off the land.

By the end of what geologists describe as the Cambrian period some recognisable forms of life were well established. By then, 530 million years ago, the animal kingdom included spiders and scorpions, oysters and octopuses, snails, shrimps, sponges, corals and jellyfish; but in the vegetable world there were only non-flowering plants such as seaweeds and similar primitives.

Fossil of a cycadophyte from France. These descendents of the great seed-ferns had fronds which spread out from the top of the trunk in a similar way to palm trees

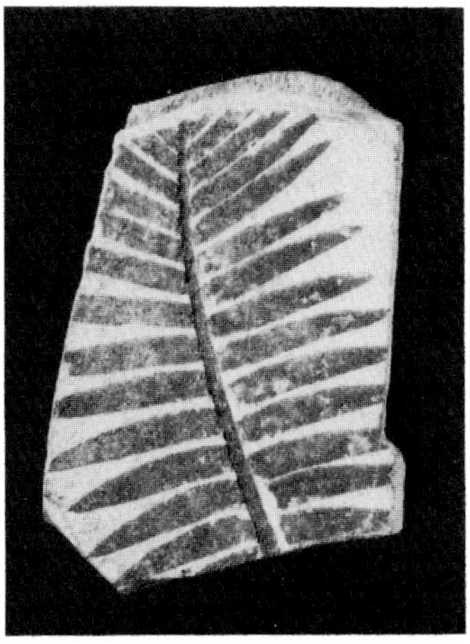

As yet there were no land plants. Mosses by the water's edge needed perpetual soaking if they were to survive. They lacked the essential structure of a land plant – roots to draw nourishment from the soil, a more or less rigid stem and a system of canals to bring water and nourishment to the leaves.

Two hundred million years later plants had come ashore. There were ferns with rigid stems soaring into the air, and anchoring roots which probed the ground beneath. The cycads (tall trees with a crown of leaves) and the cone-bearers, each representing a giant step forward in the life-history of plants, can be traced back nearly three hundred million years. By that time the world had passed through the warm Carboniferous period which began 345 million years ago when corals grew in Spitzbergen; during it our coal forests were laid down with giant horsetails and non-flowering scale-trees as a feature of the landscape.

At times Britain, except for parts of the Midlands and Wales and a peninsula linking Wales with Ireland, was awash. Scotland was uncovered, and was joined with Iceland to the north Atlantic continent.

One other change vital to the prospects for flowering plants occurred during the Carboniferous period. Insects appeared.

Then came the Permian, a drier, less oppressively hot period, which ran from 280 million years ago to 225 million years – the age of the early reptiles, which laid shelled eggs that could develop on dry land. The Triassic period, running from 225 million years ago to 195 million years ago was another dry one – and favoured the reptiles and other land-dwellers. The Jurassic period from 195 to 136 million years ago saw the first of the mammals, with Britain once more a piece of dry land – and, more sensational – the sudden unheralded appearance of flowering plants, with a structure totally distinct from what had gone before. As Darwin wrote to his friend Joseph Hooker in 1881, 'Nothing is more extraordinary in the history of the vegetable kingdom than the apparently very sudden and abrupt development of the higher plants'. To the botanist the most notable feature of flowering plants, as we know them in the garden, is not so much the petals, or the scent, as the fact that the seeds are developed in a closed capsule known as the carpel of which the bean pod is just one of many different examples.

With the seeds fully protected in this way the chances of survival were much greater than in the

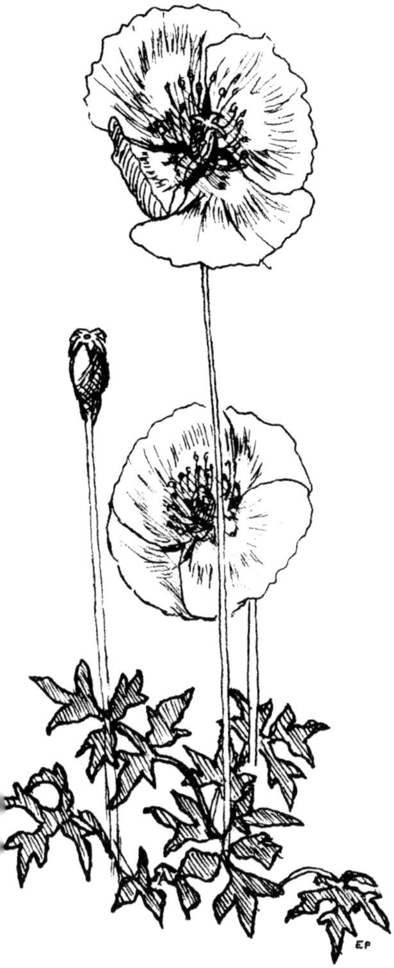

Alpine Poppy (*Papaver alpinum*), before the Ice Age began a million years ago, a native British wild flower

case of non-flowering or cone-bearing plants where the seeds were vulnerable to drought, fungi etc., and, though the first flowers were thought to have bloomed 160 million years ago, the number of their species, within 100 million years, are thought to have outnumbered by far those of the non-flowering, (though this view may have to be revised as we learn more about mosses, lichens and bacteria).

Biologists have so far failed to explain the sudden arrival of flowering plants – and there does not seem to have been any intermediate link between the non-flowering and the flowering species.

But the theory is that petals, like carpels arose from modified leaves; that nectar was originally unwanted sugar which the plant had to dispose of if its circulation canals were not to be clogged up, and was exuded – as it still is in some plants by glands attached to the leaf stalks.

The ensuing period, the Cretaceous, from 136 to 65 million years ago saw the waters once again partially closing over Britain, but the climate in the northern hemisphere remained mild, and magnolias, bread fruit and camphor trees flourished on the west coast of Greenland – 300 miles north of the Arctic Circle. It was then that the Iguanodon, an erect dinosaur walking with its head 15 feet above ground, roamed parts of Sussex feeding off the tree tops. During the next period, the Tertiary, which ended a mere two million years ago, the climate grew colder; nevertheless Britain, now partially uncovered again, still had an almost tropical climate. The vegetation of Sheppey, for instance, included ferns and palms of the kind one would expect to see today in southern India or Malaysia. There were crocodiles at Kew, hippos in the Thames Valley and Amazon-style lianas in the Isle of Wight.

Even at the end of the Tertiary period, by which time the climate had cooled still further there were about 500 species of flowering plants, including many of those we see wild today – buttercups, poppies and even the Water Soldier plant which floats to the surface of ponds and canals and thrusts its sword-shaped leaves into the air only at flowering time. There are fossil traces too, of water lilies and sedges, and insect-eating or to be more accurate insect-digesting plants related to the Common Sundew. There were evergreen flowering trees such as the *Ilex* (holly) as well as deciduous trees that shed their leaves – for example birch, alder and oak.

The Tertiary period which, as we have seen, ended only about two million years ago, was the curtain-raiser for the so-called Great Ice Age. There had been glacial periods before – at least one of them occurred more than 500 million years ago – but afterwards there had been a pause for nearly three hundred million years. Then in the relatively short space of less than a million years, there were at least seven major glaciations, each with interglacial (that is warmer) periods between. Once again there appears to be no certain explanation to account for the ice ages, though irregularities in the inclination of the earth's axis may have been one factor.

The glaciers of the Great Ice Age had probably been building up for several thousands of years before they began to creep forward. The ice came to Britain from three different bases – one wave from the Hudson Bay area of Canada, a second from Scandinavia and the third from Siberia. In parts of Britain the ice was two thousand feet – more than a third of a mile – deep. It covered most of northern Europe and what is now Canada. The earth's crust buckled under its weight. In Britain, only England south of the Thames, a small part of Ireland and one or two Welsh and Scottish and possibly Pennine mountain tops escaped the full effects.

During the most severe phase the mean temperature in southern England in July was believed to have dropped to a mere five degrees Centigrade – a 'reading' deduced partly from the types of plant that were apparently growing at the time – with due allowance for some plants being more adaptable than others. (A surprising amount of plant-life for instance survives today even in Greenland.)

The glaciers advanced across the surface of Britain like flat paint-scrapers, pushing the loose rocks before them, squeezing the soil like paste between each granite cleft, tearing up trees, levelling hills, scouring valleys, and digging vast craters where the ground was soft. As each ice-front drew near, the temperature dropped and the communities of animals and plants that had previously flourished in England 'retreated' to warmer regions nearer the equator. Plants such as the Arctic Willow and the Dwarf Birch came south. So did the Arctic fox, the musk ox and the reindeer. During the interglacial periods, the animals and plants strove to re-establish themselves in their former haunts. Land animals, birds and insects and the wind would have carried back the seeds from the south, and these would have germinated as soon as the climate became favourable. Moreover, the action of the glaciers would have created extra soil by grinding off and breaking up the rocks.

In America there were no real obstacles to this periodic north–south migration because the sheet-ice did not penetrate the southern states such as Alabama and Florida and the northern plants and insects had a natural base from which to recolonise the sites from which the ice had driven them. In China, too, large parts of the country having a plentiful rainfall and a temperate climate remained free from glaciation (which helps to account for the number of botanical treasures subsequently found there).

Britain was less fortunate in that there were physical barriers which hindered the north–south flow of animals and plants. True there was a time during which plants which grew in Britain but whose natural homes were in Spain and Portugal, could retreat (or advance) over a land bridge which formerly joined these two countries to Ireland. Similarly, land bridges at Gibraltar and Sicily joined southern Europe to north Africa, thus giving southern Europe a precarious link to the south. But when the glaciers melted and the sea level rose, these communications were cut. Britain remained isolated by the North Sea and the Irish Sea, and, from about 8,000 years ago onwards, the water of the English Channel began to cut our links with the Continent.

Thus many of the plants that we lost were not recovered. There were also permanent changes in the climate. Our summers never again became warm enough for the magnolia and the tulip tree to re-establish themselves as wild plants, though they manage to do so in the eastern part of North America where the winters are harsher than ours. Other plants found change itself to be a killer. They simply could not adapt themselves sufficiently quickly. Arctic plants, such as the delightful little evergreen twinflower (*Linnaea borealis*), found the interglacial climate over most of Britain too hot, and retreated northward until they had little more than a toehold on the mainland. The Alpine Poppy was lost for good as a wild plant.

Plants which were flowering in Britain before the last glaciation and which survived it include *Nuphar lutea*, the Yellow Water Lily; *Ilex aquifolium*, holly; *Hedera helix*, ivy; *Origanum vulgare*, marjoram; *Mentha aquatica*, Water Mint; and *Saxifraga oppositifolia*, the plant with conspicuous purple flowers that wreaths its way round the rocks of the north like some green millipede.

Several have done well in gardens.

A second group has been traced back to a more recent period when the final glaciation was at its most severe. One of these is *Dryas octopetala*, the Mountain Avens. This is a miniature member of the rose family, though its white petals and golden stamens are reminiscent of the Christmas Rose or an anemone – both members of the buttercup tribe. *Dryas octopetala* is a favourite rock garden plant, and the wild species should be, but is not at the time of writing, legally protected. Another survivor from the same period is *Thalictrum alpinum*, Alpine Meadow Rue, a foliage plant with yellow and purple

Mountain Avens (*Dryas octopetala*), a miniature member of the rose family which survived the Ice Age

anthers – always a pleasure to meet with on some ledge in Snowdonia. Others in the same group are *Filipendula ulmaria*, Meadow Sweet; *Viola palustris*, Marsh Violet; *Prunella vulgaris*, self-heal; *Viola tricolor*, heartsease – the ancestor of the gardener's pansy; some forms of Campanula; *Scabiosa columbaria*, Small Scabious and another potential rock garden plant, *Viscaria alpina*, found wild only in the Lake District and in Angus, Scotland. Its white or pink flowers with slashed petals form a cluster, cowslip-fashion, at the top of the main stalk.

A third group are known to have flourished in the warmer Late Glacial period – say onwards from 10,000 BC. They include *Centaurea cyanus*, cornflower; *Armeria maritima*, Sea Pink, the neat low-growing plant that makes a tidy green frieze along the sea-cliffs or the garden border; *Polemonium caeruleum*, Jacob's Ladder and *Saxifraga hypnoides*, *Mossy Saxifrage* – another neat border plant. The Rock Rose of the chalk and limestone hills flowered in the south of England at this time as did a close relative of *Artemisia abrotanum*, the garden shrub known as Southernwood. Later on, soon after the ice age could be considered to have ended, we find *Verbascum thapsus*, Common Mullein – still a feature of cottage gardens; *Valeriana officinalis*, Common Valerian; *Dipsacus fullonum*, Common Teasel and *Hippophae rhamnoides*, Sea Buckthorn which makes an attractive, silvery-leaved hedge with bright orange berries on the female of the species; and several more plants for the garden-to-come.

Much of the information on which plants flowered in the past comes not from fossils, but from the analysis of the pollen shed by flowers. Many pollen grains are preserved in perfect condition if they happen to fall on to a piece of ground that is permanently waterlogged or which becomes overlaid with sediment and ultimately a bed of fossil. A peat bog is the ideal resting place for pollen – if it

Cornflower (*Centaurea cyanus*), which flourished as far back as 10,000 BC

never dries out. And the fact that peat is slightly acid is an added protection against decomposition. Each year showers of pollen may land on a peat bog, with new layers covering those that fell the year before, so that in time a historic record is built up. An instrument similar to an apple corer can be driven into the ground and a sample taken of pollen going back for hundreds and in many cases, for thousands of years.

After sifting out the pollen grains, these can be stained to show up clearly under a microscope. Pollen specialists or palynologists as they have come to be called, can fairly easily pick out certain well-known types of pollen. One of the most distinctive is the pollen grain of the pine tree which is provided with two ear-like air sacs. The ash pollen grain is shaped like a square cushion, the oak like a three-bladed propeller. Vetch is oval, hogweed waisted, Spear Thistle prickly, milkwort a cog-wheel, dandelion hexagonal, lime notched. Grasses and sedges, too, yield pollen that can be identified. But the scale of the operation can be judged from the fact that it is not unusual for a single gram of soil to yield several thousand grains of pollen.

Seeds, if preserved in peat or rock, can also be identified, either by their shape or by the cell pattern.

But with seeds, as with pollen, even the expert has to tread with caution, and it is by no means easy to obtain from pollen grains buried in the soil, a representative count of the species growing in the area. Streams can carry seeds and pollen many miles from where they first fell.

The researcher has to allow for the fact that some pollen grains have a tougher outer skin than others. The pollen of composite daisy-type flowers including sunflowers and marigolds, is especially tough; other pollen grains are more easily decomposed by bacteria in the soil and don't live to tell the tale.

Some plants leave little evidence behind them

because they flower less freely or less often, or are slower growing, or increase with the help of runners without seeding.

Nevertheless, the proportion of pollen provided by herbs, in comparison to that coming from trees, can provide a general indication of the climate at the time. In warm periods the trees prosper at the expense of the herbs; and in cold periods the trees suffer.

It is in this fashion, and with the help of carbon-dating and direct geological evidence, that botanists arrive at their estimates of the flora existing in Britain at any given time.

At this point, however, in our search for the origin of garden plants, we are confronted with a very difficult and not entirely academic problem. It is to decide which of the wild flowers that subsequently appeared in the garden flower beds of castle and cottage can be regarded as true natives of Britain, and which should be regarded as introduced or naturalised aliens to be credited to some other fatherland.

Some purists have declared that only those plants which existed in Britain before the final glaciation towards the end of the ice age should be regarded as truly our own.

But are plants which can survive only in the abnormal conditions of the ice age more native than those that flourish in the countryside today?

Other botanists would argue that the census of truly native plants should have been taken later but at least before the date when man was first able to clear the forest, thus creating an artificial environment that could no longer be considered purely native.

But, as we shall see, there is still some difference between the experts on when these clearances first began to take place. Other botanists consider that only those plants known to have been established before the Channel separated England from the Continent can be considered as truly native.

But even when that question has been settled, we still have the problem of deciding how many species were flowering at the cut-off date. Many plants that are now accepted by botanists as 'natives' were not recorded for centuries after they are now believed to have been growing here. Thus we have no native record of the beautiful chequered tulip-like fritillaries that bloom in places in the upper Thames valley and in Suffolk, earlier than 1736. But neither is there any record that they were artificially planted in any of these areas. The equally beautiful Snowdon Lily, a white bell-flower striped with purple outside and orange inside that blooms near the summit of the mountain, was unknown until Henry Lloyd climbed up there in 1696. Yet it is almost certainly a survivor from the ice age. Another showy plant that spreads in cushion-like masses, *Diapensia lapponica* – it has no English name as far as I know, remained undiscovered in western Inverness until 1951 – yet is confidently believed to have flowered in the same spot since before the ice age. How many more less conspicuous or perishable plants might have flowered undiscovered at the time of the cut-off?

Even experts continually make new discoveries which discredit their earlier beliefs. It used for instance to be thought that the nettle was introduced by the Romans who used the young shoots as a pot-herb. Now we learn that it was flourishing in Britain before the end of the ice age. Let us admit then that it is difficult to assemble an authoritative list of native plants based purely on recorded seniority.

Other perplexities arise even in the case of those plants which we know to have been introduced intentionally or accidentally by man or some other agency.

Some of these aliens seem more at home here than in their original domicile.

One such example is the little Ivy-leaved Toadflax – *Cymbalaria muralis* – whose pale purple-striped gargoyle-like flowers are to be seen on almost every ancient wall. It was brought to Britain from the Mediterranean and was flowering in William Coys' garden at North Ockenden in Essex in 1617. Even more senior is another miniature plant that like *Cymbalaria* loves the haunts of man. This is the Sleeping Beauty, *Oxalis corniculata*, so called because its flowers open widest when the sun is out. This plant with the yellow flowers and shamrock-type leaves was first recorded as an introduction in 1585 during the reign of Queen Elizabeth. Should it really be considered as an alien?

Are there other, more logical, criteria that could be adopted, apart from the date when it was first recorded, to decide whether a plant is native or not? The matter is a practical one, because the Conservation of Wild Creatures and Wild Plants Act of 1981 (which makes it an offence to pick, uproot or destroy rarities with a fine of (£1000 per plant) applies only to those plants having the status of British plants. Moreover the Nature Conservancy Council are obliged, at least once every five years, to advise the Secretary of State whether any new plants should be added to the list or taken off.

What sort of factors should influence the Council in cases where there is no record of the plant having been accidentally or intentionally introduced? Especially if it is a recent discovery?

One consideration might be whether it flowers in the kind of place in which one might expect to find it growing naturally. Is it for instance growing among other flowers known to be native? Plants that are found to be flourishing on so-called waste ground, that is, ground that has been disturbed by man and not cultivated, would be suspect. Likewise those on rubbish tips or near the docks at which ships from abroad are unloaded, or in lay-bys used by continental lorries, would, in the absence of evidence to the contrary be regarded as aliens – or at least casuals and unlikely to survive. Is the plant growing near a garden? Some of our most attractive 'wild' flowers have escaped over the garden wall.

Assuming then that there is no evidence of the plant having been introduced intentionally or accidentally, what else needs to be established to qualify it for British citizenship?

Ideally it should succeed in reproducing itself naturally in the wild by means of seeds and not merely by what is called vegetable growth – i.e. underground roots or suckers. (Though one uncommon 'native' *Dentaria bulbifera*, Bulbiferous Coralroot, for want, perhaps, of suitable pollinating insects, reproduces itself by bulbils formed at the base of the upper leaves and rarely seeds in this country.) The Water Soldier, generally regarded as native since it has been traced back for 50 million years seldom, if ever, forms seed here, though it may have done so at some warmer period in our history.

Another clue can be gathered from the plant's vital statistics. Aliens often increase at a prodigious rate or die out altogether, though here again, one can think of exceptions. One is *Trifolium stellatum*, the Starry Clover, whose seeds are believed to have been brought to Shoreham in Sussex in the ballast of Wellington's ships returning around 1809 from the Spanish peninsular campaign and so launched as a wild plant. This clover has appeared here and there in Shoreham ever since but has rarely been found elsewhere.

Then there is also the possibility that an alien well established in Britain may develop characteristics not found in the original alien plant – and so become worthy of protection as a native plant.

Thus, we see that the answer to the question of how many of our garden plants were derived from native wild ones must remain a matter of fine tuning by the second factor in the equation, man himself, whose role in the production of garden plants we shall now attempt to consider.

2 *Before the Gardeners Came*

With the end of the ice age – say 10,000 years ago – the climate in Britain and therefore the vegetation changed decisively. As the weather improved, the birch and dwarf willow which had survived by virtue of a low profile gave way to pine and then to alder, elm, oak and beech. The advance was a measured tread rather than a surge, for new trees do not grow overnight and, even if seeds are cast immediately on maturity (40 years or so in the case of elm and beech), they would not travel long distances. (One and a half times the height of the tree is normal maximum in a pine forest.)

As the forest front-line advanced, man's first reaction was to retreat. But he was not defenceless. He had learnt how to make axe-heads by chipping flakes off the sides of a blade, and over the years, wooden handles had been added, allowing the axe to be swung, so that he had less hesitation in cutting down a tree if one stood in the way. Traces of ashes dating from this period suggest that burning out the forest to make clearings may have been a more general practice than had been hitherto suspected.

Neolithic men when they crossed the Channel and landed on English soil brought with them farming techniques that had been used in the more favourable conditions of the Middle East and Central Asia since 8000 BC. They may even have brought seeds of cornfield weeds as well as of wheat with them.

Camelina sativa, Gold of Pleasure, a plant belonging to the cabbage family, provided neolithic man with part of his fat ration, and linseed oil from flax helped to light the lamp. He sowed wheat in furrows marked out with a staff tipped with flint, and the straight rows allowed the chosen field to be regularly hoed and perhaps even manured, for with the extra crop yield, it became possible to keep domestic animals, without moving from one station to another, though in poor years many of them had to be killed off in the winter.

Thus the main meat supply of the tribe no longer came from hunting but from domestic animals based more and more on a single village with more or less permanent huts. Grazing, of course, became more of a problem now that the tribe was settled in one centre. Large areas of the South Downs were cleared altogether and used for grazing sheep. Three thousand or so years later, they are still bare, and have remained the haunt of the first orchids to have been noted by early British writers on gardening matters. In the north of England, on the steeper slopes of the Pennines, the effects of clearance were more dramatic. Once the trees and scrub had been cleared, the rain washed away the soil for good, adding significantly to the metal content of the lakes below. Perhaps, in the north, this may have aided the survival of the 'alpine' wild plants which would otherwise have been smothered by forest trees.

As yet, there was no plough. About 500 BC, the Celts arrived, in a second wave, bringing with them the weapons of the Iron Age – an event which led to even more clearance, because charcoal and therefore wood was needed for smelting the iron.

The general effect must have been to open up the country and thus encourage the group of plants known as cornfield weeds – for instance the cornflower, *Agrostemma githago*, the corncockle with its carmine trumpet and green starfish sepals, *Melampyrum arvense*, the beautiful and almost extinct Purple Cow-wheat, a startling bottle brush beneath the waving corn, *Sinapis arvensis*, the flashy yellow

Papauer Rhoeas.
Red Poppy, or Corne-rose.

Corn Poppy, from John Gerard's *Herball*, 1633 edition

charlock, the Field Poppy, *Papaver rhoeas*, ancestor of the Shirley Poppy, *Chrysanthemum segetum* the golden Corn Marigold, *Achillea*, yarrow and not yet golden, and *Viola arvensis*, the Field Pansy.

A working model of a 300 BC Iron Age Celtic farm has been set up at Butser Hill, near Petersfield in Hampshire, with these and other contemporary cornfield weeds on show.

The farm is enclosed in a typical earthwork – a ditch and a bank which would originally have had a palisade or thorn hedge to keep in the cattle. Hay was stored by draping it round an upright post. The cattle byre was made of puddled clay, animal dung and straw, supported by posts and covered with a thatched roof. The main house is of oak stakes with hazel rods, daubed with clay, earth, chalk, animal hair and straw, again with a thatched roof.

Emmer (*Triticum dicoccum*) and Spelt (*Triticum spelta*), both bearded wheats, had replaced the original wheat used by neolithic man but Celtic Broad Bean (*Vicia faba*) and woad were also cultivated, the latter for the blue dye obtained from the first year leaves.

An improved plough which actually turned the soil was introduced to England by the Belgae tribe whose warriors landed in 75 BC, a few years before Julius Caesar.

Up to this point we have been talking mainly about the Garden of England; but from now on we can begin to talk about the Gardeners of England. For, much as the neolithic new stone age men brought the techniques of settled agriculture with them across the Channel, so the Romans imported the pleasure garden.

Virgil who published his four-volume work on husbandry, usually referred to as *The Georgics*, in 30 BC wrote enthusiastically about the success of an old peasant who took over a piece of waste ground unsuited to ploughing, grazing or wine-growing and grew lilies, verbena, poppies, hyacinths as well as roses and limes for his bees.

Roses, periwinkles and poppies appear on the walls of the Casa di Livia on Rome's gracious Palatine Hill, and the younger Pliny was delighted with the rosemary hedge and the violets that grew in his garden overlooking the Bay of Ostia.

Flowers were in demand for garlands and wreaths, and the Romans were familiar with grafting techniques used to improve the quality of plants and trees. But they were even more concerned with the structure of gardens which they considered should feature terraces and avenues, fountains and shaded bowers. Box hedges were favoured and were cut to give geometrical and other effects.

Other plants, *Hemerocallis fulva* and *H. flava* – the orange and yellow Day-Lilies – were grown too, but for medical use, and the Romans were also connoisseurs – as today – of vegetables: onions, garlic, globe artichoke, cabbage, cucumbers, peas, radishes, and of course the leek especially beloved by the Emperor Nero.

We know very little about Roman gardens in Britain, but neither the climate nor the available local skills could be relied on. Britain was a garrison colony and the tendency was to take wealth out in the form of wheat rather than invest it in real estate. There was little need anywhere in the country for cooling fountains. Possibly rosemary may have been introduced to Britain in Roman times either by seed or cuttings, but if so it seems to have been lost sight of for 900 years when Queen Philippa, wife of Edward III, claimed to have introduced it for the first time.

But pollen analysis does not help much to decide what flowers the Romans favoured. One reason for this – as J.R.A. Greig of the Department of Botany, University of Durham, has pointed out in his investigations of the Roman Palace at Fishbourne,

(*Isatis tinctoria*), from Gerard's *Herball*

West Sussex, is that gardeners' soil can be unfavourable for pollen research.

Where the soil is gravel or clay rather than peat, bacteria get to work and break down the wall of the less resistant pollen grains. They are still more encouraged if the clay has been marled with chalk in order to lighten it, as seems to have happened in Roman times. Furthermore, the showy flowers that would have been grown for display in the gardens would be insect pollinated and comparatively little pollen would have been shed.

We cannot even be certain whether the Romans either imported box plants or replanted the local species. For if they cut it, as they were wont to do either to trim the hedge or to line a coffin, it might not have flowered and so would not have shed pollen from its diminutive yellow flowers.

The main significance of the Romans would seem to lie in the vegetable garden to which they introduced *Foeniculum vulgare*, fennel, admittedly a pot herb but sometimes grown in gardens for its decorative thread-like foliage, and several other flavoursome plants such as *Smyrnium olusatrum*, Alexanders now a wild plant, and *Peucedanum graveolens* (dill). The Romans were also partial to *Coriandrum sativum*, coriander, grown for its digestive and aromatic qualities, though the authoritative *Clapham Tutin and Warburg Flora of the British Isles* declares it can be distinguished because 'the whole plant smells strongly of bed-bugs'. *Atropa belladonna*, Deadly Nightshade, and *Hyoscyamus niger*, henbane, were used medicinally.

On the fringes of the garden, the Romans encouraged *Ficus carica*, fig, *Juglans regia*, walnut, *Morus nigra*, mulberry, *Mespilus germanica*, medlar, and *Prunus domestica*, the cultivated plum.

Over the countryside as a whole, the coming of the Roman legions helped to reintroduce some of the southern species that had been temporarily lost, and to establish newcomers. The legionaries brought seeds in their clothes, in the mud of their horses' hooves, in the horses' fodder. Their system of roads spread seeds far and wide and the sloping verges on either side of the roads provided a convenient apron for the newcomers. Among them *Papaver somniferum*, the stately pale mauve opium poppy, and the humble Scarlet Pimpernel and in all probability that pest of the garden, *Aegopodium podagraria*, Ground Elder.

Onopordon acanthum, the giant woolly ultra prickly plant usually called Scottish Thistle – though it doesn't grow there – was a Roman importation. It is decorative enough to be grown in gardens and, if given enough space, looks impressive. *Malva sylvestris*, the Common Mallow and *Conium maculatum*, hemlock, were two more contemporaries.

But there may have been many more which shed their pollen on to unsuitable or undiscovered sites and a hint in this direction is provided by the Roman words used by the Anglo-Saxon invaders to describe the plants they found growing. *Gladiolus* – the word means little sword – was used by the Romans to describe the leaves of *Gladiolus illyricus* which still grows wild in part of the New Forest. 'Gladdon', a corruption of this word, was used by the Saxons, and is still used in country districts to describe a similar but much more common plant, *Iris foetidissima*. Which of these two plants flourished in Roman times is unclear – it could have been both. Neither appears to have left pollen traces. Gladiolus is sufficiently rare, and gladdon usually flowers on chalk soils inimical to the survival of pollen grains.

Another flower of the chalk hills and grasslands is *Rhinanthus minor*, Yellow Rattle – so called because its seeds rattle in the capsule when ripe. (In Sweden it is said to be the signal for hay-making to commence.) The Romans called it *Crotalum* which was the word used by Cicero for the rattle or

(*Iris foetidissima*), known in Saxon times, from Gerard's *Herball*

castanets used to accompany certain types of dance. The Anglo-Saxon word for the plant is Hratele. There is similar twinning between the Roman and Anglo-Saxon words for almond, beet, chestnut, lettuce, lily and mallow – confirmation in the last two cases of evidence we have from other sources. (And conversely the Romans – and Greeks too – may have inherited their names from the peoples whom they conquered.)

The Romans finally withdrew from Britain in 410 AD and a period of confusion followed during which the British were attacked from north and west by the Picts and Scots and from the east by Saxon raiders, and from 787 onwards by the Vikings and when William the Conqueror-to-be landed in 1066 AD he found a country that was still divided.

In the meantime clearance of the forests had continued. The Saxons had invested in ploughs drawn by teams of oxen, which were not easily turned round, so that the fields tended to be ploughed in long strips surrounded by hurdles which were removed after the harvest to allow the area to be grazed. The farmer's hedge and the plants that shelter in it – the dog rose, the wild honeysuckle and at times the primrose and blubell – came later. But flowers containing nectar were encouraged, for no sugar was imported and families kept their own bees.

The Norman kings put an end to the chaos which had prevailed so long over the tenure of land. All land from the largest estates down to the smallest freehold were first declared to be forfeited to the crown. Those who had not fought in the battle of Hastings were permitted to recover their estates but only as dependents. Those with large properties swore an oath of fealty as tenants-in-chief directly to the King, others pledged themselves to one of the tenants-in-chief, and so on down the line.

Large stretches of the countryside were set aside

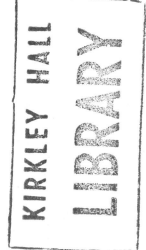

for hunting – the New Forest was one – and they became the country's first nature reserves sheltering plants that would otherwise have been lost, including of course the gladiolus itself.

Another development which affected, if indirectly, the plants grown in our gardens, was the position of the Church, and the monastic movement.

For one of their special cares was for the herb garden preserved within the safety of the monastery walls.

3 *The Virtuous Plants*

From the first, some flowers which have since appeared in the garden were blessed with divine sponsorship, and were linked to the gods. The hyacinth was said to have sprung from the blood of Hyacinthus, a youth beloved by both Apollo and Zephyrus. When Hyacinth showed his preference for Apollo, Zephyrus' revenge was untypical of a soft west wind, but effective. During a game of quoits between Hyacinthus and Apollo, Zephyr blew one of the heavy metal discs on to a rock. It recoiled, striking Hyacinthus a fatal blow on the head; and this, according to Ovid, is the reason why the wild hyacinth still keels over.

Iris was the messenger of Juno, and she walked between heaven and earth over the bridge made by the rainbow; the flower had almost as many different colours. Narcissus, the golden-haired youth was changed by the gods into a flower after he had gazed so longingly at his own image in the waters of a stream in the belief that it was that of his long-lost sister. (I greatly prefer this explanation to the one which links Narcissus with narcotics.) Dianthus was the flower of Dios or Jove. Centaurea healed the wounds of Chiron the Centaur.

Furthermore certain flowers have been given symbolic values. *Lilium candidum* was singled out by the venerable Bede as an emblem of sanctity, the white petals symbolising the purity of the Virgin Mary's body, and the golden anthers the beauty of her soul. Rosemary was cherished by Sir Thomas More as well as by Shakespeare as sacred to remembrance, love and friendship. Violets are still the symbol of modesty if not humility. Other plants have been linked to particular saints – as, for instance, St Patrick's Cabbage and St Barnaby's Thistle, though the latter, as David McClintock, I believe has pointed out, flowers in Britain well after 11 June, the saint's festival day – on 8 August when I last saw it in Sussex.

Some plants, with or without divine help, were credited with magic properties. Thus the Christmas Rose – probably brought to Britain by the Romans along with *Lilium candidum* was used by both Greeks and Romans to ward off evil spells. The root could be dug up only after drawing a circle round the plant, turning to the east and praying for permission to dig; and then the leaves were strewn around the rooms of the dwelling to be protected – to the sound of appropriate Greek or Roman chants.

Finally, witch doctors, and then physicians were able to show that dosage was more effective than incantation. The day of the herbalist had arrived.

Some of the herbs used could, of course, be found growing wild in the countryside, at least during certain months of the year. Perhaps they had even been introduced by Romans and survived unaided. Other plants, however, were unable to establish themselves in the wild, and would flourish only in gardens where they were sheltered not merely from the wind but from the competition of other weeds.

Few if any such gardens existed in the years which followed the Roman withdrawal from Britain. First the country was invaded by the Saxons who destroyed the cities set up by the Romans. Then came the quarrels among the Saxons themselves. St Augustine and his followers made converts to Christianity around the beginning of the seventh century, but prolonged civil war between the country's leading chieftains, disturbed the peace of the cloister and therefore of the herbalist.

Towards the end of the eighth century the

Vikings arrived, setting fire to churches and Augustine monasteries alike. The struggle between Alfred and the Danes followed, with the country partitioned between them. Some Benedictine communities of monks pledged to poverty, charity and obedience, were set up in the tenth century in the days of St Dunstan, yet, at the time of the Norman conquest only 48 houses of men and 12 nunneries still remained.

Thereafter discipline improved. Towards the end of the eleventh century the Cistercian Order was founded to institute stricter observance of the original monastic ideals. Labour in the fields and the development of the wool trade were encouraged. This conception agreed so well with the spirit of the times that within a century some 600 Cistercian houses had been founded. The Carthusians, founded in 1084, were stricter still, with the monks living in separate cells isolated from each other, unsustained by an infirmary or even a coffin on the day of their burial. Though their cells had a small garden attached they would have had little to tell us about the origin of garden flowers.

Meanwhile in Britain, as the monasteries increased in size and wealth, more space had to be found for the monastery garden. One reason for this was the amount of entertaining that had to be provided for travellers, rich, comfortably off and poor. Monasteries in those days were often the only building for miles around at which travellers could hope to find somewhere to sleep, and monasteries were expected as a condition of their endowment to provide accommodation and food for all that came. The nobility were entertained by the Abbot or Prior, the less exalted guests by the Hosteller in the Guest House and the poor in the Almonry or Alms House, which, like the Guest House was usually near the entrance gate. Often the visitors stayed for an indefinite period, and we are told for instance that in Edward II's reign, resources of the priory on the Wirral peninsula were strained to their uttermost by having to feed and house travellers who were waiting for fair weather to allow them to cross the Mersey estuary to the Liverpool side.

It therefore became necessary to grow herbs for the pot. These included *Borago officinalis*, Borage; *Chamaemelum nobile*, Camomile; *Foeniculum vulgare*, Fennel; Mint species; *Petroselinum crispum*, Parsley; Sage species; Thyme species; *Satureja montana*, Savory; *Crocus sativus*,* Saffron (still the vital element in bouillabaisse); *Origanum vulgare*, Marjoram. Mallow and Chicory were used in salads; *Artemisia absinthum*, Wormwood and *A. abrotanum* (Southernwood) for preserving the taste of ale, and *Brassica nigra*, the Black Mustard (whose seeds are actually brown) was one of the main sources of mediaeval mustard.

A second group of plants was grown for general use. Violets were needed for their fragrance; a shirt washed in lavender water would it was said, be free of lice as long as the scent persisted; linen table cloths derived from flax, now covered the Abbot's table. There were two kinds, both potentially garden flowers, the native *Linum perenne*, Perennial Flax and *Linum usitatissimum* cultivated in Britain with the earliest cereals, if not before, for its oil; they were not replaced as a source of cordage until Tudor times when a royal edict made it compulsory for *Cannabis sativa*, the Hemp plant, to be cultivated to equip the newly established Royal Navy.

Other useful plants were those yielding dyes. The red stigmas of the saffron provided the yellow and it was said that 4,300 flowers were needed to yield one

Verbascum Matthioli.
French Sage.

French or Jerusalem Sage (*Phlomis fruticosa*), from Gerard's *Herball*

* A member of the Iris family to be sharply distinguished from *Colchicum autumnale*, an extremely poisonous plant, also mauve and autumn flowering, and often described as Meadow Saffron or even Autumn Crocus, but which belongs to the lily and not the iris family.

ounce of the pure dyestuff. Madder provided red dye, privet berries afforded green, and the stately golden-flowered woad, the blue, apart from which it was credited with medicinal values being used to alleviate St Anthony's Fire (the popular name for Erysipelas).

Wild Catmint, *Nepeta cataria*, the white flowered, pale-leaved upright plant so different from the straggling purple sprawl of the garden plant, was grown for its fragrance.

Sugar was still imported in those days although it grew wild in southern Italy, and other warm places in Europe. Honey remained the main source of domestic sweetness, and was used not only in confections but also for the production of mead. Bees also helped to provide the wax for altar candles. The hives would have been placed near lime trees and fields of clover, or banks of heather, but lavender, used since Roman times for this purpose, would have lured the bees too.

Apart from this, the monastery garden included a selection of medicinal herbs. These were needed not only for the 'Farmery' to which the monks were sent when ill, but to the infirmary proper which was at the disposal of visitors.

In the days before anaesthetics, it was essential for the surgeon to be able to call on drugs that would stupefy. Few today would care to see *Atropa belladonna* with its 'hollow floures bel-fashion of an overworn purple colour' growing in their flower bed. But both this and *Papaver somniferum*, the Opium Poppy, were welcome inside the monastery gate. So was *Hyoscyamus niger*, henbane, equally poisonous but with not unattractive funnel flowers of cream veined with purple markings. Even less acceptable (to us) would be Ground Elder, *Aegopodium podagraria* which was cherished as a remedy for gout, as well as on occasions as a pot-herb.

Tussilago farfara, coltsfoot, the yellow daisy with

the scaly stem that sends up flowers in early March in advance of the leaves, was recommended for coughs which were all too prevalent within the monastery walls. *Symphytum officinale*, comfrey, was widely used for poultices, and valerian was the 'keep well' plant as its name, derived from the Latin *valere*, to be strong, testifies. *Chrysanthemum parthenium*, feverfew, was, as its name implies, cultivated as a herb for lowering the temperature, and its strongly aromatic foliage no doubt helped to sustain its image as a herb of considerable efficacy. Its white daisy flower and pale green chrysanth foliage can be detected on the fringes of many walled gardens. Its name is said to have been derived from an incident related in Plutarch's *Life of Pericles* during which a man who fell while working on the Parthenon escaped death by grabbing hold of a clump of feverfew. Our own native *Alchemilla vulgaris* whose name suggests some magical connection with the alchemists of the middle ages, was another widely used healing herb.

The purple-flowered *Salvia horminoides* – clary, and the rarer and more showy *Salvia pratensis*, Meadow Sage, were both believed to clear the eyes. Various members of the woundwort family grew wild and were used for healing the kinds of injury that can happen even to monks – from a sickle or a chisel or a carving knife. Two of these, the Hedge Woundwort, *Stachys sylvatica*, and the Marsh Woundwort, *S. palustris*, are common wild plants. But the Downy Woundwort, *S. germanica*, whose covering of long silky white hair reminds one of its near relative *S. lanata*, Lamb's Ear, is extremely rare outside gardens.

It was recommended for bronchitis and other 'griefs of the chest'.

The Iris was said to have been first adopted as an emblem in the sixth century by King Clovis of the Franks, after a clump of *Iris pseudacorus*, Yellow

Alchimilla.
Lyons foot, or Ladies mantle.

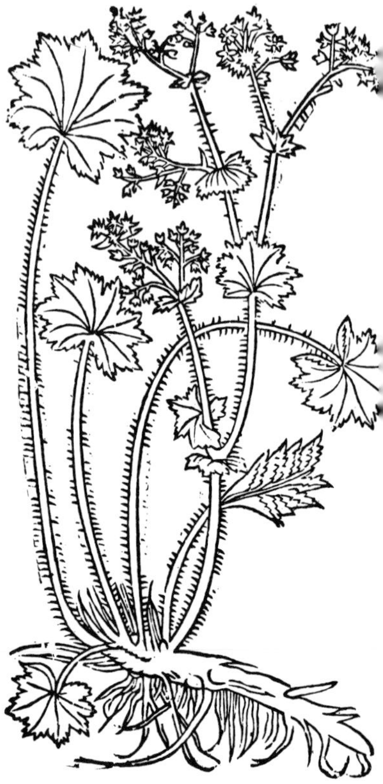

Lady's Mantle (*Alchemilla vulgaris*), a widely used healing herb in medieval times, from Gerard's *Herball*

Iris susiana, a native of Lebanon, from Emanuel Sweerts' *Florilegium* (1612)

Water Flag, had shown him where he could ford a river and so escape from a superior force of Goths. It was revived as an emblem, the Fleur de Louis, by Louis VII of France in 1147 when he set off on the disastrous second crusade. It figured at one time in our own royal coat-of-arms and still appears on the dials of non-digital compasses to show the way to the north. But the Iris was used in medicine as well as in heraldry. It was said to be a remedy against dropsy, jaundice, the ague, stones in the kidney and a number of less serious though distressing complaints. The blue garden variety, *Iris germanica*, was cultivated even in the ninth century by Walafrid Strabo, abbot of Reichenau, the famous monastery on Lake Constance, and no doubt soon spread to gardens this side of the channel.

Bats-in-the-Belfry, alias *Campanula trachelium*, the Nettle-leaved Bellflower, was, as its Latin name implies, used as a remedy for inflammation of the trachea or windpipe. It was the original Canterbury Bell – and the larger double-flowered *Campanula medium* was known – for no very obvious reason, as the Coventry Bell. But in the end the plant with the larger flowers was accorded the name with the greater status.

Rue (*Ruta graveolens*), which is no relative of our own native Meadow Rue (*Thalictrum flavum*) and one which has never established itself in Britain outside gardens was popular in monastery gardens.

Knautia scabiosa, the scabious, was the sovereign remedy for scabs, running or spreading ulcers or 'the breaking out of the itch' though in places it was probably too common in the wild for it to be taken notice of by the herb-gardener.

Tutsan, *Hypericum androsaemum*, the smaller version of the Rose of Sharon – St John's Wort – also grew wild but not perhaps in sufficient quantities for the needs of the physician, for the whole plant was 'toute saine'.

Ruta hortensis.
Garden Rue.

(*Ruta graveolens*), from Gerard's *Herball*

Monkshood, *Aconitum anglicum*, the close relative of the delphinium, is also a native British plant, seen more frequently in the west and Wales than elsewhere. It yielded the pain-killing alkaloid drug aconitin and was probably specially cultivated, despite its reputation as a poisonous plant.

But it would be wrong to conclude that plants were grown in monastery gardens only for the dinner table, the dispensary or the workshop. The monks had other duties that compelled them to be gardeners. From the twelfth century onwards, it was usual for most of the monks to be in priests' orders and therefore qualified to celebrate not only mass but christenings, marriages and the like. They had obligations towards the laity who lived around them. Some monasteries, particularly of the Augustine and Benedictine Orders, had inherited the site and endowments of a parish church; others reserved an aisle in the monastic church for the use of parishioners. In either case the church had to be decorated, and flowers provided not only for weddings but for funerals. On the occasion of the main Christian festivals such as Christmas, Easter, Whitsun and the Harvest-home and those saints' days of special significance to the foundation, there would be processions outside the precincts. There were also shrines to be honoured. For all these purposes flowers were needed – daffodils, carnations, roses, lilies and periwinkles – a most suitable plant for wreaths and garlands and well established outside gardens even though its seed rarely ripens in our climate. In one instance a flower garden was enjoined by the terms of the foundation: Henry VI in the will which provided for the establishment of Eton College stipulated that a space of 38 feet should be left between the wall of the church and the cloister so that certain trees and flowers needed for the service of the church could be planted there.

Some abbots and priors treasured private flower beds of their own, set apart from the official monastery garden. One of these was Alexander Necham, foster brother of Richard, Coeur de Lion; he was elected abbot of the Augustine monastery of Cirencester in 1213 AD, two years before the Magna Carta was signed. In his work *De Naturis Rerum*, published in 1190 AD, he sang the praises of two more garden plants not hitherto mentioned. One is *Acanthus*, species not stated, but probably not a native plant. (Our own *Acanthus mollis*, Bear's Breeches, was first recorded as growing wild in the south-west of England in 1820.) Its name commemorates a decision by the Greek sculptor Callimachus in the fifth century BC to use the plant's leaf as the basis for a design of the top of his Corinthian columns.

The other plant, which was named after Paeon, the physician who healed the wounds of the gods during the Trojan War, was *Paeonia officinalis*; it was credited with general toning up properties contained in the roots, and was said to have healed the wounds given by Hercules to Pluto.

Necham also mentioned the 'turnsole', probably *Calendula officinalis* although he may have seen this while studying in Paris rather than in England.

The two military Orders closely connected with the crusades may have played some part in bringing back plants used in monasteries. These Orders were the Knights Hospitallers and the Templars. The Knights Hospitallers Order was founded in 1092 AD at the time when a hospital was built in Jerusalem to assist the crusaders and pilgrims visiting the Holy Land and to protect them on their way. They were at one time extremely powerful and the Grand Prior was accorded a seat in the House of Lords. The Templars fulfilled more or less the same function, and were supposed to protect the Holy Places as well as the routes leading to Palestine. The original

Star of Bethlehem (*Ornithogalum umbellatum*), which may have been brought back to Britain by Crusaders, from Sweerts' *Florilegium*

hollyhock is one of the most likely importations dating from the time of the crusades; it was mentioned as far back as 1373 AD and probably loitered on the way here before that date. *Ornithogalum umbellatum*, the Star of Bethlehem, may also have been a crusader's capture, but by no means for sure. We shall meet other plants in the same category later on.

Monastery gardens were not, of course, the only sanctuaries for flowers during the middle ages. A layman, describing himself as Mayster Ion Gardener wrote a five-page poem, the 'Feate of Gardening' which appears to have been transcribed into a book of Miscellanies around 1440 though it had probably been written earlier. 'Ho so wyl a gardener be, Here he both hyre and se,' the poem begins. A study of the 'Feate' is included in Alicia Amherst's scholarly work, *A History of Gardening in England* and as she points out, provides firm evidence of what was cultivated at the time. What surprises, perhaps, is the large number of those plants which would today be considered wild – although in a garden they would naturally do better and appear more desirable than in the wild.

Thus, included on Gardener's list are *Betonica officinalis*, Betony, a close relative of the woundworts; *Geum urbanum*, Wood Avens; *Bellis perennis*, the Common Daisy; *Ajuga reptans*, Bugle; *Chrysanthemum segetum*, Corn Marigold; *Calamintha ascendens*, Common Calamint; *Chamaemelum nobile*, Camomile; *Primula veris*, cowslip; *Eupatorium cannabinum*, Hemp Agrimony; *Smyrnium olusatrum*, 'Elysauwder' Alexanders; *Gentianella amarella*, Felwort; *Lychnis flos-cuculi*, Ragged Robin; *Digitalis purpurea*, Foxglove; *Iris foetidissima*, Gladdon; *Lithosperumum officinale*, gromwell; *Senico vulgaris*, Groundsell, 'Growdyswyly'; *Hypericum perforatum*, Common St John's Wort; *Geranium robertianum*, Herb Robert; *Marrubium vulgare*, White Horebound; *Artemisia vulgaris*,

Mugwort; *Apium graveolens*, Wild Celery; *Sanicula europaea*, Sanicle; *Ranunculus flammula*, Lesser Spearwort; *Stellaria holostea*, Greater Stitchwort; *Verbena officinalis*, Vervain; *Sedum acre*, Biting Stonecrop; *Egrimoyne*, Agrimony; *Asperula odorata*, Woodruff; *Oxalis acetosella*, Wood Sorrel; and a teasel – probably *Dipsacus fullonum* subspecies Sativus, used in the wool trade to prepare wool for spinning.

Cultivars of some of these, for example the daisy, the foxglove, survive in the modern garden today. The little yellow Biting Stonecrop invests the walls and pavements where it can, and other garden flowers mentioned in Ion Gardener's list include daffodil, a native plant, honeysuckle, lavender, lily, periwinkle, rose and water lily.

Many more garden plants were adopted by the herbalists as a result of the writings of Theophrastus Bombast von Hohenheim (1493–1541) better known by his Latin synonym, Paracelsus. Like his father he was a doctor, and he was elected to a professorship at the University of Basle. But his arrogance and his contempt for the convictions of his colleagues and for anyone who preferred other opinions to his own, lost him the post. His views were unusual to say the least. In a treatise based on the Doctrine of Signatures he maintained that every plant had virtues which could be deduced from its signs or outward appearance. Thus the perforations in the leaves of Common St John's Wort indicated that it was a remedy for 'inward or outward holes or cuts in the skin'. Giambattista Porta, who lived in the latter half of the sixteenth century, even extended the theories of Paracelsus. He suggested that herbs with yellow sap – *Chelidonium majus*, the Greater Celandine was one – would be good for jaundice. So would a very different looking plant of the same family, *Glaucium flavium*, the Yellow Horned Poppy of the sea shore. Plants such as *Picris echioides*, the Bristly Ox-tongue, rough to the touch, would help to ensure a smooth skin, and *Cynoglossum officinale* (the adjective proclaimed that it would be sold by herbalists) which had acquired the popular name of houndstongue from the nature of its leaves, was a remedy for 'Mad doggebit'. The forget-me-not tribe – particularly *Myosotis scorpioides*, of which the flowering stem recurves after the manner of a scorpion, would be an effective remedy for the bite of that arthropod, and *Lathraea squamaria*, the Common Toothwort, drew its name from the white toothlike scales, which suggested that it would relieve toothache.

William Langham's *Garden of Health* published in 1579 gives other herbal remedies infallible in cases of Stomach Gnawing, Falling Sickness and Fundament Griefes, and a seventeenth-century English writer, William Cole, suggested that the walnut with its cranium-like shell and wrinkled 'brain' inside would be the ideal remedy to take after blows on the head.

Herbalism has never before and perhaps never will be again so irrational and it is perhaps with a sense of relief, not induced by any herb, that we close the gate of the herb garden behind us.

4 *Lovesome Flowers*

We can trace the English love of flowers for their beauty's sake at least as far back as 1300 AD – sixty years before English had replaced French as the official language of the Law Courts and Parliament.

At that time an anonymous poet wrote of woderove (woodruff) springing up and of the rose that 'rayleth hire rode' (puts on her [robe of] red) as well as of the lilie that is lossom (lovesome) to see.

The woodruff would have been wild – encouraged perhaps by the anti-bandit laws passed in 1285 which called for no trees, bushes or ditches to be left within 200 feet on each side of roads linking market towns. But the rose and the lily would be more likely to appear in a flower garden. Another nameless poet of about the same period offers his mistress the lilie of largesse, the parvenke (periwinkle) of prouesse (prowess) and the solsecle (sun-seeking marigold) of sweetness.

The poet's love of flowers persisted even through the closing years of the fourteenth century when England and the world generally seemed to be in a parlous state. In 1348 the Black Death had struck carrying off more than half the population. King Richard the Second had come to the throne in 1377 as a boy of ten. Four years later he had to deal with the Peasants' Revolt during which the mob broke into the Tower of London and beheaded the Archbishop of Canterbury. The Church was at war with itself with two rival Popes, one in Rome and the other in Avignon, and in England John Wycliffe was questioning the conventional authority of the priests.

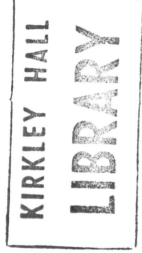

Yet despite all the turmoil, flowers were not overlooked and praise for their beauty comes from mandarin-bearded Geoffrey Chaucer himself, although he had spent much of his life on diplomatic missions abroad or in London, and spent little time at his house in Kent.

Chaucer wrote:

There sprange the vyolet al newe
And freshe pervynke rich of hewe
And Floures yelowe, white and rede
Suche plants grewe there never in mede

The pervynke rich of hewe was likely to have been the red-purple variety of periwinkle which is not normally found outside gardens.

It was nearly two hundred years before another English poet comparable to Chaucer emerged. He was Edmund Spenser, an admirer of Chaucer – and also of flowers. Writing in 1579 in praise of Eliza, he calls for a presentation bouquet to be assembled:

Bring hether the Pincke, and purple
  Cullambine,
    With Gelliflowres
Bring Coronations, and Sops-in-Wine,
    Worne of Paramoures;
Strowe me the ground with Daffadowndillies,
And Cowslips, and Kingcups, and loved
  Lillies;
    The pretie Pawnce,
    And the Chevisaunce,
Shall match the fayre flowre Delice.

This would seem to be a mixture of garden and wild flowers. The 'pincke' would probably have been the single pink *Dianthus plumarius*, now known as the Common Pink. This is an introduced pink of impeccable lineage; its deeply fringed petals are to

Dames Violet (*Hesperis matronalis*), from Gerard's *Herball*

be seen on the walls of castles such as Sherborne and Rochester dating from the Norman times and it has been suggested that the seeds were originally carried to England with the stone that the Normans used for building these fortresses. The Gelliflowres would normally be the *Dianthus caryophyllus* – the Clove-scented Pink, another introduced plant naturalised on some old walls. It was already to be found in double as well as single flowers, and earned its popular name from the fact that it flowers mainly in July – along with other companion flowers such as wallflowers, stocks and even the fragrant crucifer *Hesperis matronalis*, Dame's Violet, which were also referred to occasionally as gillyflowers. The Coronations were semi-doubles or doubles, larger than the gillyflower and without its clove scent; as their name implies, they were impressive enough to be used on crowns and head-dresses. Sops-in-wine were smaller single clove-scented pinks used to sweeten wine or ale, which, with hops not yet in general use – and no pressure kegs – would keep for only a few days. The cowslips to which Spenser refers and the Lillies and Daffadowndillies need no comment and Kingcup is still the countryman's name for *Caltha palustris*, the Marsh Marigold.

The Pawnce is the pansy and the Chevisaunce is the wallflower so called from the old English word for achievement. The Delice is better known as the Fleur-de-lys or Iris.

Shakespeare, however, prefers to think that Fleur de Lys was derived not from Louis' name but from Lis, the Latin word for lily for in The Winter's Tale, he allows Perdita to say 'lilies of all kinds, the fleur-de-luce being one'.

The passage, however, is too interesting not to be quoted more fully.

Perdita was the princess unjustly disowned by her father as illegitimate and banished from his kingdom. The ship carrying her away is all but wrecked and she is cast up, still in her cradle, on the shore of an island forming part of 'the deserts of Bohemia' ruled by King Polixenes. She is brought up by a shepherd and, in Act IV of the play, she is acting as hostess at a shearing festival attended – in disguise – by King Polixenes, his son Florizel and an attendant.

The celebration opens inauspiciously with Perdita offering the king winter flowers suitable for an old man.

PERDITA . . . Reverend Sirs,
For you there's rosemary and rue; these
keep
Seeming and savour all the winter long:
Grace and remembrance be to you both
And welcome to our shearing!

POLIXENES Shepherdess –
A fair one are you – well you fit our ages
With flowers of winter.

PERDITA
Sir, the year growing ancient
Not yet on summer's death nor on the birth
Of trembling winter, the fairest flowers o'th'
season
Are our carnations and streaked gillyvors,
Which some call Nature's bastards; of that
kind
Our rustic garden's barren, and I care not
To get slips of them.

POLIXENES
Wherefore, gentle maiden,
Do you neglect them?

PERDITA
For I have heard it said
There is an art which in their piedness
shares
With great creating Nature.

POLIXENES

Say there be;
Yet Nature is made better by no mean
But Nature makes that mean; so over that
art
Which you say adds to Nature is an art
That Nature makes. You see, sweet maid,
we marry
A gentler scion to the wildest stock,
And make conceive a bark of baser kind
By bud of nobler race. This is an art
Which does mend Nature – change it, rather
– but
The art itself is Nature.

PERDITA

So it is.

POLIXENES

Then make your garden rich in gillyvors,
And do not call them bastards.

PERDITA

I'll not put
The dibble in earth to set one slip of them:
No more than, were I painted, I would wish
This youth should say 'twere well, and only
therefore
Desire to breed by me. Here's flowers for
you:
Hot lavender, mints, savory, marjoram;
The marigold that goes to bed wi'the sun
And with him rises weeping; these are
flowers
Of middle summer, and I think they are
given
To men of middle age. Y'are very welcome.

CAMILLO (the attendant)
I should leave grazing, were I of your flock,
And only live by gazing.

PERDITA
Out, alas!
You'd be so lean that blasts of January
Would blow you through and through. (to Florizel) Now my fair'st friend
I would I had some flowers o' the spring that might
Become your time of day – (to the Shepherdesses) and yours, and yours,
That wear upon your virgin branches yet
Your maidenheads growing. O Proserpina,
For the flowers now that, frightened, thou let'st fall
From Dis's wagon! Daffodils,
That come before the swallow dares, and take
The winds of March with beauty; violets dim
But sweeter than the lids of Juno's eyes
Or Cytherea's breath; pale primroses
That die unmarried ere they can behold
Bright Phoebus in his strength – a malady
Most incipient to maids; bold oxlips and
The crown imperial; lilies of all kinds,
The fleur-de-luce being one: O, these I lack
To make you garlands of . . .

So Perdita (parentage apparently unknown) is advancing arguments against marrying Prince Florizel (though she eventually does so) while the King is arguing in favour of marrying 'a gentler scion to the wildest stock' until he discovers that Perdita the shepherdess, the wildest stock, is secretly betrothed to Florizel. In parallel with this, a philosophical discussion seems to have been going on about the ethics of 'improving' garden flowers by grafting.

On firmer ground, so to speak, it can be confirmed that the growing interest in gardening at this time was not limited to poets.

Many new influences were at work. The waning power of the church had led men to turn more readily to secular pursuits. Caxton's printing press set up in 1476 and others like it brought a new thirst for knowledge which could be communicated to others.

The suppression of the monasteries had endowed the nobility with money to build country mansions of their own, and the law and order established by the Tudor dynasty made it unnecessary for them to rely on battlements and the portcullis for security, or to limit the flower bed to a bank of earth heaped up against the castle wall.

There was no one style. Some of the manors were newly built. Others were conversions.

Most of the newer houses were designed without the enclosed courtyard to be entered only through a turreted gateway, and, instead, presented an apron walled in on three sides only – or not at all. Little Moreton Hall, near Congleton in Cheshire, kept its moat, its chapel and its great hall, but the walls were of 'magpie' timber work and no match for cannon fire.

Great or small, the trend was there, and one of those who noted it was Francis Bacon, one of Queen Elizabeth's Counsellors and afterwards Lord Chancellor. He wrote, 'There was never the like number of fair and stately houses as have been built and set up from the ground, since Her Majesty's reign: insomuch that there have been reckoned in one shire that is not great, to the number of thirty three, which have been all new-built within that time – whereof the meanest was never built for two thousand pounds'. He added that just as the Emperor Augustus had said that he had received the city of brick and left it of marble so, the queen might say 'she received it a realm of cottages and hath made it a realm of palaces'.

Bacon, according to gossip-writer and antiquary John Aubrey, had a 'delicate lively hazel eie. Dr Harvey told me it was like the eie of a viper'. The Lord Chancellor-to-be was also a man of sensitivity. He had 'musique in the next room when he meditated' and insisted that his men should wear boots of Spanish leather not ordinary neat's (bull's) leather of which he disliked the smell. 'Sweet herbs and flowers were always before him when he dined' Aubrey wrote.

Thus it is not surprising that Bacon should have chosen for one of his essays the subject of gardens. 'God Almighty first planted a garden,' he wrote, 'And indeed it is the purest of human pleasures. It is the greatest refreshment to the spirits of man; without which buildings and palaces are but gross handiwork.'

The essay, published in 1625, but written earlier, gives an excellent check-list of Bacon's favourite flowers selected to provide 'ver perpetuum' a perpetual spring in the garden through the year. 'For December, and January, and the latter part of November, you must take such things as are green all winter: holly; ivy; bays; juniper; yew; pine-apple trees; fir-trees; rosemary; lavender; periwinkle, the white, the purple and the blue; germander; flag; orange trees; lemon trees; and myrtles, if they be stoved; and sweet marjoram warm set [planted against a wall in the sun]. There followeth, for the latter part of January and February, the mesereon tree, which then blossoms; crocus vernus, both the yellow and the grey; primroses; anemones; the early tulippa; hyacinthus orientalis; chamairis [a name applied to two species of dwarf iris]; and fritillaria.

'For March, there come the violets, specially the single blue; the yellow daffodil; the daisy; the almond tree in blossom; the peach tree in blossom; the cornelian tree in blossom; sweet-briar. In April follow the double white violet, the wall-flower; the stock gilliflower; the cowslip; flower-de-lices, and lilies of all natures; rosemary flowers; the tulippa; the double piony; the pale daffodil; the French honeysuckle; the cherry tree in blossom; the dammasin and plum trees in blossom; the white thorn in leaf; the lilac-tree.

'In May and June come pinks of all sorts, especially the blush pink; roses of all kinds, except the musk, which comes later; honeysuckles; strawberries; bugloss; columbine; the French marigold; flos Africanus ['African' marigold]; cherry tree in fruit, ribes; figs in fruit; rasps; vine flowers; lavender in flowers; the sweet satyrian with the white flower [*Gymnadenia conopsea*] the Fragrant orchid of which white varieties sometimes occur. Herba muscaria (the Grape Hyacinth); Lilium convallium [lily-of-the-valley]; the apple tree in blossom; in July come the gilliflowers of all varieties.'

In August and September the writer seems mainly preoccupied with fruit – though he mentions 'monks-hoods of all colours' and later 'holy-oaks'.

In his view the garden should be divided into three sections – a green in the entrance 'because nothing is more pleasant to the eye than green grass kept finely short', then the main garden, then a 'heath or desert'.

There are to be shaded alleys at the side up against a stately hedge which is to enclose the garden so that in great heat it is not necessary to 'buy your shade' by going first across the open lawn.

Then comes Bacon's finest passage – a declaration of revolt against the earlier Tudor practice of regarding the geometrical design of the beds, often imitating designs worked in wool and silk, as the most important feature of any garden. What he particularly objected to was the so-called 'knot

Monkshood (*Aconitum napellus*) from Sweerts' *Florilegium*

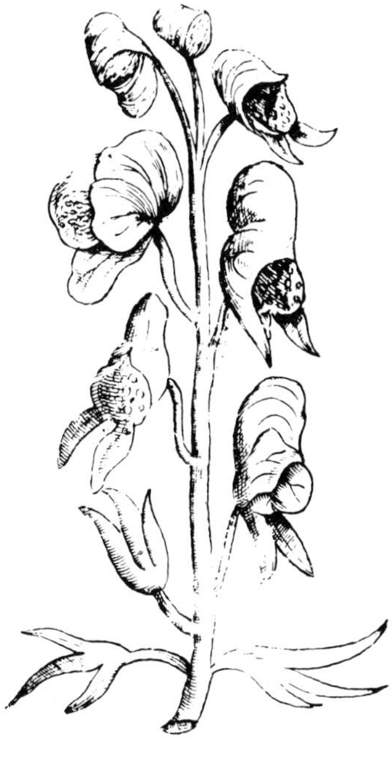

garden' consisting of a pattern of mirror-image small beds edged with box, rosemary, lavender or cotton lavender, arranged cross-word puzzle fashion in a position to be viewed from afar from the living rooms then usually on the first floor, without the labour of going to look at the flowers. 'As for the making of knots and figures with divers coloured earths, that they may lie under the windows of the house on that side which the garden stands, they be but toys; you may see as good sights many times in tarts.'

He does not like his hedges 'too busy or full of work'. 'I for my part do not like images cut out in juniper or other garden stuff; they be for children.'

Fountains are all right with him – 'but pools mar all, and make the garden unwholesome, and full of flies and frogs'. The main matter, as he saw it, was to convey the water so that it never stays either in the bowls or in the cistern, discolouring or encouraging 'mossiness and putrefaction'.

Hollyhock or 'Holy-oaks' (*Althaea rosea*), from Sweerts' *Florilegium*

In the heath or desert at the far end of Bacon's 'plot' as he called it we find the beginnings of the earliest English wild garden . . . 'a natural wilderness'. 'Trees I would have none in it, but some thickets made only of sweet briar and honeysuckle, and some wild vine amongst. For these are sweet and prosper in the shade. And these to be in the heath, here and there, not in any order.' Most of the flowers he prescribes for this 'heath' grow wild in Britain today. But he spoils the picture to some extent by adding 'standards' of little bushes to be planted on top and around 'little heaps in the nature of mole-hills (such as are in wild heaths)'. The bushes would be roses, juniper, holly, berberries, red currants, gooseberries, rosemary, bays, sweet-briar etc.

At this point we may feel entitled to ask how many of the plants described by poets and essayists actually existed in Tudor gardens. An opportune reply comes from the practical Elizabethan gardener William Turner, whose list of plants used by the gardeners of his time gave names in Greek, Latin, Dutch and French as well as in English.

Turner was a man of his time and apart from being a serious botanist held strong religious beliefs and suffered for them. He was a north countryman, the son of a tanner from Morpeth, Northumberland, who took his degree at Pembroke Hall, Cambridge, in 1533 and must have been highly regarded there since he became Fellow and Senior Treasurer of his College. In 1538 while still at the university he published his first botanical list of herbs. He was one of the first botanists to assemble a collection of dried plant specimens.

In 1540 Turner spoke out against some of the measures taken by King Henry VIII in his quarrel with the Church and felt obliged to leave England with his wife and children. He travelled in France, Germany, Italy and Switzerland, and discovered, while doing so, that his own country possessed no work linking the English names of herbs used in England with those employed, sometimes for different purposes by apothecaries on the Continent. While in Switzerland he came to know the famous botanist and Alpine mountaineer, Konrad Gesner, Professor of Greek at Lausanne and later of Physics and Natural History at Zurich. Gesner collected some 500 plants previously unrecorded by classical botanists – a shock for the traditionalists. He also devised a system of classifying plants according to their fruits. He wrote treatises on medicine, and encouraged Turner to study the art of healing. Turner took his medical degree in Italy, then one of the leading centres of study in that field.

On Henry VIII's death, Turner felt able to return to his native land and was appointed Chaplain and physician to the Duke of Somerset, who had been installed as Protector during the minority of the new king, Edward VI.

Somerset had been given the estate of Syon near Brentford in Middlesex as a gift from the Crown, and Turner helped him to lay out the gardens there. He had his own garden at Kew, and also visited those of Dr Richard Bartlot, President of the Royal College of Physicians, at Blackfriars, and of Lord Cobham at Gravesend.

In 1548 he published a second list containing not only the names of plants growing in England but where they could be found. Among those recorded for the first time were *Physalis alkekengi*, the Winter Cherry, with its decorative 'Chinese lanterns'; *Cistus salvifolius*, the shrubby Cistus with the leaves of a sage and white flowers stained with yellow; *Spartium junceum*, sometimes called Spanish Broom; *Jasminum officinale*, the white scented jasmine from Persia. The Moors had brought it with them at the time they occupied the Spanish peninsula from 712 AD to 1492 AD. The Moors also brought at least one species of lilac, which, although known for centuries in the gardens of 'Turkey' which then included those of Romania and Bulgaria to say the least – was not found in the wild state till 1828. *Aristolochia longa*, a species of birthwort was also on his list.

In 1553, when Edward VI was succeeded by Mary Tudor, Turner had to go into exile again, but he was able to return home in good Queen Bess's time and his invaluable herbal, linking names used on the Continent with 'the common names that herbaries and apothecaries use' was completed and dedicated to the Queen shortly before his death in 1568.

Among plants listed in it were *Tagetes erecta*, the so-called African Marigold, a single flowered species. It was a native of Mexico, brought back to Spain, and only then naturalised in north Africa, where the warriors who accompanied the Emperor Charles V on his expedition of 1535 to free Tunis

Solanum Halicacabum.
Red winter Cherries.

Winter Cherry (*Physalis alkekengi*), mentioned for the first time in 1548 by William Turner, from Gerard's *Herball*

A page from Sweerts' *Florilegium* showing the African Marigold (*Tagetes erecta*) and the French Marigold (*Tagetes patula*), both of which probably originated in Mexico (right)

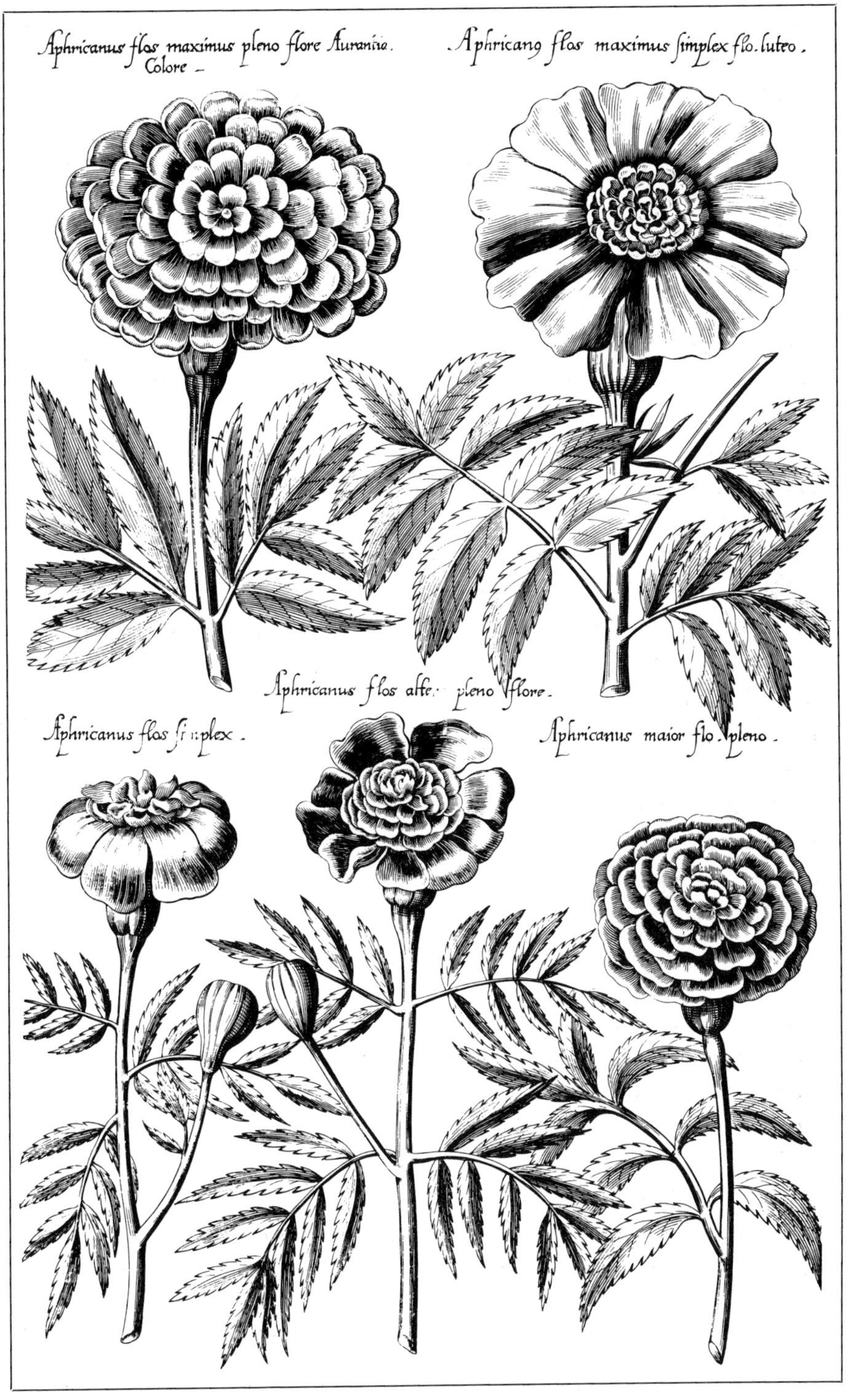
Aphricanus flos maximus pleno flore Aurantiæ. Colore.
Aphricanꝰ flos maximus simplex flo. luteo.
Aphricanus flos alte: pleno flore.
Aphricanus flos simplex.
Aphricanus maior flo. pleno.

from the Moors, found it growing, and assumed it was native. *Tagetes patula*, the Velvet Flower or French Marigold, was also described by Turner and probably took the same route to Britain via Paris. But the two plants are similar and easily confused.

The Spanish conquests of central Mexico, Panama, Costa Rica, Nicaragua, Guatemala, Honduras and Ecuador were completed between 1511 and 1525 with Peru, Yucatan, Venezuela and Florida to follow soon after; and besides the Marigolds the Spaniards also brought home the Nasturtium, *Tropaeolum minus*; *Mirabilis jalapa*, the Marvel of Peru; *Canna indica*, Indian Shot, and *Passiflora incarnata*, the passion flower.

Several other plants in Turner's list of 1568 deserve mention. One of these was *Santolina chamaecyparissus*, Lavender Cotton, known to the French as Garde Robe because it kept the clothes' moths at bay. It was also favoured as a plant suitable for the edges of the knots featured in Tudor gardens. There was, too, *Nigella sativa* – a cousin of *Nigella damascena* later called love-in-a-mist; the seeds of *N. sativa* had long been used as a relish and stimulant for the taste buds. Turner also recorded *Lilium martagon*, the Turkscap Lily with its whorls of dark glossy green leaves topped with dropping pink and purple blooms; it still flowers wild in some southern counties, and so does another of Turner's flowers, *Inula helenium*, Elecampane. Turner grew the garden snapdragon from seeds sent from Italy. He called it Broad Calf's Snout in counter-distinction perhaps to the small wild red snapdragon, *Misopates orontium*, still known to countrymen as Weasel's Snout.

Several other literary gardeners can be conveniently mentioned here. Thomas Tusser believed to have lived between 1515 and 1580, was himself a farmer at Cattawade, a village in East Suffolk south west of Ipswich, and he wrote largely with fellow-

Turkscap Lily (*Lilium martagon*), from Sweerts' *Florilegium*

yeomen in mind. But his advice published in 1573 under the title 'Five Hundred Points of Good Husbandry' was in the form of rhymed couplets. Tusser's recommended list of garden plants contains little that is unexpected except perhaps for the annual, *Delphinium consolida*, Branched larkspur or Larks Heel as it then was. But he makes the interesting suggestion that some plants 'should be set in Spring and at Harvest Time in pots, Pailes or tubs or for summer in beds' possibly after they had been grown under cover. In short, so many 'outlandish' plants are supplementing the native ones, that bedding out has to be considered. Twenty years later, Sir Hugh Platt in 'The Jewell House of Art and Nature' commended the notion of window boxes of wood, sealed with pitch or lead. The suggestion should have appealed to Thomas Hyll, a contemporary of Tusser's and a Londoner.

He wrote for the owners of modest gardens and, in his best-known work, *The Gardener's Labyrinth*, published in 1577, he conjures them to study the humble marigold: 'the follower of the Sunne'. 'This Marigold is a singular type of Herbe, sowen in gardens, as well for the potte as for the decking of garlands, bewtifying of Nosegays, and to be worne in the bosom.'

Then, just as the century draws to a close we meet with John Gerard, probably the most frequently quoted garden writer of his day. Gerard was born in 1545 and qualified as a Member of the Court of Assistants of Barber-Surgeons in 1595 and as Master in 1608. He was in charge of the gardens at Theobalds, near Cheshunt in Hertfordshire, the mansion which Lord Burleigh (or Burghley), Elizabeth I's Lord High Treasurer and Chief Minister was building for his son, Robert, first Earl of Salisbury. (Robert never lived there, having been compelled by King James I to exchange it for the bishop's palace at Hatfield.) Gerard had his own

(*Inula helenium*), from Gerard's *Herball*

Consolida regalis syluestris.
Wilde Larkes heele.

rk's Heel (*Delphinium consolida*),
m Gerard's *Herball*

garden, situated in Holborn, and his catalogue of plants, which listed more than a thousand species, many for the first time, is believed to have been based on those growing there at the time, that is, in 1596. The famous *Herball or Generall Historie of Plantes* was published in the following year, in somewhat discreditable circumstances. The publisher John Norton had commissioned a Dr Priest to translate from Latin into English a comprehensive work by the Flemish botanist Rembert Dodoens – but Priest died before finishing the work. The text came into the hands of Gerard who completed the translation, altered the arrangement of the plants and released it under his own name – without acknowledgement. Indeed he went so far as to say that Dr Priest's translation of Dodoens' work had 'likewise perished' at the time of the doctor's death.

Most of the 1,800 woodcuts used by Gerard were first published in 1590 as illustrations to a widely read work, *Neuw Kreuterbuch* by Jacob Bergzaben, better known by his Latin equivalent name, Tabernaemontanus. They in turn had come from others. The whole collection of illustrations was bought by John Norton for use in the *Herball* but Gerard's knowledge of botany was not sufficient to allow him to match the illustrations to the text. (The wild orchids are especially lamentable.) Some of the errors were corrected with the help of a fellow gardener and expert botanist, Mathias de l'Obel (for whom the plant Lobelia was later named), who was then in charge of Lord Zouche's garden in Hackney. Others remained uncorrected until a second edition 'very much enlarged and amended by Thomas Johnson, citizen and apothecarie' appeared in 1633. John White contributed the potato* plant which Gerald is shown holding in his hand.

*It had appeared in Raleigh's account of Virginia, but neither he nor Drake had brought the first home with them.

Nevertheless, the *Herball*, running to nearly 1,400 foolscap pages, printed in clear easy-to-read Roman type was read in many a home, and its authoritative style must have carried conviction and even brought relief to many a sufferer.

The descriptions which it gives of even the most commonplace plants are highly readable, and the style is confidential so that one might imagine that we are strolling alongside John Gerard, dressed for the part, four hundred years ago. Of *Filipendula ulmaria*, Mede-sweet, or Queene of the Meadowes (which Queen Elizabeth liked to be strewn on the floors of the houses she visited), Gerard wrote: 'This herbe hath leaves like Agrimony, consisting of divers leaves set upon a middle rib like those of the ash tree, every small leafe snipt about the edges, white on the inner side, and on the upper side crumpled or wrinkled like unto those of the Elme tree; whereof it tooke the name Ulmaria, of the similitude or likenesse that the leaves have with the Elme leaves. The stalke is three or four foote high, rough and very fragile or easie to bee broken, of a reddish purple colour: on the top whereof are very many little floures clustering and growing together, of a white colour tending to yellownesse, and of a pleasant sweet smell, as are the leaves likewise: after which come the seeds, small crookedly turning or winding with one another, made into a fine little head: the root has a sweet smel, spreading far abroad, black without, & of a darkish red colour within'.

Of the Thorn Apple, *Datura stramonium*, he had this to say: 'The stalkes of Thorny-apples are often times above a cubit and a halfe high, seldom higher, an inche thicke, upright and straight, having very few branches, sometimes none at all, but one upright stemme; whereupon doe grow leaves smooth and even, little or nothing indented about the edges, longer and broader than the leaves of

Spanish Broom (*Spartium junceum*), mentioned in Dr Bartlot's list of 1548, from Parkinson's *Paradisus Terrestris*

Matthias de l'Obel (1538–1616), after whom Lobelia was named

1 *Stramonium Peregrinum.*
The Apple of Peru.

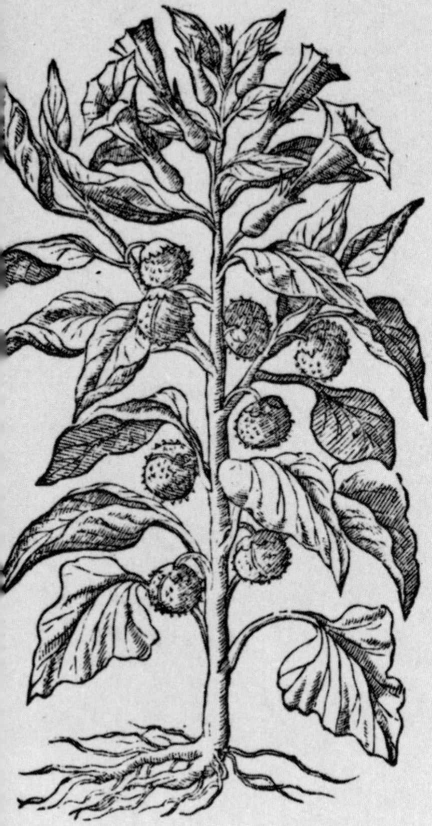

2 *Stramonium ſpinoſum.*
Thorny Apples of Peru.

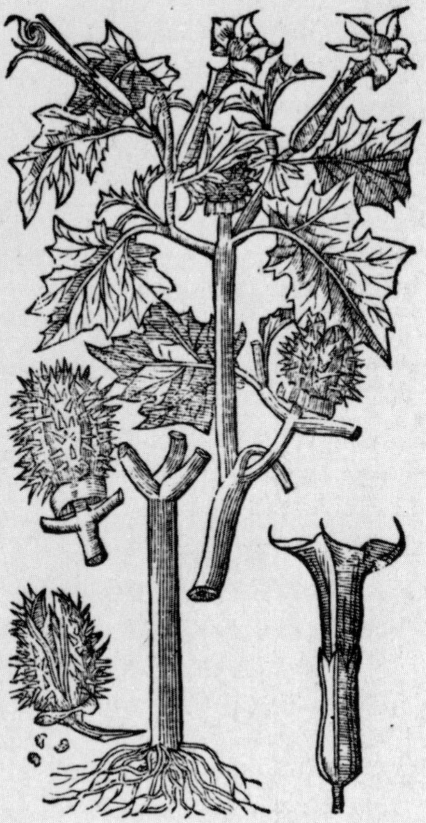

¶ *The Place.*

1 This plant is rare and ſtrange as yet in England: I receiued ſeeds thereof from *Iohn Robin* of Paris, an excellent Herbariſt; which did grow and bare floures, but periſhed before the fruit came to ripeneſſe.

2 The Thorne-apple was brought in ſeed from Conſtantinople by the right honourable the Lord *Edward Zouch*, and giuen vnto me, and beareth fruit and ripe ſeed.

¶ *The Time.*

The firſt is to be ſowen in a bed of horſe-dung, as we do cucumbers and Muske-melons.
The other may be ſowen in March or Aprill, as other ſeeds are.

Two species of *Datura* (Thorn Apple), from Gerard's *Herball*

Nightshade, or of the mad Apples. The floures come forth of long toothed cups, great, white, of the forme of a bell, or like the floures of the great Withwinde that rampeth in hedges; but altogether greater and wider in the mouth, sharpe cornered at the brimmes, with certain white chives or threds in the middest, of a strong ponticke savour, offending the head when it is smelled unto . . .'.

Even the Woody Nightshade, *Solanum dulcamara*, a pest in many gardens acquires a new interest when described by him: 'Bitter-sweet bringeth forth wooddy stalks as doth the Vine, parted into many slender creeping branches, by which it climbeth and taketh hold of hedges and shrubs next unto it. The barke of the oldest stalks are rough and whitish, of the colour of ashes, with the outward rind of a bright green colour, but the yonger branches are green as are the leaves: the wood brittle, having in it a spongie pith: it is clad with long leaves, smooth, sharp pointed, lesser than those of the Bindweed. At the lower part of the same leaves doth grow on either side one smal or lesser leafe like unto two eares. The floures be small, and somewhat clustered together, consisting of five little leaves apiece of a perfect blew colour, with a certain pricke or yellow pointal in the middle: which being past, there do come in place faire berries more long than round, at the first green, but very red when they be ripe; of a sweet taste at the first, but after very unpleasant, of a strong savoor, growing together in clusters like burnished coral. The root is of a mean bignesse, and full of strings'.

Gerard is sceptical about the virtues of Mandrake, and rejects the superstition that the root grows in the shape of a man or woman: 'In truth it is no otherwise than the roots of carrots, parseneps and such like'. But his faith in other nostrums is undiminished.

St James his wort or Rag-wort, the flowers of which 'stand in a pale round about, which turn into down as doth Groundsel' has several virtues. 'The decoction hereof gargarised is much set by as a remedy against swellings and impostumations of the

John Gerard (1545–1612), author of *The Herball or General History of Plants* first published in 1597

throat, which it wasteth away and thoroughly healeth. The leaves stamped very small, and boiled with some hogs grease unto the consumption of the juice, adding thereto in the end of the boyling a little Masticke and Olibanum, and then strained, taketh away the old ache in the huckle bones called Sciatica.'

On the other hand, the tobacco plant, relative of the Petunia, is said to provide 'an oile to be taken out of the leaves that healeth merri-galls, kibed (chapped) heeles, and such like'. The cyclamen, 'being beaten and made up into trochisches, or little flat cakes is reported to be a good amorous medicine to make one in love, if it be inwardly taken'. (How else?)

Most modern gardens would be overflowing if they showed just one specimen of each of the plants appearing in Gerard's Catalogue.

But let us begin at the beginning with *Eranthis hyemalis* – the Winter Aconite with its golden flowers set off by a slashed bib of bright green stem leaves which will flower even amid the snows of January. It was an introduced plant – we don't know for certain when, but probably at least 20 years before Gerard wrote about it. Gerard has 10 species of Auriculas (Mountaine Cowslip), a pitcher plant (*Sarracenia*) which he describes picturesquely as Friers Cowl, and an *Aristolochia* (birthwort) which he says is 'very common in most gardens'. He has five kinds of *Nigella* (love-in-a-mist), two dozen *Cistus* (if you count in the helianthemums) and a small nasturtium, known then as Indian cress.

Another Gerard plant, *Sternbergia lutea*, is also yellow but a complete contrast to *Eranthis*. Its brilliant shining yellow crocus-like flowers appear in the autumn and thrive in the lightest, warmest and most well-drained pockets of the rock garden. It remains a favourite among the cognoscenti. It was named after the Austrian botanist, Count Caspar Moritz Sternberg.

Then there is *Anemone coronaria*, the Great Double Windflower of Bithynia, the ancestor of the garden red, white, blue and purple varieties. The original red species was said to have been brought back by the crusaders with earth used as ballast in ships (a most unwise procedure) – and in any case there was no need to do so, for the plant already grew wild in Italy.

Phlomis fruticosa, French Sage to Gerard and Jerusalem Sage to other gardeners, was a standby that first appeared in his work. It is a long-lived shrubby plant with roughish pale grey leaves and striking helmeted sage-like flowers – but alas, no sage-like smell.

Astrantia major, masterwort, could have stepped out of an old-fashioned print with its small pink and white flowers and its spiky green and purple collar. It took up rather a lot of room but, as William Cole pointed out in his work *The Art of Simpling* (that is,

Love-in-a-mist (*Nigella*): Spanish and 'Double Blew' varieties, from Parkinson's *Paradisi in Sole*

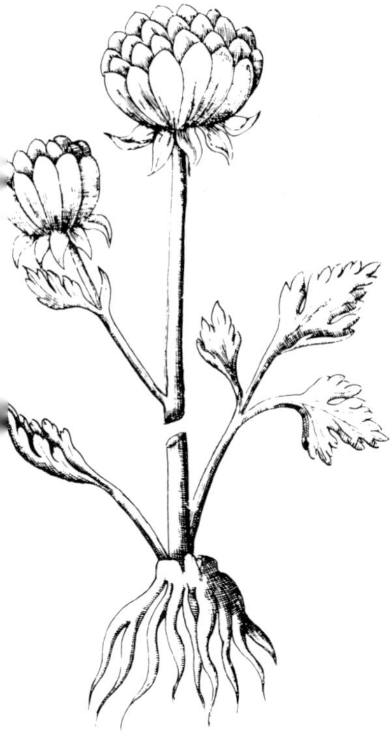

Ranunculus asiaticus: brownish red 'from Tripoli', and double form in orange vermilion, from Sweerts' *Florilegium*

of choosing simple herbs) 'as a lyon bringeth forth but one whelp, so this mighty plant is not very numerous in its progeny'.

Lunaria biennis, honesty, which Gerard knew as the White Satin Flower had, to judge by the number of its different nicknames, been in circulation for a considerable number of years.

And *Yucca gloriosa*, with its whorls of sharp leaves and spire of white flowers had also been known from the middle of the sixteenth century.

Another intriguing plant, *Colutea arborescens*, the Bladder Senna – so called from its inflated pods, had arrived at some undetermined time in the sixteenth century before Gerard wrote about it; and so had *Cercis siliquastrum*, the Judas Tree, with its purplish-red blossoms in May.

Ranunculus asiaticus, the Double-flowered Red Crowfoot or Buttercup – was something that Gerard could well be proud of. This rather than *Anemone coronaria*, could have been the lily of the field referred to in the Gospel of St Matthew. But Gerard found it hard to keep, and had to be content with the single form of the flower akin, it would seem to our own wild plant *Adonis annua*, Pheasant's Eye. Another conspicuously red plant was *Impatiens balsamina* (Busy Lizzie); its capacity for scattering its seeds in a burst of temper had already been noted before Gerard's day.

The Cockscomb Amaranths – now called *Celosia* – also impressed Gerard. He listed *A. cristata*, Common Cockscombe; *A. tricolor*, the leaves of which show stripes of red, yellow and white stemming from the green ribs; and *A. caudata*, love-lies-bleeding. Of *Hibiscus syriacus*, the white hollyhock with the red-blotched centre, he had only the seeds, but was filled with hope that they would mature.

Looking over Gerard's list one is alarmed at its length. Yet so many of our common garden plants or their ancestors figure in it, that it just cannot be abridged too drastically.

Among the garden trees is *Laburnum alpinum* – not the Laburnum with which we are most familiar but a fair approximation with brown, not black, seeds; we know it as the Scotch Laburnum.

Lychnis chalcedonica is another plant which appears to have been misrouted on its way here. Once again we have a plant that was supposed to have been brought home by the crusaders and indeed it is known as the Cross of Jerusalem in French, Spanish, Italian and German as well as in English. So did it deserve to be attributed to Chalcedonia, an ancient city at the entrance to the Bosphorus? The Portuguese called it the Maltese Cross, which rather suits the shape and metallic red-lead colour of the flowers. Its cousin, *Lychnis coronaria*, which for some reason is called the Rose Campion although its petals are deep reddish purple, is with us still, grey silk fur and all, both in and out of gardens. It seems to have arrived later than *L. chalcedonica*.

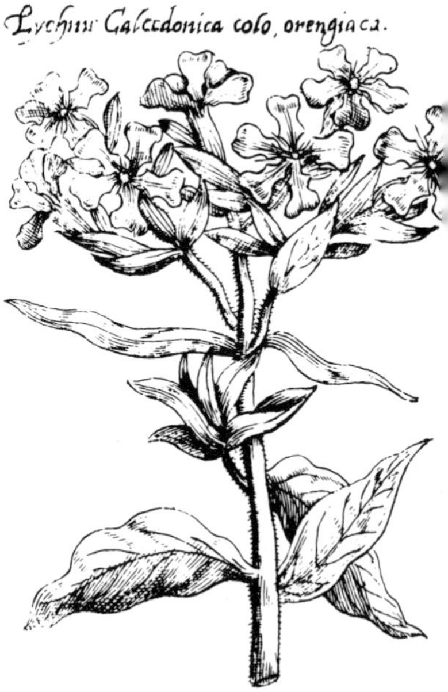

Jerusalem or Maltese Cross (*Lychnis chalcedonica*), from Sweerts' *Florilegium*

Turning back for a moment to the shrubbery we find *Philadelphus coronarius*, the Mock Orange and *Jasminum fruticans* – a yellow jasmine but, unfortunately flowering in July. Among the climbers he listed a red clematis.

Some flowers which we know as wild are given an honoured place in Gerard's. There is our native *Clematis vitalba* for which Gerard provided the unforgettable name of Traveller's Joy. There is *Polemonium caeruleum*, Greek Valerian to Gerard, but better known as Jacob's Ladder. There is *Lysimachia nummularia*, Creeping Jenny, the plant with the yellow bell-like flowers, which covers the ground of so many cottage gardens, despite the fact that it is not known to seed in Britain. There is *Chamaenerion angustifolium*, Rosebay Willowherb which Gerard cultivated in his garden without realising that it grew wild. There is *Saponaria officinalis*, soapwort, which had probably become naturalised by the time

(*Doronicum pardalianches*), from Gerard's *Herball*

Gerard wrote about it – and *Doronicum pardalianches*, Leopard's Bane, a well-known herb, but sufficiently decorative and early flowering to keep its place in the border. There is also *Pulmonaria longifolia*, the native species of lungwort or Soldiers and Sailors, as it is sometimes called because it has red (young) and blue (mature) flowers showing at the same time. There is *Epimedium alpinum* with its tiny jewel flowers and its almost impenetrable screen of pointed heart-shaped leaves, crowding together in a tiled arbour of greenery and extending a little each year. An introduced plant, this, from Austria. There is *Calendula officinalis*, the double Pot Marigold, and *Erythronium dens-canis*, Dog-toothed Violet.

Finally there are the varieties of well-known plants beginning for the first time to appear in uncomfortably large numbers – warning of hybrids to come. We have already seen some of the pinks, but now Gerard tells us of the Orange Tawnie Gilliflower from Poland. It was given to him by John Leete who was a member and three times Master of the Worshipful Company of Ironmongers. He probably had commercial links with East Europe.

The Iris had already become a specialists' plant, and Gerard featured a dozen species including the Portingale Fleurdeluce – which came not surprisingly from Portugal; *Iris florentina*, predictably from Florence and *Iris susiana*, called the Mourning Iris because of its sombre black, brown and dark purple markings. It was supposed, wrongly, to grow among the ruins of the ancient Persian city of Susa. There was also *Iris sibirica*, blueish mauve, which does grow in Russia as well as in central Europe. *Iris tuberosa*,* the Snake's Head Iris, which Gerard also grew, showed falls (lower petals) of velvet black edged with greenish yellow and standards (upper

* Now called *Hermodactylus tuberosus.*

petals) of the same colour. *Iris xiphioides*, which came to be known as the English Iris seems to have arrived around 1570 in ships plying between Spain and Bristol. It is deep blue with a golden patch. *Iris pallida* with the milk-blue flowers and greyish mauve leaves appears in Gerard's catalogue as the Great Fleurdeluce of Dalmatia and he had red, yellow, white and violet varieties of *Iris pumila*, the miniature which seldom grows to six inches in height.

Gerard's collection of narcissi includes what he calls the Yellow Daffodil Double, *Narcissus pseudonarcissus* and *N. poeticus* with appropriate English titles such as the 'timely purple-ringed daffodil', 'the more timely purple ringed daffodil' and 'the very hasty flowering daffodil'. He includes the double white Daffodil of Constantinople '*Narcissus orientalis*' – 'which was sent into England unto the right Honourable the Lord Treasurer, among other bulbed flowers; whose rootes when they were planted in our London gardens, did bring foorth beautiful flowers, very white and double with some yellowness mixed in the middle leaues [we call them petals] pleasant and sweete in smell; but since that time we neuer could by an industrie bring them unto flowring again'.

Gerard's lilies included *Lilium croceum*, Orange Lily, which could be dark red orange, or saffron spotted with black; and *Fritillaria libanotica*, Persian Lily of which 'the floures grow alongst the naked part of the stalk like little bels, of an overworn purple colour, hanging down their heads, every one having his own footstalk of two inches long, as also his pestell or clapper from the middle part of the flower; which being past and withered, there is not found any seed at all, as in other plants, but is encreased only in his root.' The red Lillie of Constantinople we are told, 'groweth wilde in the fields and mountaines, many daies journies beyonde

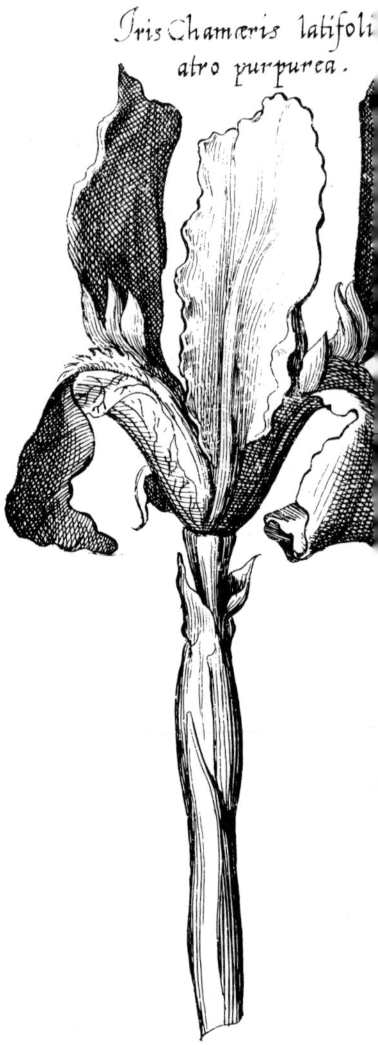

Iris pumila, purple, from Sweerts' *Florilegium*

Marvel of Peru (*Mirabilis jalapa*), from which the purgative jalap is derived, white and multi-colour varieties from Sweerts' *Florilegium*

Constantinople, whither it is brought by the poore peasants to be solde, for the decking up of gardens. From thence it was sent among many other bulbs or rare and daintie flowers, by Master Harbran, Ambassador there, unto my honorable good Lord and master, the Lord Treasurer of England, who bestowed them on me for my garden'. The envoy referred to was William Harborne, the first English ambassador to Turkey. His term ran from 1582 to 1588, during the reign of Suleiman the Magnificient.

Gerard also grew the bunch-of-flowers Tazetta type narcissus, so called because of the Italian word for a small cup which the flowers resemble, and he also cultivated jonquils with small sweetly scented flowers and rounded leaf-tips.

Among the smaller bulbs were blue and yellow Grape Hyacinths, *Crocus susianus*, Cloth of Gold Crocus, a new companion for the familiar purple and white spring-flowering plants; it had been sent to him by Robinus of Paris, 'that painful and most curious searcher of Simples'. There were also two species of cyclamen: *Scilla amoena* – a bright blue species; *Convallaria majalis*, Lily of the Valley, in a pink variety; *Hyacinthus orientalis* in pink, blue and white; *H. romanus* and, naturally, *Endymion non-scriptus*, our Wild Hyacinth or bluebell.

Part of the attraction of Gerard's writings lies in the unlooked for names given to familiar plants. Thus *Acacia vera* becomes the Aegyptian Thorne of Matthiolus; *Leucojum vernum*, known to botanists as Spring Snowflake, becomes the Early Bulbous Stocke Gilloflower, and *Galanthus nivalis*, our snowdrop, is 'a lesser sort thereof'. *Leucojum aestivum*, Summer Snowflake, becomes 'Early Sommer fooles or Somer Sottekins'. 'Wild Panick' turns out to be another name for Indian Oatmeal. *Iberis amara*, candytuft, is demoted to being Peasant's Mustard.

But the sense of wonder prevails when Gerard comes to describe the so-called Marvel of Peru,

(*Mirabilis Jalapa*) with heart-shaped leaves and trumpet flowers, from the roots of which the purgative Jalap is prepared, its petals 'glittering ofttimes with a fine purple or crimson colour, many times of an horse-flesh, sometimes yellow, sometimes pale and sometime resembling an old red or yellow colour, sometime whiteish, and most commonly two colours occupying half the floure, or intercoursing the whole floure with streaks or orderly streames, now yellow, now purple divided through the whole, having sometime great, sometime little spots of a purple colour sprinkled and scattered in a most variable order and brave mixture'. The botanical name *Jalapa* for this plant is, however, undeserved as Jalap comes from the roots of Ipomoea purga, an unrelated plant.

5 *Cottagers and the First Explorers*

It was about this time that the cottage garden – and the flowers in it – became traditional. Ever since the mid-fourteenth century when the Black Death had halved the population, there had been scarcity of labourers and the cottager, the small-holder and the yeoman farmer had profited in consequence. Many had the resources – and felt the need, in the days when doctors were few and far between – to grow their own medicines. The trend was not confined to the countryside, for in those days, except in the centres of large cities, houses were seldom closely packed or terraced. There were spaces between, and some families had a few fruit trees around the house and perhaps even a hen tethered nearby for safety.

In the town there might be a wall; in the country, a hedge to keep out wandering goats, horses, sheep, geese and even hares. Wild briar, blackthorn and holly provided the best defence, with possibly a gorse bush nearest the back door as an anchorage for the washing hanging out to dry.

Some of the more showy plants in cottage gardens were 'throw-outs' from larger estates, and, in this way, many species which might otherwise have been lost for good have survived. Other plants persisted – were chosen even – because they were self-perpetuating either through seed or creeping roots. A few, such as paeonies, which resent being disturbed, prospered through neglect.

And then, from about 1540 onwards, there were the Huguenots who never seemed to neglect anything. Driven from France and the Low Countries because of their religious beliefs, they settled in

Norfolk, Suffolk, Essex, near London in Bermondsey and Spitalfields on the main route to London from their first haven in East Anglia and further afield in Yorkshire and Lancashire, bringing with them not only an enthusiasm for Garden Societies but the plants themselves – especially auriculas, which, because of the shape of the leaves and the hair growing on some of them, were known as Bears' Ears.

Honeysuckle and privet were favoured near the porch, as well as two native shrubs, *Viburnum lantana*, the Wayfaring Tree with its leathery leaves and bright red berries and *Viburnum opulus*, the Guelder Rose. Furthermore the box was not invariably a cut down miniature hem for the edge of the border; for were not the conspirators in *Twelfth Night* told to 'get you all three into the Box Tree – Malvolio's coming down this walk'?

If the cottage had a wall, *Kentranthus ruber*, Red Valerian, already known to Gerard, would flourish, and so would *Matthiola incana*, Wild Stock – both of them naturalised from an early date. Cottages on the chalk or limestone would be good for *Salvia pratensis*, the Meadow Sage, and *Aquilegia vulgaris*, the columbine, the spurs of which, unlike those of the garden variety, curve towards each other like the necks of cooing doves. *Knautia arvensis*, the light mauve scabious, also flowers naturally on chalk. *Borago officinalis* would be there and *Chrysanthemum vulgare*, tansy, for tansy pudding provided, not as you might think as a delicacy but as a bitter tasting privation to be endured during Lent or at other times as a penance. *Digitalis purpurea*, foxglove, is another cottager's joy which, once installed, looks after itself by self-seeding; the 'glove' part of the name is said to have been derived from the old Saxon word for 'bell'. Another self-assertive introduced plant hard to eject once planted is *Campanula rapunculoides*, the Creeping Bellflower, with spires of

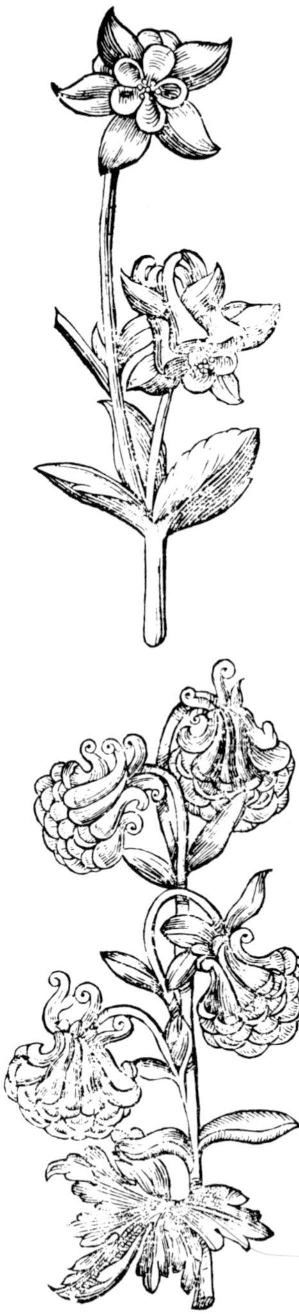

Columbine (*Aquilegia vulgaris*): single and 'partly coloured', from Parkinson's *Paradisus terrestis*

Leucoium syluestre.
Wilde wall floure.

(*Cheiranthus cheiri*), from Gerard's *Herball*

mauve flowers. I've not been able to trace the date of its first landing in Britain.

Aconitum anglicum, monkshood, with its darker blue-mauve racemes was a native plant which found shelter in some gardens. Another cottage favourite from the hedgerow was *Lathyrus sylvestris*, the narrow-leaved pea, first cousin of *Lathyrus latifolius*, the Everlasting Pea. Other transients from the wild included *Chrysanthemum leucanthemum*, the Oxeye Daisy; *Geranium pratense*, the pale blue-mauve Meadow Cranesbill; *Sedum telephium*, the rose-flowered stonecrop; *Convallaria majalis*, lily of the valley; *Centaurea cyanus*, cornflower; *Viola odorata*, Sweet Violet; *Althaea officinalis*, Marsh Mallow, and one or other species of *Myosotis*, forget-me-not.

The wallflower was there – it too probably came over with the Normans – and it was not threatened until the mid-nineteenth century with rivalry from the Siberian Wallflower, which experts tell us is not really a wallflower at all but allied to the Treacle Mustards, and by then blood red, golden and pale yellow varieties of real wallflower had been bred. *Kniphofia uvaria*, the Red Hot Poker, a feature of some cottage gardens, is said to have been first described in a book published in Amsterdam in 1644 about the time of the Battle of Marston Moor. The plant was named after a German professor, Johan Hieronymus Kniphof, and I find this more easily remembered if I pronounce the name as it would have been in German, namely Knip-hof, with the 'p' and the 'h' kept separate.

Cerastium tomentosum, Snow in Summer, the chickweed with the wedding-cake flowers and silvery foliage, would have been available from around 1648.

When writing of native flowers in cottage gardens I should have mentioned three other bulbous treasures although they might not have been too common. They are all Stars of Bethlehem and two are native. The smallest, *Gagea lutea*, Yellow Star of Bethlehem, a native plant, is seen at its best in damp woods; it has yellow flowers with a green band across the outer surface of the petals. *Ornithogalum nutans*, the Drooping Star of Bethlehem, is a striking looking hyacinth-like plant with a raceme of chinese-white blossoms which nod downwards after flowering. It is an introduced plant but does well in the wild on shaded chalky banks. *O. pyrenaicum* was once so abundant in the West Country that it was known as Bath Asparagus. It has many more flowers than its nodding cousin; they are yellowish and held erect.

The cottage garden, of course, drew its inspiration from the manor, and the renewed interest in plants for their own sake which had so impressed William Turner during his travels on the Continent had in turn been inspired in the previous century by the fall of Constantinople to the Turks in 1453. The Mussulman invasion sent a wave of intellectual Christian savants fleeing across the face of Europe. With them they brought news of gardens in the Middle East that were more delectable than any to be found in the west. Furthermore many of the strange and beautiful plants in them could, with care, be raised in Italy, France, Germany, the Low Countries and perhaps even in England.

At the same time, advances in the study of medicine added to knowledge of the effects of drugs, and to the need to identify more accurately the plants from which those drugs were derived. The ferment of the Renaissance was already at work in Italy and the world's first university botanical garden had been laid out at Padua in 1545. Others were set up before the end of the sixteenth century in Pisa, Montpellier, Heidelberg, Breslau and Leyden.

Equally there was an increasing desire among scholars to recover and make use of the store of

Drooping Star of Bethlehem (*Ornithogalum nutans*), from Sweerts' *Florilegium*

botanical knowledge once possessed by writers during the golden age of ancient Greece or even Rome – if indeed the plants they wrote about could still be found.

Aristotle, the pupil of Plato and tutor of Alexander the Great (338–23 BC), was known to have written about plants and their relationship with other life-forms but none of his writings on this subject survived at first hand. Aristotle's library was left to his pupil Theophrastus, whose work, *Enquiry into Plants*, was translated into English more than two thousand years later (1916) by the Harrow School housemaster, Sir Arthur Hort. It follows Aristotle's attempt to devise a logical classification for plants and suggests that they might be divided into trees, shrubs and undershrubs – a convention respected in practice today by many nurserymen if not by botanists. Theophrastus also advocated the separation of flowering plants from non-flowering and of deciduous from evergreen plants. Parts of the teachings of both Aristotle and Theophrastus were preserved in Greek schools set up in Aleppo, Damascus and elsewhere in the Middle East; their words were translated into Arabic probably in the ninth century and survived the Middle Ages in this form before being rendered again into Greek, or even Latin when the Arabs established themselves in parts of Europe.

But the most influential Greek writer of the pre-Christian era in the botanical field was probably Kratevas, physician to Mithridates the Great, King of Pontus in Asia Minor, who ruled during the final century BC. Kratevas was a contemporary of Pliny the Elder, whose encyclopaedia of natural history ran to 37 volumes and, according to Pliny, Kratevas prepared a herbal containing coloured illustrations of the plants he described. No trace of the original has been found but Kratevas' work survived in that of a more famous contemporary of his, the botanist

Pedanios Dioscorides. This work, in five volumes, usually known under its Latin title of *De Materia Medica* listed some five hundred plants known to the ancient world.

No copies of *De Materia Medica* appear to have been taken at the time but a later transcription believed to contain extracts from Kratevas' writings and copies of his illustrations was made in the sixth century AD for Anicia Juliana, daughter of Flavius Anicius Olybrius, one of the 'phantom' Roman Emperors who ruled Rome under the domination of the barbarians after the sack of the city. The transcript found its way to Constantinople and lay there undiscovered for more than a thousand years, until 1562 AD, when it came to the notice of a diplomat, Ogier Ghiselin de Busbecq. He had been sent from Vienna by the Emperor Ferdinand I as ambassador representing the Holy Roman Empire at the Court of the Sultan. The precious document was then in the possession of a man whose father had been physician to the Sultan, and, although the manuscript was in very poor condition – worm eaten and decrepit – De Busbecq urged his master to acquire it. The price asked was a high one, however, and it was seven years before it was safely locked up in the Imperial Library in Vienna.* Other versions of Dioscorides' work turned up in Constantinople as well as illustrations probably derived from Kratevas' work.

De Busbecq was also able to send back choice plants which included the Crown Imperial Fritillary and a flower whose European name tulip was said to have been derived from the tulband or turban worn by the Turks. He first noticed it in the fields while on a journey from Adrianople to Constantinople in 1554 and brought the seeds or bulbs of a red, garden

Corona Imperialis cum semine.
Crowne Imperiall with the seed.

(*Fritillaria imperialis*), from Gerard's *Herball*

*A facsimile has been published by Akedemische Drucke Verlag Anstalt of Graz, Austria.

Charles de l'Ecluse or Carolus Clusius (1526–1609), who helped to popularise the tulip from Constantinople

variety back to Vienna. By 1561 the tulip had reached Antwerp before crossing the Channel. Richard Hakluyt, nephew of the Elizabethan explorer, referred to it when he wrote (1582): 'Within these four years there have been brought to England from Vienna divers kinds of flowers called tulipas and those and others procured a little before from Constantinople by an excellent man called Carolus Clusius'. (This Clusius, more often referred to as Charles de l'Ecluse became Director of the Botanical Garden at Leyden and helped to launch the Netherlands' bulb growing industry.)

The spectacle of strange new flowers and the illustrations of some of them in Dioscorides' work led to the appearance of two early plant-hunters. One of them, Pierre Belon, who was both a doctor and a botanist, travelled at the expense of the Cardinal of Tournon on a journey that took him to Crete, Cairo, Greece, Constantinople and Jerusalem. His mission was to describe and draw the plants – and animals – that had once fascinated classical writers. He travelled the hard way, and noted for the benefit of others visiting Crete that 'monasteries give such provisions as they have gratis to all travellers whatsoever, as pickled or dried olives, onions, bisquet, salted fish, sometimes fresh for they often go a-fishing, their vessels or boats being cut without great difficulty of the thick trunks of Plain (*sic*) trees; their nets for want of corks are supported by gourds'. Belon described several new species including a white form of oleander and *Paeonia clusii*, discovered in Crete in 1546.

Belon climbed Mount Ida, reporting that there was snow there all the year round. 'T'is so cold that the shepherds cannot inhabit it in the summer time, but are forced every night to descend and leave their flocks of goats and sheep feeding. . . .'

'Near around this famous Mountain Ida are found Salvia pomifera which is carried to all the markets,

Caper shrubs, Mandragora mas & foemina, a Trifolium moenianthe [perhaps the modern palustre], Heliochryson which grows so thick as to cover and shelter the hares. Also Lotus arbor, and Zizyphus or Jujube. There is a sort of Carline Thistle called Chamaelean albus, whose odorate root sweats out a gum which the women in Kandy chew as they in Scio do mastick or they in Lemnos the Gum of Condrilla.'

Belon seems to have lost some of his interest in flowers as his tour progressed and devoted more attention to animals – he was impressed by the giraffe he saw in captivity in Cairo. He escaped the perils of the Levant – travelling much of the way in the party of the French Ambassador to the Sultan, but met his death in the Bois de Boulogne, then part of the forest encircling Paris where he was set upon and killed by brigands.

A journey of a more adventurous kind was made by the German physician, Leonhardt Rauwolff or Rauwolf whose *Travels* were translated into English by the botanist, John Ray.

Rauwolf set out from Augsburg in May 1573 with the strictly practical aim of identifying the herbs referred to by older writers including Dioscorides, in order to ensure that the herbalists of his day were supplying their customers with genuine traditional and authentic remedies.

It was no voyage for a weakling. Rauwolf and some of those who had sailed with him from Marseilles were attacked even as they stood outside the gates of the middle-eastern city of Tripoli, their first call. He was compelled to seek refuge in the Fondique, the large warehouse under the protection of the French Consul. It contained extensive underground cellars with space for the merchants to sleep alongside their goods. Next door to it, as could be clearly heard, was the place where those guilty of drinking wine or of not observing fasts, or not

Paphiopedalum victoria-regina subsp. *liemonianum*; allied to *Cypripedium*: from *The Botanical Magazine (1787—)* also known as *Curtis's Botanical Magazine*

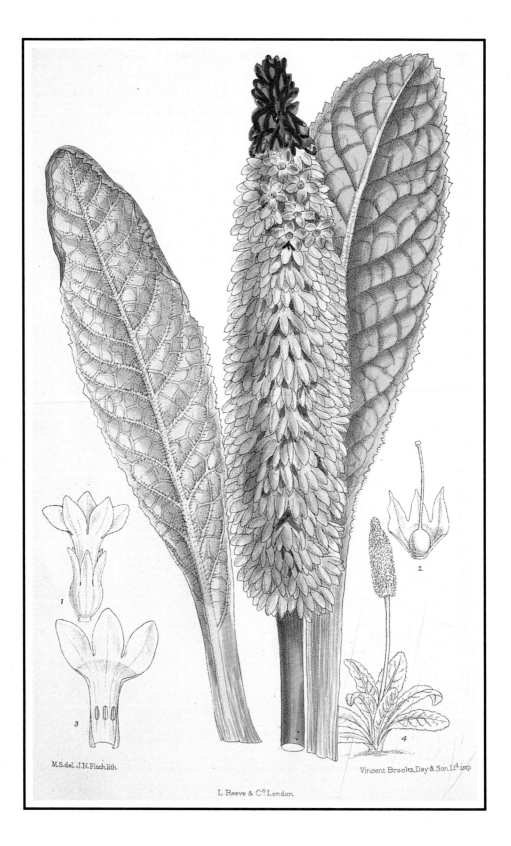

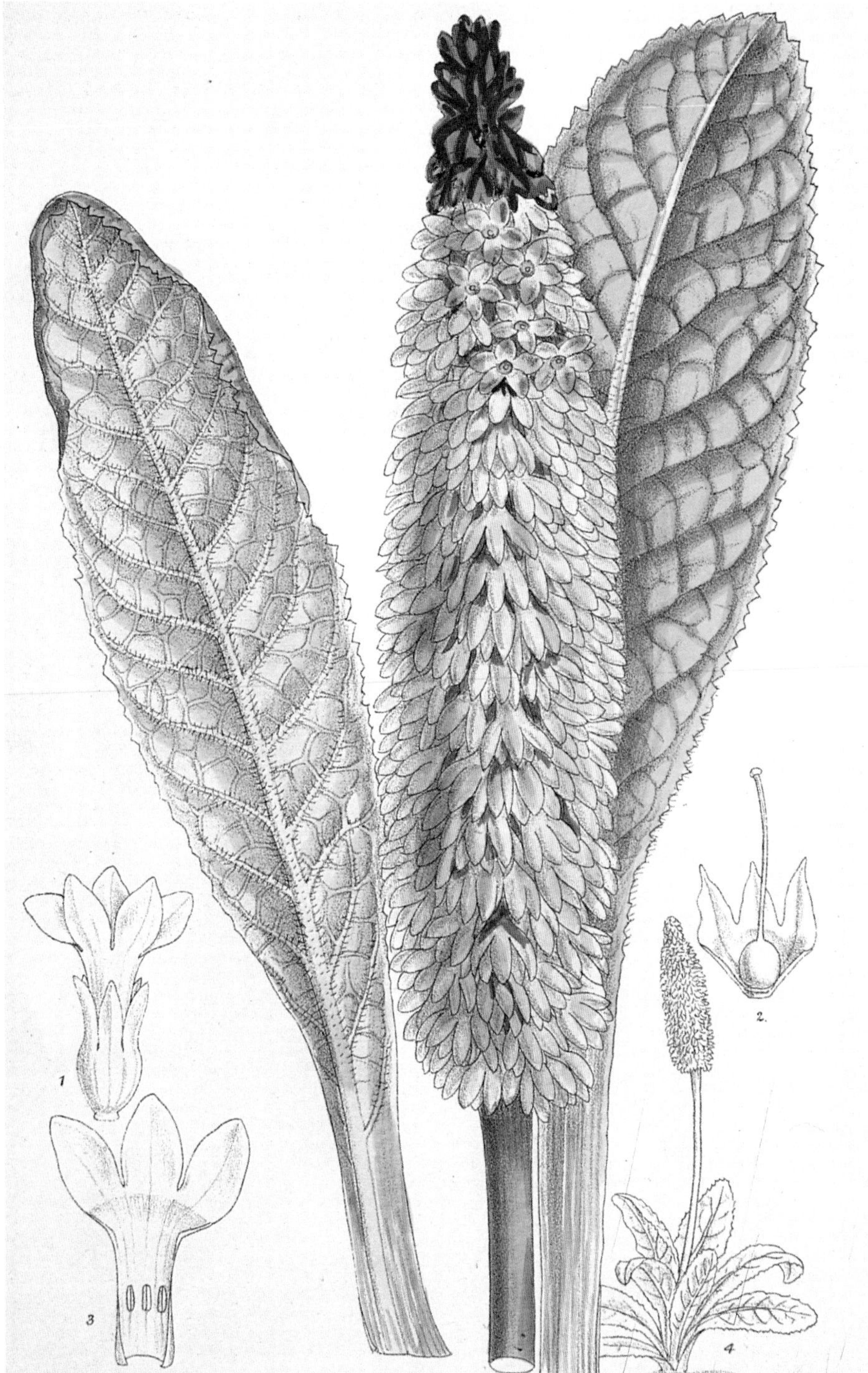

1
2.
3
4
M.S.del. J.N.Fitch lith.
Vincent Brooks, Day & Son Ltd imp
L. Reeve & Co. London.

attending prayers often enough, or of defaulting on their debts, were 'condemned to receive a certain number of blows on the soals of their feet and besides pay half a penny for each blow'.

Rauwulf was glad to discover that 'in their gardens, the Turks love to raise all sorts of flowers wherein they take great delight, and use to put them in their turbants so I could see the fine plants that blow, one after another, daily without trouble'. Violets were to be seen in December, then tulips, hyacinths and narcissus including one rare kind with a double yellow flower.

Other Turkish customs, however, were less attractive. Malefactors, Rauwolf noted, were tied to a cross, and between the cross and the men's shoulders were placed 'two burning torches prepared with bacon so that the grease ran all over their bodies burning them severely'. Other habits were peculiar if not outlandish. There were no tables or chairs in the houses, and attempts to make social contact with Turkish women could be a dangerous sport – 'but that you may know where the women are, they commonly hang cloth over the door towards the street, so that if any man should intend to go in there, he may find himself another entrance'. At times Rauwolf found it difficult not to be conspicuous, for the Turks, if they see a man making water standing up, conclude he is a Christian.

In Tripoli Rauwolf saw the banana and *Brassica marina*, with rather square leaves instead of round ones, and an unusual *Echium* 'at a mile's distant as you go to St James's church'. In the hills behind he encountered '*Zizypha alba*', '*Absinthum ponticum*' and '*Eleagnus matthiolus*'. Unlike Belon, Rauwolf took the trouble to pack his finds between sheets of paper, glueing them to the paper with great care, so that they dried with their natural colours preserved.

Primula littoniana from *Curtis's Botanical Magazine*

Near Aleppo he found 'many sorts of cornflowers

quite differing from ours'. He also encountered 'papaver erratic, in their language called Schuck of which they make a conserve with sugar and use it in confits'. In the same area he came across 'Glauctum corniculatum' the Horned Poppy, 'with stately purple [most people would say deep red] flowers', Eryngium with bluish tops and starred heads with two sorts of henbane 'whereof one that groweth in the fields hath red and purple coloured flowers; the other which I found in the town upon the old walls had white ones by the Latines called apollinaris'.

He continues: 'Yet I cannot but describe to you one more plant for the taking of which I and my two comrades fell into great danger . . . This is called by the inhabitants Rhafut and also Rumigi; it hath a strong yet unpleasant savour and about four stalks of a whitish colour and so tender towards the root and so small as a pack thread wereon at each side grown seven or eight tender ash coloured leaves distributed like unto those of Osmond Royal, only they have round Ears towards the stalk like unto small Sage. . . . (It has) flowers like Aristolochia yet a great deal bigger and more brownish colour and hanging on longer stalks. The root striketh very deep and is very like to our Pellitory, of a drying quality and somewhat hot as the bitter taste intimates. [Speculation is, as they say, rife, as to the name of the plant.]

'When I was busy about this tender plant and strove to get it out whole which took me up the more time because I had no proper tools by me, a Turk, well-armed came galloping upon us to see what we were doing.' Each of the group gave him some coins and he rode away apparently satisfied. But before Rauwolf could lift the plant the Turk came back at full speed and 'came down upon me with his cymeter drawn and fetched one blow after the other at me, which I still declined running from one side of the (olive) tree to the other, so that they went into the tree and mangled it mightily.' Rauwolf concluded that if the Turk decided to make use of his bow and arrow, he would have to put aside the cymeter for a moment and that this would make it possible to engage the infidel in close combat. But the coin was mightier than the sword, and Rauwolf was able to buy off the Turk, who nevertheless insisted on taking away Rauwolf's 'tablebook' of records which had fallen out of his pocket in the struggle.

Undeterred, Rauwolf and a friend, Hans Ulrich Rafft, decided to journey overland to the Euphrates river and coast down it to Baghdad, and to make themselves less conspicuous they posed as merchants, dressed in blue cabans buttoned right down and cut about the neck, white cotton drawers falling to the ankles, shirts without collars and white 'turbants' with a blue brim such as Christians usually wore. The outfit included yellow shoes painted in front and guarded with nails and a 'frock', narrow and without sleeves, reaching to the knees. It was woven out of goat or asses' hair though finer than the material used for tents, or for a portmanteau for carrying the food for camels and mules.

This trip yielded fewer flowers particularly as the barge would often glide past tempting plants on the river bank without stopping. But it taught Rauwolf much about the tent-dwellers of the desert. 'These vagabond people that are used to idleness from their infancy and will rather endure hunger, heat and cold than get anything by their handiwork or till the fields or plant garden herbs although they might do in several places of their own possession.'

Rauwolf was arrested by the Turks when he got back to Tripoli, allegedly for spying, but in his view merely as a pretext for extorting a fine from him.

He was able to extricate himself from trouble and even practised medicine before returning home with his botanical spoils.

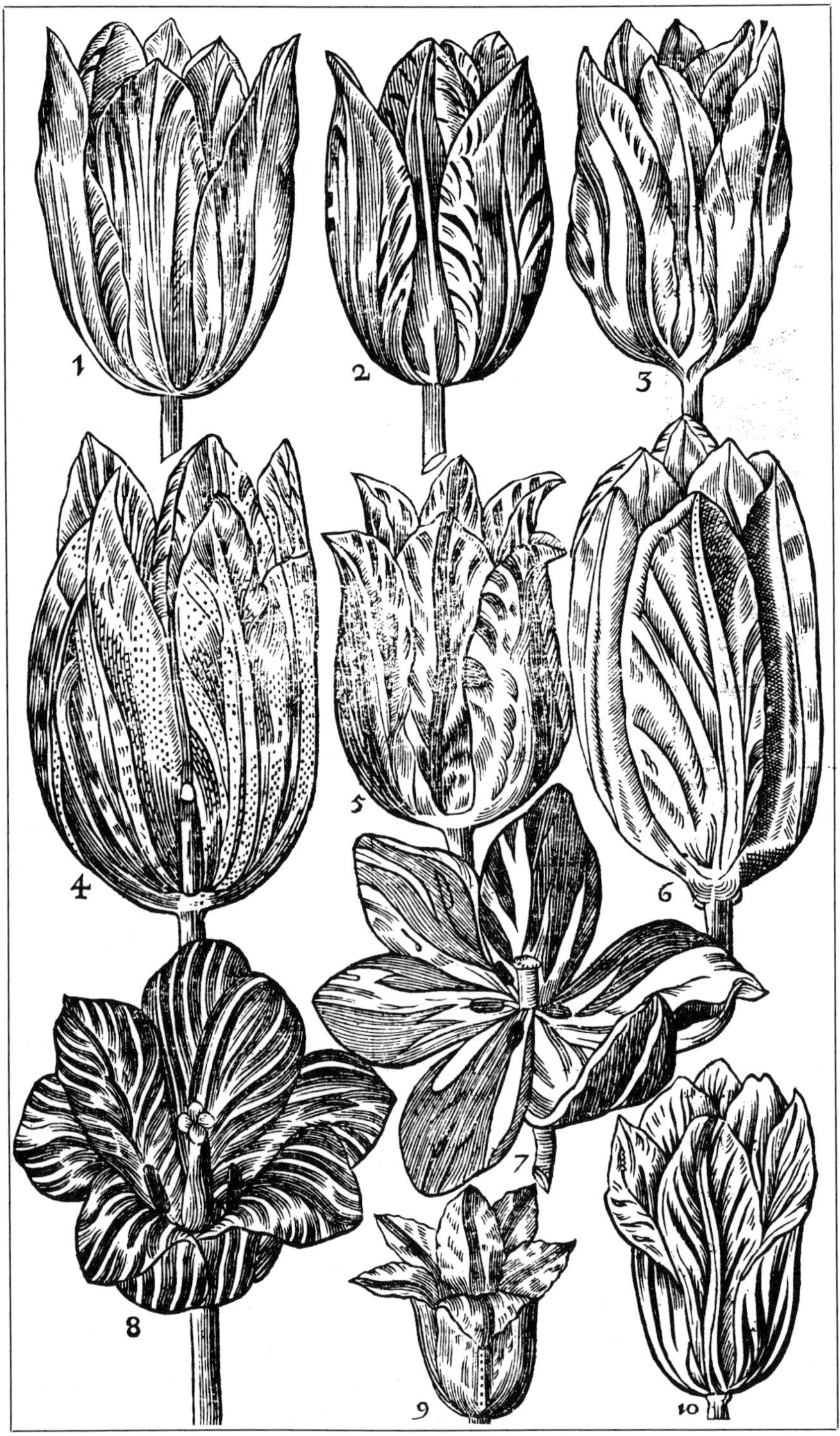
1
2
3
4
5
6
7
8
9
10

For the English, the opportunities lay further afield. In 1493 Pope Alexander VI had awarded to Spain all newly discovered land west of a line drawn 100 leagues to the west of Cape Verde Islands. Portugal was granted all new discoveries to the east, and later the line was pushed further west to give Portugal Brazil.

It was a challenge which the Tudors could not ignore. Up to the reign of Henry VIII the royal navy had consisted of conscripted merchant ships which could engage enemy vessels only by heaving a grappling line and boarding them. But in the first half of the sixteenth century, things changed. Dockyards were established at Woolwich and Deptford and ships were built which could fire broadsides from guns mounted athwartship. The vessels were highly manoeuvrable and in Elizabeth's time Drake was able to raid the Spanish Main and the Pacific coastline. In 1577 he set sail on his voyage round the world.

And lest it be thought that Drake, and for that matter Raleigh, brought back nothing but silver with them, it should be recorded that Clusius made a special trip to England to see what plants the two mariners had collected.

There was also plenty for Clusius to do on the Continent.

A cottager's plant was about to give rise to what has been called tulipomania. The disease had set in gradually, for the bulbs were, as we have seen, known in Europe in the middle of the previous century. The first tulip to make a real impact was a red-petalled long scented variety, named at the time for Conrad Gesner, Zurich-born botanist who had seen it in bloom in the garden of Johan Harwart in Augsburg, in 1559. It would now be regarded as a variety of *Tulipa suaveolens*. The first double-tulip was recorded by Clusius in Vienna in 1581 and from then on was taken up enthusiastically in France, and

A page of tulips from Parkinson's *Paradisus Terrestris* '1 A Tulipa of three colours. 2 The Tulipa of Caffa purple with pale white stripes. 3 A pure Claret wine colour variable. 4 Mr. Wilmers Gilloflower Tulipa. 5 A Crimson with white flames. 6 A kind of Zwisser called Goliah. 7 A Tulipa called the Zwisser. 8 Another white Flambat or Fooles Coate. 9 The Vermillion flamed. 10 The featherbed Tulipa red and yellow.'

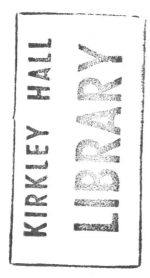

England where, by 1629, 150 different varieties were listed.

But Holland – the country to which Clusius had moved after working for 14 years in Vienna for the Emperor Maximilian II – led the van, so much so that in later years Dr Evrard Forstus, Professor of Botany at Leyden, could not see a tulip without whacking at it with his walking stick.

Tulip breeding was a lottery in which everyone could join. All you needed was an ordinary self-coloured tulip which you hoped would 'break', that is, develop stripes of a different colour – as it was afterwards learnt from a virus infection. No one could say for certain in advance when the breaking in a self-coloured tulip might occur. But once this had happened, the same pattern would occur on all the offsets – bulbs – derived from that plant, and so on more or less *ad infinitum*. And the breaking or partial loss of colour due to the virus seemed to add intensity to the parts of the petal that were not affected. If the edges only were streaked, the bloom was said to be feathered, and if the centre was pencilled, the flower was 'flamed' with that colour.

Brand new combinations of colour made fortunes for small-holders overnight – for it was in the soil of cottage gardens that most of the breaks seemed to occur. Regular tulip auctions were held from June till September, though many a sale took place over a glass of Genever in some alehouse.

Bulbs were bought on margin by those who could not afford to pay but assumed that the price would rise after the next flowering season. Those who had no ready cash mortgaged even their houses.

The uncertainties were great. Seed was unwanted, as it took several years for the flower to appear. Only offsets produced by the bulbs themselves would suffice and even then who could be certain that the offset had really come from the plant that was said to have produced it?

Nevertheless, vast sums changed hands both in cash and kind, and a single bulb, named Viceroy, was bartered for two loads of wheat, four of rye, eight fat pigs, 12 fat sheep, some cheese, silver, some liquor and a carriage and pair. And even this bulb was considered inferior to the most famous strain of all, *Semper Augustus*, of which the flower, though not very large, was well veined, and striped with pale yellow on deep crimson with a bottom of dark violet purple. It was put about that there were only 12 such bulbs in existence and the going price seems to have been 4,000 to 5,000 florins which at present (1982) prices, would be equivalent to around £1,750. Such madness could not last, and the demand for freak tulips had almost collapsed by 1640, ruining hundreds of speculators.

But the interest of the ordinary gardener in tulips persisted and was sustained towards the end of the century by the introduction of the parrot tulip with its slashed petals and by the fact it was possible to buy plants which would provide four rows in a bed, one behind the other, each taller than the last. In the middle of the nineteenth century, nurserymen still found it possible to ask £100 for a single bulb.

6 *The Tradescant Connection*

The opening years of the seventeenth century witnessed a number of special appeals made to women as gardeners. William Lawson's *The Countrie Housewife's Garden*, published in 1618, was one of the first, and, though it suggests no special adventures in the flowerbed, it often offers sound advice, emphasising at one point that 'if you be not able or willing to hire a gardener, keep your profits to yourself, but then you must take all the pains'. He also suggests that there is little point in building a stockade round your orchard if you are niggardly with the fruit. 'Liberality is the best fence,' he declares.

John Parkinson, apothecary and herbalist to James I, was another seventeenth-century garden writer to address himself especially to women. His most famous work, *Paradisi in sole Paradisus terrestris*, usually referred to as *Paradisus* – a gardening treatise as well as a treasury of desirable flowers – was dedicated to Queen Henrietta Maria, wife of King Charles I, and in it he makes many references to the names most often used by 'gentlewomen' when referring to garden plants.

Nor is this deference a mere form of words to be forgotten, when once taking up the trowel. Thus, after describing the 'Purple Pasque Flower; the Passe flower of Denmarke; the red, yellow and white Passe Flower; the white wilde broad leafed Windflower; the purple Starre Anemone; the great double Orange tawney Anemone; the double crimson Velvet Anemone; and the double Carnation Anemone', he continues, 'I cannot (Gentlewomen) withold one other secret from you, which is to informe you how you may so order Anemonies, that after all other ordinarily past, you may have them in flower for two or three moneths longer then are to be seene with any other, that useth not this course I direct you. The ordinary time to plant Anemones is most commonly in August, which will beare flower some peradventure before, but mostly in February, March and Aprill, few or none of them abiding untill May; but if you will keepe some rootes out of the ground unplanted, untill February, March and

John Parkinson (1567–1650), author of *Paradisus Terrestris*

Pasque Flowers (*Pulsatilla vulgaris*): 'The purple Pasque flower with leafe, seed, and root; Swertz his red Pasque flower.' from Parkinson's *Paradisus Terrestris*

Aprill, and plant some at one time, and some at another, you shall have them beare flower according to their planting, those that shall be planted in February, will flower about the middle or end of May, and so the rest accordingly after that manner'.

It was *Paradisus*, published in 1629, that obtained for Parkinson the appointment of Royal Botanist to King Charles I but, in his search for royal favour, Parkinson never loses the common touch and is far less regal than Bacon.

Thus in the section headed 'The Ordering of the Garden of Pleasure' he writes, 'The severall situations of mens dwellings, are for the most part unavoidable and unremoveable; for most men cannot appoint forth such a manner of situation for their dwelling, as is most fit to avoide all the inconveniences of winde and weather, but must bee content with such as the place will afford them; yet all men doe well know, that some situations are more excellent than others'.

He goes on to say that if the house cannot be built on the north side to protect the garden from weather 'which might else spoyle the pride thereof in the bud', then 'every ones pleasure thereof shall be according to the site, cost and endeavours they bestow, to cause it to come nearest to this proportion, by such helpes of bricke, or stone wals to defend it, or by the helpe of high growne and well spread trees planted on the North side to keepe it the warmer'.

Parkinson had his own garden in Long Acre, not far from Covent Garden, once the Convent Garden of the monks of Westminster, and throughout, he emphasises that he is aiming for a garden of pleasant flowers and not herbs. His philosophy is well set out in his paragraph on *Verbascum*, Mullein: 'There be divers kindes of Mullein, as white Mullein, blacke Mullein, wooddy Mullein, base Mullein, Moth Mullein, and Ethiopian Mullein, all which to distinguish or to describe, is neither to my purpose, nor the intent of this worke, which is to store a Garden with flowers of delight and sequester others not worthy of that honour. Those that are fit to bee brought to your consideration in this place, are first, the Blattarias, or Moth Mulleins, and then the wooddy Mullein, which otherwise is called French Sage [some confusion here], and lastly the Ethiopian Mullein, whose beauty consisteth, not in the flower, but in the whole plant; yet if it please you not, take it according to his Country, for a Moore, an Infidell, a Slave, and so use it'.

He also makes a plea for another far from popular wild flower: 'You may somewhat marvaile, to see mee curious to plant Thistles in my garden, when as you might well say, they are rather plagues than pleasures, and more trouble to weede them out, than to cherish them up, if I made therein no distinction or choise; but when you have viewed them well which I bring in I will then abide your censure, if they are not worthy of some place, although it be a corner of the Garden, where something needes be to fill up roome'.

One of the thistles he favours is the 'Friers Crowne' more usually known to us as *Cirsium eriophorum*, the Woolly Thistle. It is anything but that for the spines of the leaves are directed both upwards and downwards as a keep-off warning and would be quite unsuitable as part of a nosegay or tussie-mussie which was Parkinson's name for a garden posy. Nevertheless the plant's globe-shaped involucres are strongly reminiscent of a friar's newly cropped hair-style.

Pyracantha coccinea, the Fire Thorn, is a shrub on Parkinson's list which has kept its popularity. Its show of scarlet berries lasts well into the autumn; birds eat them but re-sow them. Another plant befriended by Parkinson was *Hieracium aurantiacum*, the fiery Orange Hawkweed more popularly known as the Fox and Cubs. He called it the Gold Mouse Ear. Another half wild plant on Parkinson's list was *Saxifraga umbrosa*. London Pride is a hybrid of this and *S. spathularis*.

Some of Parkinson's favourites are garden favourites still. There was also *Centaurea moschata*, Sweet Sultan, of which Parkinson writes: 'As a kinde of these Corne flowers, I must needes adjoyne another stranger, of much beautie, and but lately obtained from Constantinople, where, because, (as it is said) the Great Turke, as we call him, saw it abroade, liked it, and wrote it himselfe; all his vassals have had it in great regard . . . the circling leaves [petals] are of a fine delayed purple or blush colour . . . very beautiful and of so exceeding a sweet sent that it surpasseth the finest civet that is'. He also cultivated *Kochia scoparia*, a native of southern Europe, a sub-shrub grown for its decorative foliage and often known as Summer Cyprus because of its inability to survive the English winter.

The dark red scabious *Scabiosa atropurpurea* was also on his list having been first described by Clusius (who found it growing plentifully in Austria and passed it to Gerard). The brilliant scarlet *Lobelia cardinalis* which he featured seems to have arrived back in 1626 from America via France.

Morning Glory, *Ipomoea violacea* (synonym: *Ipomoea rubro-caerulea*) or was it, perhaps *I. learii* also fascinated him. He called it the Greater Blew Bindeweed and described how the plant 'riseth up with many long winding branches, whereby it climbeth and windeth upon any poles, herbes, or trees, that stande neare it within a great compass, alwaies winding itself contrary to the course of the sunne; on these branches doe growe many faire great round leaves, pointed at the end, like unto a Violet leafe in shape, but much greater, of a sad greene colour; at the joynts of the branches, where the leaves are set, come forth flowers on pretty long stalkes, two or three together at a place, which are long and pointed almost like a finger while they are buds, and not blowne open, and of a pale whiteish blew colour, but being blowne open, are great and large bels, with broad open mouths or brims ending in five corners, and small at the bottome, standing in small greene husks of fine leaves; these flowers are of a very deepe azure or blew colour tending to a purple very glorious to behold'. This was by no means its first appearance, for it had been noted eight years earlier by John Goodyer, the Hampshire naturalist.

Oenothera biennis, which Parkinson calls *Lysimachia siliquosa*, the Tree Primrose of Virginia, had also been described by Goodyer and it had been known in the Padua botanic garden in 1619 as was *Helichrysum orientale*, the first of the everlastings. *Lilium canadense* came to Parkinson from France; Jacques Cartier, the navigator who helped establish the French in Canada, had brought the plant back with him on his return in 1535. *Paradisea liliastrum*, St Bruno's Lily, with its white flowers is mentioned in Parkinson's *Paradisus*, which could have inspired the name. Parkinson cultivated the Blue Agapanthus from the Cape, presumably through the Dutch merchantmen although their permanent settlement there was not set up till 1647.

One other garden plant deserves a mention here – though surprisingly enough it does not get a specially commended one from Parkinson. This is *Gladiolus byzantinus*, or, as he calls it, the Corne Flag. From his description it sounds rather like our own native *Gladiolus illyricus*. Of the Corne Flag, Parkinson says, 'The stalke riseth up from among the leaves, bearing them on it as it riseth, having at the toppe divers huskes, out of which come the flowers, one above another, all of them turning and opening themselves one way, which are long and gaping like unto the flowers of the Foxglove, a little arched or bunching up in the middle, of a faire reddish purple colour, with two white spots within the mouth thereof, one on each side, made like unto a lozenge that is square and long pointed. If it be suffered any long time in a Garden, it will rather choake and pester it, than be an ornament unto it'.

Parkinson adds 'They grow in France and Italy, the least in Spaine and the Byzantine, as it is thought, about Constantinople, being (as is said) first sent home from thence. John Tradescant assured mee, that hee saw many acres of ground in Barbary spread over with them'.

And so, through Parkinson we are introduced to the Tradescants, the family who presented our gardens with Virginia Creeper, the Tulip Tree, *Cotinus coggygria*, the Smoke Bush, *Lupinus perennis*, Perennial Lupin and many other delights.

John Tradescant senior came of an old Suffolk family which moved to London in 1578, and his first recorded employment dating from 1609 was with Robert Cecil, 1st Earl of Salisbury. It seems likely that before this he had worked for Henry Brooke, Lord Cobham at Cobham Hall, near Meopham, Kent, and in this way was brought to the notice of the Cecil family who came to own two other Kent properties, the Manor of Shorne near Rochester, and St Augustine's Palace at Canterbury, and were also linked by marriage to the Brookes.

At that time, Salisbury's main interest was the rebuilding of Hatfield, for which the French hydraulic engineer and fountain expert, Salomon de Caux, was called in. Tradescant's work was largely concerned with alterations to the garden which were needed to match the new lay-out of the estate. Mulberry trees were imported in large quantities to please King James, who hoped to establish a flourishing silk industry at home though he chose *Morus nigra* a species good for fruit instead of *M. alba* preferred by silk worms. Twenty thousand vines were ordered through Madame de la Boderie, wife of the French Ambassador, and hundreds of peach, pear, apple, quince, medlar and cherry trees.

In 1611 Tradescant was sent abroad for three months on a buying expedition. He visited Flushing, Leyden, Rotterdam, Haarlem, Brussels and Paris. There he met Jean Robin, Royal Arborist to three kings – Henry III, Henry IV and Louis XIII. Robin had already laid out a garden for the Louvre, and established a plot for the Royal School of Medicine which afterwards developed into the Jardin des Plantes. Though preoccupied with fruit-bearing trees, Tradescant returned with at least five worthwhile border introductions – the 'debble Epatega' (Hepatica) and two lilies the 'Martegon pompone blanche' and the 'Martagon pompone oreng coller', so called because their recurved petals were thought to resemble the martagon, a special form of turban adopted by the Turkish ruler, Sultan Mohammed I.

But the 1st Earl did not live to see all these acquisitions in their full glory. He died in 1612, deeply in debt, without ever having lived at Hatfield.

William Cecil, the new Earl, however, was undaunted and continued to spend freely on his properties, whether at Hatfield, Cranborne, Greenwich or at Cecil House in the Strand. He furnished Hatfield extravagantly, built a family chapel for private worship and entertained royalty in an alarmingly lavish manner. Possibly he had to cut down on the garden. At any rate around the year 1615, we find John Tradescant, his wife Elizabeth, a farmer's daughter, and his seven-year-old son John, back in Kent. They appear to have kept Pitfield Cottage, Meopham, which they had occupied from 1607 onwards but Tradescant was now chief gardener at St Augustine's Palace in Canterbury which had been bought from the 2nd Earl of Salisbury by

Allium ostrowskianum – carmine-coloured Garlic from Western Turkestan, *Curtis's Botanical Magazine*

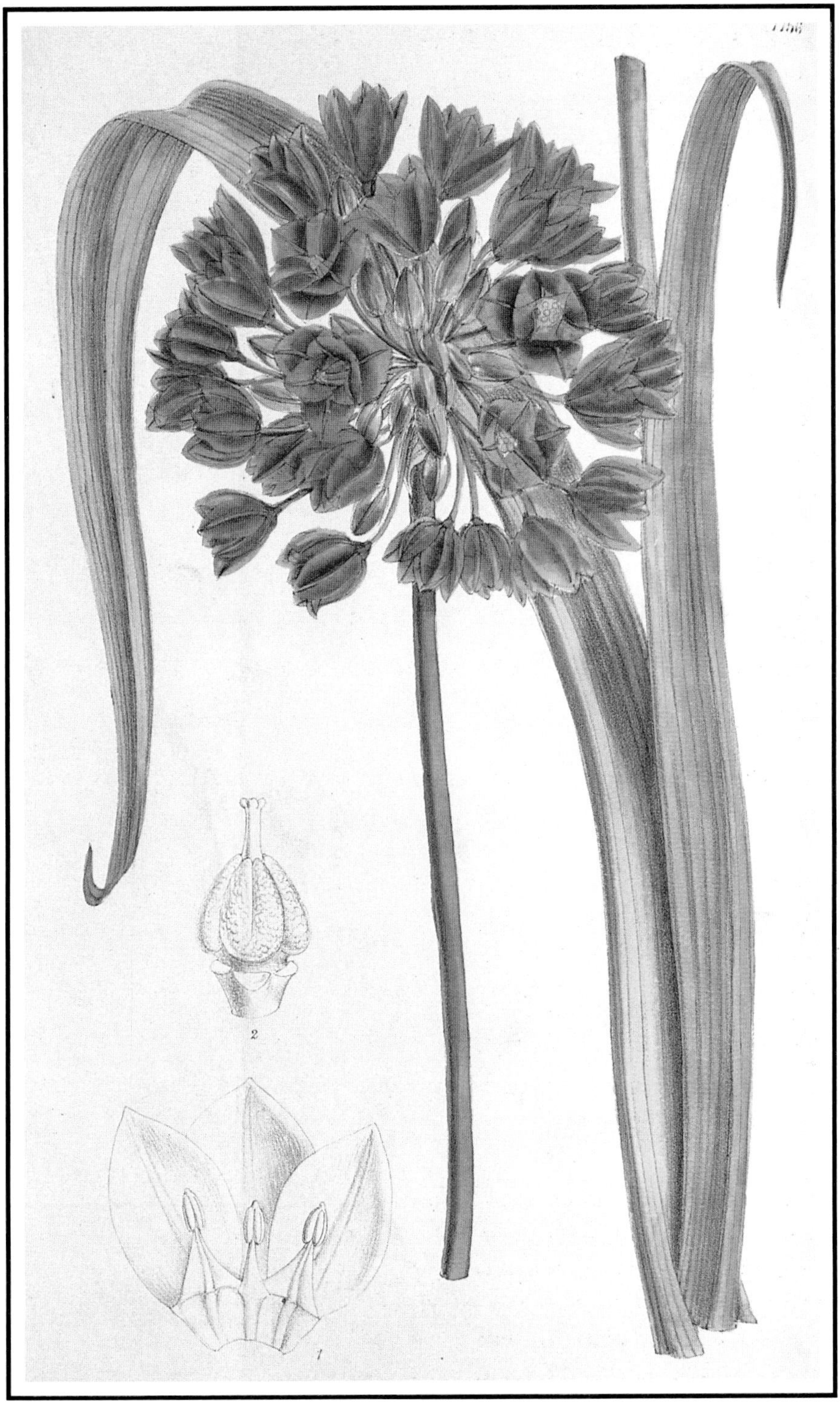
2
1

3801.
Miss Dally Delᵗ
Pub. by S. Curtis, Glazenwood, Essex, June 1. 1840.
Swan Sc.

John Tradescant the younger (1608–62)

Sir Edward Wotton.

Young John remained at school at Canterbury until 1625 when the Tradescant family moved to Lambeth.

In the meantime, however, John Tradescant Senior, had embarked on the first of his own plant-hunting adventures abroad. The chance came when his name came to the attention of Sir Dudley Digges who had recently acquired the manor and castle of Chilham in Kent and had ambitious plans for laying out new gardens there. Sir Dudley was already a man of substance, a formidable lawyer with the intention of making his mark in politics. He was a leading member of the East India Company, had invested in the new colony of Virginia, and was also a member of the Muscovy Company. In short he was just the man to head a diplomatic mission sent in 1618 to the new Czar Mikhail Romanov to arrange a loan to the Czar to be provided by the East India and Muscovy companies in return for valuable and exclusive trading privileges.

The mission as such was a failure as Sir Dudley never reached Moscow, turning back after he heard that it was under siege from the Polish army, but Tradescant made good use of his three weeks spent in and around Archangel. One of these finds was *Angelica archangelica*, Angelica, with the greenish white flowers and green stem which is still used in confectionary. Another was *Andromeda arborea*, a cousin of our somewhat rare pink flowered Bog Rosemary.

But his best find was a species of larch, the tree which provides unmatched splashes of green in the spring. It had seldom been seen before in England.

By this time the wanderlust seems to have gripped Tradescant and when he heard that an expedition was being sent to suppress the slave trade conducted by the Barbary Corsairs in the Mediterranean, he was accepted as a volunteer aboard a ship

Fuchsia fulgens, the Glowing Fuchsia, from *Curtis's Botanical Magazine*

captained by Phineas Pett, Commissioner of the Navy; the vessel reached Alicante and cruised the Mediterranean for the best part of seven months. During this time, Tradescant was able to secure seeds or bulbs of several popular plants which appeared later on the list of those he was able to grow himself.

The *Gladiolus*, of course, was one.

Other plants from the Mediterranean area were still growing in the Tradescant garden towards the end of the century. One was *Tamarix anglica*, which despite its name, is a native of Portugal and Spain. Alicia Amherst attributes its original introduction to Edmund Grindal (1519?–83), the staunchly Protestant Archbishop of Canterbury in Elizabeth I's reign. *Viburnum tinus*, the evergreen variety with flowers tinged with pink, was another of Tradescant's importations from the Mediterranean though it had been first introduced to England in the sixteenth century.

And there were also some Rock Roses: *Cistus monspeliensis* with sticky leaves and white flowers and *C. hirsutus*, another white species with yellow stamens as showy as those of a Christmas Rose.

His *C. ladanifer*, the Gum Cistus described earlier by Gerard is also white but the petals are decorated with a chocolate-coloured blotch.

A white lupin from Crete appeared on Tradescant's list but the best of the bunch was undoubtedly *Syringa persica*, the lilac which Tradescant called the dark violet-coloured Persian Jasmine. Who would be without it today? It may originally not have been Persian at all but just one more of those plants brought west with them by the Chinese whose empire, already in being at the time of the Pharaohs, stretched at one time to the Caspian Sea.

The next year Tradescant accepted employment with an even more illustrious patron – Charles Villiers, Duke of Buckingham and favourite-to-be of King Charles I. Buckingham had recently bought Newhall, near Chelmsford, in Essex, the great mansion formerly used by Henry VIII and Anne Boleyn, and was planning improvements to its gardens.

Tradescant accompanied Buckingham in 1625 to the ceremony in Paris at which King Charles in England was married by proxy to Louis XIII's sister, Henrietta Maria. No sooner had he arrived than he was sent back to recover a trunk containing his master's ceremonial apparel which had been left behind, but, as the celebrations lasted for three weeks, there was plenty of time for him to see his old friend Jean Robin and Robin's son, Vespasien.

That year, it will be remembered, the family finally moved from Kent to Lambeth, the site of the famous Tradescant nursery, which was combined with a collection of unusual curiosities, some of which are still to be seen in the Ashmolean Museum in Oxford.

Two years later Tradescant was once more a volunteer, this time on Buckingham's unsuccessful attempt to storm the Isle of Rhe, opposite to La Rochelle on the west coast of France. That failure led a discontented officer, John Felton, to assassinate Buckingham with a knife which he had bought for a shilling.

But by now Tradescant was his own employer. His nursery, situated in an area now midway between Stockwell and Vauxhall stations, was well established. Turret House, as it was officially called, looked out over green fields without another house in sight; and the Tradescants seemed to be able to raise plants there that had been failures everywhere else.

In 1630 John Tradescant Senior was appointed Keeper of His Majesty's Gardens, Vines and Silkworms at Oatlands, the palace between Walton and Weybridge which was the special delight of the royal pair. It had five gardens, the great garden, the long garden, the King's privy garden, the Queen's privy garden and the new garden.

He was by now receiving many new and strange plants from abroad. For in 1617, Tradescant had become a shareholder in the Virginia Company and, having paid for the transport of 24 settlers to the new colony, had been entitled to buy 1,200 acres of land there. He was also in a position to arrange for seeds, bulbs, and even 'flower laid betwin paper leaves in a book, dried' to be sent home to him. Indeed while still in the service of the Duke of Buckingham, he had been able to write as from the Duke to Edward Nicholas, Secretary to the Navy, who asked diplomats such as Sir Thomas Roe, who had been ambassador to the court of Jehangir, the Mogul Emperor of Hindustan between 1615 and 1618, as well as at Constantinople, and even the Chartered Merchants of the Virginia Company who might need the navy's protection or patronage, to search for new species of all kinds.

Tradescantia virginiana, as shown in Parkinson's *Paradisus terrestis*. One of many plants introduced by John Tradescant the younger

Mea Allen, in her deeply researched biography of the Tradescants, has prepared a list of new plants introduced from 1617 – the year when Tradescant took up membership of the Virginia Company – up to and including 1634 when he produced the list of plants growing in his own garden.

They include *Amaranthus (Celosia) hypochondriacus*, 'The Great Floramour or Purple Flower Gentle' – more generally called the Prince's Feather; *Dodecatheon meadia*, ineptly named the American Cowslip, for its pink flowers are anything but funnel-shaped, and bloom, candelabra fashion, at the top of a candle stalk with petals swept back, styles pointing like storks' bills to the ground, as if they were cranberry flowers, and *Robinia pseudacacia*, sometimes called the Locust Tree, sometimes (wrongly), the acacia.

But it is sometimes difficult to know how many American introductions to ascribe to Tradescant alone. This is because he frequently passed on plants to his friend, Parkinson, to cultivate and these, if earlier than 1629 would have appeared in Parkinson's catalogue. Parkinson specifically credited some plants on his list to Tradescant, among them 'Tradescant's Spiderwort (*Tradescantia virginiana*)'; but others may not have been, and it is only after 1629 that Tradescant began to keep his own notes of new plants received, which he wrote in onto blank pages at the end of his copy of Parkinson's list.

One of these would be the silkweed with two-tiered dull purple flowers; its Latin name is *Asclepias syriaca*, though the species is as north American as blueberry pie. Of this Parkinson wrote, 'it cometh to me from Virginia', but he did not say how or through whom. Also, we cannot be certain that all American plants listed separately by Tradescant can be automatically or even entirely credited to him as 'firsts'. The Dutch, for example, were in possession of New Amsterdam, later New York, until 1667, and the French did not give up Canada till nearly a century later. Louisiana and Florida remained in French or Spanish hands until the beginning of the nineteenth century, and new American plants may have come to London from other collectors in Paris, Amsterdam – or even Madrid.

Cone Flower (*Rudbeckia laciniata*), recorded by Tradescant in 1632, originated in America

Rudbeckia laciniata, the Cone Flower, which Tradescant recorded in 1633 and Parkinson in 1640, was not secured directly from America. Vespasien Robin sent it to Tradescant, as well as *Zephyranthes atamasco*, which we know as the Jamestown Lily. In the same year Tradescant recorded *Solidago canadensis*, a species greatly superior to our own native *S. virgaurea*, Golden Rod. The Tradescant plant had presumably migrated to England from Canada via Paris.

Nevertheless the notes of plants received and kept by Tradescant from 1629 onwards, show that he was handling some species considerably in advance of the date of introduction given, for example, in the invaluable *Dictionary of the Royal Horticultural Society*. Thus in 1630 he recorded a plant identified as *Tiarella cordifolia*, the Allegheny Foam Flower, which apparently was lost sight of until 1731; and *Ptelea trifoliata*, the Canadian Hop Tree, with the sweet scented yellow flowers, which Tradescant recorded as received in 1633, was not apparently established until 1704.

The next year, 1633, witnessed the arrival of *Chrysanthemum serotinum*, 'the Great Tufted American Daisy' and the white-flowered form of *Tradescantia virginiana*, Moses in the Bulrushes. The original plant with its three-petalled violet flowers peeping from within a casket of dark green spears, had apparently been known in Europe for nearly forty years, though not, it would appear, to Parkinson.

Tradescant made little to-do about his *Aster tradescanti*, an ancestor of our Michaelmas Daisy – perhaps because of its straggling habit, or because it looked no more distinguished than Gerard's earlier *Aster amellus*, the Purple Starwort from Italy.

The official records of the State Paper Office show that John Tradescant Junior paid a visit to Virginia in 1637. He had meantime been admitted to the Mystery of the Gardeners of the City of London which had been incorporated by Royal Charter in 1606. It had power to remove and burn plants that were dead or corrupt and also to insist on seven years' apprenticeship for those intending to set up as gardeners. He went via Barbados where he collected *Mimosa pudica*, called the Humble Plant, merely, I suppose, to distinguish it from its near relative, *M. sensitiva*, the Sensitive Plant. In either case the leaves are so responsive that they fold together at the slightest touch. The plant had a legendary reputation, but no one at home had seen it perform.

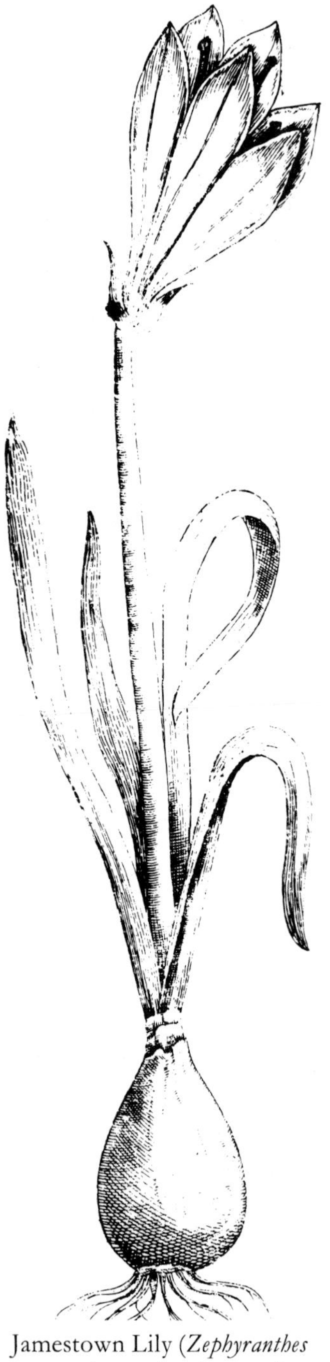

Jamestown Lily (*Zephyranthes atamasco*), another import from America, from Sweerts' *Florilegium*

Purple Starwort (*Aster amellus*), imported from Italy, from Sweerts' *Florilegium*

Another curiosity was *Sarracenia purpurea*, the Pitcher Plant which flowers wild in Roscommon and Westmeath in central Ireland, where it was introduced in 1906. The flowers, usually more than an inch across, are globular and purple; the root leaves are tubular pitchers marked with purple and usually filled with water and noxious secretions from the plant in which the insects on which the plant depends for its extra ration of nitrogen, are drowned and absorbed. The genus was named, rightly or wrongly, after Dr Michel Sarrazin, a physician in Quebec.

Another winner to come from this trip was *Campsis radicans*, the Trumpet Vine, an orange red spectacular hardy in most parts of Britain on a south-facing wall. There was also *Aquilegia canadensis*, the Canadian Columbine – red and yellow with straight spurs more like the modern varieties.

John Tradescant Senior died in 1638 but his son made two further expeditions to America, in 1642 and 1654 and published another garden list in 1656. This included *Acer rubrum*, the glorious Red Maple that sets Canada and the eastern United States on fire each autumn. There was also a new species of passion flower, *Passiflora lutea*; *Anaphalis margaritacea*, an everlasting plant; *Parthenocissus quinquefolia*, Virginia Creeper, and *Liriodendron tulipfera*, the Tulip Tree with its bluntly snipped leaves and curiously banded greenish tulip-flowers. There was *Yucca filamentosa*, sometimes called Adam's Needle and *Chelone glabra*, the handy border plant with the lower petals of its rose-white flowers protruding from beneath an upper lip like a turtle's head. There was also the European shrub, *Rhododendron hirsutum*, which has a better claim to the title Alpine Rose than its near relative, *R. ferrugineum*. Fine hauls which could only stimulate gardeners to search for more.

In the meantime, however, England had other problems. The Civil War between the Roundheads and Cavaliers broke out on 2 August 1642 in a field outside Nottingham. In that meadow bordering the wall of a ruined castle, King Charles set up his battle standard.

There were gardeners on both sides of the struggle. Sir Ralph Verney, a true royalist, was interested in sweet briars, in *ranunculi* and Persian tulips. Thomas Johnson, who edited the second edition of Gerard's *Herball* was also a royalist. He had a shop on Snow Hill, not far from Fleet Street, and drew attention to himself by exhibiting a bunch of bananas in its window – the first that had been seen in England. 'Some have judged it to be the forbidden fruit,' he said, 'But other-some the grapes which were brought to Moses out of the Holy Land.' Johnson died of wounds received during Cromwell's attack on Basing House in Hampshire.

But equally Cromwell's General Lambert, Lord of the Manor of Wimbledon, was a tulip enthusiast who obtained the double striped pomegranate and other plants from merchants travelling to Algiers and Constantinople. He was later tried for high treason and spent the last twenty years of his life in prison. Sir John Danvers who was one of those who signed the King's Death Warrant was wont, we are told by John Aubrey 'on fair mornings in the summer to brush his Beaver-Hat on the Hyssop and Thyme which did perfume it with its natural spirit and would last a morning or longer. He had a very fine fancy which lay (chiefly) for gardens and architecture'. He died in 1650 forestalling any attempt to bring him to trial.

England's oldest physic garden was established in 1621 by Henry Danvers, Early of Danby on the site of the old Jewish Burial ground opposite Magdalen College, Oxford and was opened in 1642, the very year when the Civil War began. Yet within six years it had amassed a collection of 600 native and twice as many plants from abroad. It was to produce the first

London plane tree, *Platanus acerifolia*. One account suggests that this might have been an accidentally bred hybrid between two other trees that grew there – *P. orientalis* and *P. occidentalis*, one of Tradescant's importations, but experience suggests that cross-pollination is rather unlikely in our climate and that the first London plane was an imported seedling.

Cromwell's men vandalised the gardens at Oatlands, but, on the other hand, the Protector revitalised the navy and sent out an expedition which not only took Jamaica from the Spaniards but captured plant specimens intended for Spain; and when John Vaughan, 3rd and last Earl of Carbery, went out as Governor of Jamaica, he took with him Thomas Willisel who had been General Lambert's gardener.

One man who managed to hold aloof from the struggle was Sir Thomas Hanmer who lived at Bettisfield in Flintshire, or Clwyd as it is now called. An influential landowner, he had married one of Queen Henrietta Maria's Maids of Honour, and had apparently undertaken special missions abroad for the King. While Cromwell ruled, he found it prudent, if not essential, to live quietly at home, taking no part in public affairs. He devoted the years to cultivating his estate and preparing *The Garden Book of Sir Thomas Hanmer* written around 1659 but rediscovered and published nearly three hundred years later as a transcription by Ivy Elstob.

Hanmer's treatise is on the grand scale, and presented in great detail. The show beds are arranged in 12 ranks with anemones along the sides, cyclamens at the corners and tulips and narcissi in the middle. He describes 26 types of tulip and 60 varieties of iris. His larkspurs range from violet purple and blue to ash, lead, white, pink blush and tawny. He keeps a careful note of the season and which plants did best in each year. In short, he is a gardener's gardener. One of his treasures was *Nerine sarniensis*, the Guernsey Lily from the Cape of Good Hope, which was thought at one time to have reached Britain as the result of a shipwreck on Guernsey in the 1660s at the time Christopher Hatton was governor of the Island. Hanmer's book published in 1933 proved that it was not so. But his main significance lies in the evidence which he provides of the number of cultivars that were now to be found of plants that 20 years earlier had been considered novelties.

Well might John Aubrey write, 'I do believe I may affirm that there is now in 1691 ten times as much gardening around London as there was in 1660'.

7 *Getting the Names Right*

The profusion of different names given by enthusiasts to the same plant has provided endless perplexities for researchers into the origins of garden flowers.

In plain English, the Ginny-hen Floure turns out to be the fritillary. Mullein, according to Gerard 'is called in shops Tapsus barbatus: of divers Candela Regia, Candelaria and Lanaria: in French, Bouillon: in English, Mullein, or rather Woollen, Higtaper* (sic), Torches, Longwort, and Bullocks Longwort; and of some, Hares Beard'. Nor, at first would one recognise Serapia's Turbith as referring to *Aster tripolium*, Sea Aster, a common native shoreplant or 'Seamarch Buglosse' as an English name for Pitcher Plant.

But for centuries the situation was equally confusing in the case of Latin names – at least up to half way through the eighteenth century. Thus Tradescant's Latin rendering of the passion flower was '*Amaracock sive Clematis Virginiana*', and, for Poison Ivy, '*Epimedium fruticans virginiana, sive hedera trifolia canadensis cornut*'. 'Virginian Bindweed' probably a species of Ipomoea, was listed by Tradescant as '*Convolvulus Virginianus, cordato folio flore obsoleto Tradescanti*'.

Clearly matters were getting out of hand. What was wanted was a ruling first on which plants really belonged together, and then on universally recognised names to be given to them. Carl Linné (more often known by his Latinised surname, Linnaeus),

*probably Hag or Witches' Taper.

Carl Linné or Carolus Linnaeus (1707–1778), the Swedish botanist whose nomenclature of plants is still used today

the son of a Lutheran pastor in the village of Stenbrohult, South Sweden, was the genius who brought some order into the system.

He was, of course, not the first to attempt to set out a logical system of grouping plants. Some classical writers had discerned a basic distinction between evergreen plants which keep their leaves during winter, and deciduous plants that shed them. But then, what to do about privet, a common plant which keeps its leaves if, but only if, the winters are mild enough; and most brambles shed some but not all their leaves. Other writers, in their turn, considered that plants should be classified according to the surroundings in which they flowered. But that would mean separating the irises that flower in water from those that don't. And when is a marsh not a marsh?

Other thinkers believed that plants should be

classified according to their uses, with the most useful taking preference. But which was to be preferred – the saffron, the oak or the olive? Parkinson reckoned that plants might be grouped according to their herbal virtues, but Adam Zaluziansky, the sixteenth-century botanist, introduced the more advanced notion that plants should be studied for their structure and that botany should therefore be regarded as a science entirely separated from the study of medicine.

His contemporary, Andrea Cesalpino, carried things one step further by grouping plants according to one special structural characteristic, their seeds – just as Tournefort later believed that the formation of the petals should be the determining diagnostic of a plant's species and Gesner earlier, the fruit. Mathias de l'Obel, gardener to Lord Zouche at Hackney, and later to King James I, drew attention to dissimilarities which we recognise today between plants that develop from two seed leaves (the dicotyledons or 'dicots'), and those like the orchids and lilies that have only one – the 'monocots'. He also pointed to the differences between plants that have net-veined leaves and those with parallel-veined leaves. But neither of these distinctions narrowed the field to any great extent.

Nehemiah Grew, in his *Anatomy of Plants* published in 1682, was the first to go to the heart of the matter. The Grews were indeed a singular family. Nehemiah's father Obadiah was a militant royalist; he had pleaded with Cromwell for the king's life to be spared, and favoured the royalist rising of 1659. But he was also a militant churchman, and was one of those Presbyterian ministers to be outlawed from the national church in 1662 as a Dissenter.

In 1682, the very year that his father was sent to prison, Nehemiah Grew began to publish his four-volume *Anatomy of Plants*, which fully sustained the family reputation for non-conformity. In it he suggested that the stamens of flowers were the male organs and that the pollen, or farina, as he called it, was the fertilising agent. Then, amongst others, Tournefort's pupil, Sebastien Vaillant, went further and declared that the male stamens and female pistil were the vital elements in plants – not the petals. It was an essay of Vaillant's that encouraged Linnaeus to study the sex organs of plants and eventually to base his own system of classification on them. He divided the flowering plants into 23 categories according to the number of stamens, their length, formation and position relative to the female organs (sometimes they are even on separate flowers). Linnaeus' sexual system made it easy for anyone with a magnifying glass to determine the identity of any given plant – except in a few cases where the plants are clearly closely allied but flowers show a different number of stamens – in fuchsias, for instance.

Linnaeus got himself into trouble with the prudish who considered it improper to use flowers as sex symbols, more especially since flowers were clearly promiscuous if not polygamous. His classification was also a highly artificial one. Thus henbane was grouped with cyclamen, centaury with Deadly Nightshade, gentian with dodder, and Golden Saxifrage with the Pink. Nonetheless, despite these handicaps, Linnaeus' mode of classification held the field for more than a century.

Even more important to botanists, and eventually to gardeners too, was the simplified system which Linnaeus introduced for naming plants. As a young man, he, too, had used Latin chain-names – one quoted by Wilfrid Blunt in his definitive biography of Linnaeus ran: '*Convolvulus foliis palmatis cordatis sericeis: lobis repandis, pedunculis bifloris*'. An excellent description if one had but the time to follow. But step by step, Linnaeus pared down the names of some 5,900 plants to the bare essentials for everyday use – one word to represent the genus or type of plant and a second word to represent the individual species.

The group of plants within each genus was assembled with meticulous care. Linnaeus would begin by setting out a detailed description of the individual plant that he thought would best typify the genus he had in mind, and used this as a model. He would next take another of the plants he intended to include in the same genus and compare it with his model, deleting from the model any details not common to both, and he would repeat the process with the remaining plants to be included in the same genus. He would thus be left with a description of the genus which would fit all the plants belonging to it. The fourth edition of *Genera Plantarum* describing nearly 2,000 different genera was completed in 1752.

When deciding what to call a genus, Linnaeus tried to find a name that sounded well, was simple to remember, and could not easily be confused with any other. In many cases the name chosen for the genus would be that of the plant most typical of it. Other names, if suitable, were taken from classical mythology, as for example, Andromeda, the Grecian princess who was chained to a rock over which the waters washed before she was rescued by Perseus, and indeed our own *Andromeda polifolia*, Bog Rosemary, flourishes best in situations where its own roots are washed in water. In his sketchbook Linnaeus even drew a newt to represent the dragon waiting to devour Andromeda if she had not been rescued in time.

On other occasions Linnaeus was able to honour friends who had helped him to success and even his pupils. The *Moraea* (Butterfly Iris), a genus of lilac and yellow sweet-scented cool greenhouse plants, was named after Linnaeus' father-in-law, J. Moraens. The *Magnolia* genus was named after Pierre Magnol, Professor of Botany and Director of the

Botanical garden at Montpellier, southern France, whom Linnaeus admired. *Rudbeckia* was named after Olaf Rudbeck and his son, both Linnaeus supporters and Pehr Kalm, one of Linnaeus' students is commemorated in *Kalmia latifolia*, the modest evergreen shrub with umbels of shallow delicate pink and white bell-flowers.

Linnaeus himself is immortalised in *Linnaea borealis*, the twin-flower, which sets an evergreen mat of small oval leaves, topped with sweetly scented pink bell-flowers and blossoms gallantly in the wastes of Siberia across the globe to arctic America and is even still to be found in some pinewoods in eastern Scotland. Johan Gronovius selected the name for Linnaeus who approved the choice as appropriate because the plant is 'lowly, insignificant and disregarded, flowering for a brief space, like Linnaeus who resembles it'.

Once the genera had been established, Linnaeus was faced with the problem of choosing the right name to distinguish each species in it from all the others. The name had to sum up what was specifically different about the plant in question and emphasise its most distinctive feature. Linnaeus was careful to avoid, as far as possible, labelling species with names to which the plants did not invariably conform; a plant might be large in one area but small in another under less favourable conditions; it might flower in the spring in one place, in the summer in another, so adjectives denoting size or season were suspect. He fought shy of using 'value judgement' adjectives relating to taste, smell, colour on which there could be more than one opinion. He liked to found the name of the species on the numbers, shape or position of some distinctive part of the plant – often the leaves.

In the end he had his way. In the Botanical Congress of 1905, held in Vienna, it was agreed that the first edition of Linnaeus' *Species Plantarum* published in 1753 should be the earliest valid publication from which plant names set out in the modern simple style (one word for the genus and one for the species) could be taken. All the names in it, therefore, have priority over any others for the particular plants which it covers. From that time on, new species have been distinguished by the first validly published name given to them – unless perhaps the species is transferred to a new genus already having a species with the same name, or unless (sometimes) and in the case of a genus not a species, an original valid first name is discovered in some dusty file long after people have got used to a later upstart.

Linnaeus, however, dealt only with wild flowers, and priority for garden flowers is based on the sixth edition, published in 1752, of Philip Miller's *Gardener's Dictionary*.

Miller, a Scotsman would employ only Scottish assistants and was so canny that he was said to have succeeded in growing *Anthemis pyrethrum* from seeds found sticking to a bunch of Malaga grapes. He was gardener to the Worshipful Company of Apothecaries founded in 1617. The Physic Garden in Chelsea, extending over three-and-a-half acres, had been handed over to the company for a nominal rent by Sir Hans Sloane, on condition that it would provide the Royal Society, of which Sloane was President, with pressed specimens of 50 new plants grown each year until the number should reach two thousand. The garden lay off the Kings Road, which Charles II had driven through Chelsea as his private short cut between Whitehall and the Palace of Hampton Court. (Residents needed special permission to use it.)

Miller was appointed superintendent of the garden in 1724, and easily achieved his quota of pressed plants during his 46 years as superintendent, and when he retired in 1771, the garden was

Sir Hans Sloane (1660–1753), who brought back some 800 plant specimens from Jamaica

cultivating more than five thousand different species. His equipment included a fire basket on wheels to heat soil from beneath. He also grew Alpines including those delightful fringed cousins of the primroses, the *Soldanellas*, with leaves that resemble the small Italian coins known as *soldi*. *Malcolmia maritima*, Virginia Stock, is one of many plants recorded by Miller though without attribution. It is a south European plant.

His *Dictionary* was planned by the Society of Gardeners, an association of nurserymen who were anxious to protect their good name by identifying clearly the species they were selling. They met regularly at Newall's Coffee House in Chelsea. The first edition of the dictionary was published in 1731, and at least seven others followed it. One of these editions followed the classification used by de Tournefort, and another, that of John Ray, who favoured grouping plants according to their natural affinity rather than by one particular feature. Nevertheless in the seventh edition, completed in 1759, Miller followed the fashion and changed over to Linnaeus' sexual system.

In July 1736, Linnaeus visited England and was said to have knelt in admiration when he saw gorse flowering in profusion on Putney Heath (no wonder – for *Ulex europaeus* rarely does show flowers at that time of year). He was able to meet both Miller with whom for want of English he conversed in Latin, and Johan Jacob Dillenius, Sherardian Professor at the Oxford Botanic Garden. (Dillenius first complained that Linnaeus was 'throwing all botany into confusion' but soon became his warm friend.) But the greatest honour accorded to Linnaeus during his visit was a meeting with the great Sloane.

Sloane, then 76, was not only President of the Royal Society but was a foreign member of the Academies of Sciences at Paris, St Petersburg and Madrid. He was President of the Royal College of Physicians and had attended both Queen Anne and King George II.

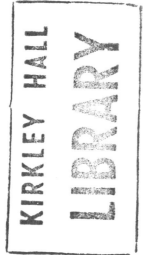

He was the youngest of seven brothers and at 16 nearly died of tuberculosis of the lungs. His schooling was cut short and he was obliged to remain a near teetotaller for the rest of his life. As a botanist he had attended lectures given by de Tournefort at the Jardin du Roi (they started at 6 a.m.) and had also studied under Professor Magnol at Montpellier. As a young medical student, he had accompanied the Duke of Albemarle, son of the General Monk who had stage-managed the restoration of Charles II, to Jamaica in 1687 when Albemarle took up the post of Governor there. When the Governor died the following year, the Duchess decided to return home and Sloane came with her, bringing some 800 plant specimens and some livestock not all of which survived. An iguana jumped overboard, a crocodile died after taking a tub of some salt water. A yellow snake, seven feet long, escaped and took possession of the deck-house roof, feeding on the ship's rats until some passengers complained and in Sloane's words 'footmen and other domestics of Her Grace, being afraid to lie down in such company shot my snake'.

Sloane duly received Linnaeus but remained true to the beliefs of de Tournefort to whom pollen was a form of waste material excreted by plants and not the agent of life. The two men parted, however, with expressions of mutual respect. The first sections of Sloane's famous work, *Voyage to the Islands of Madeira, Barbadoes, Nieves, St Christopher's and Jamaica* began to appear in 1707 near twenty years after the journey itself, and the final chapters were not completed until 1725. Neither the text nor the illustrations were inspiring, but Sloane initiated many other forays by contemporaries and subscribed to the cost of most of them.

Sir Arthur Rawdon, who, like Sloane, was born in Ireland, and was his close friend, sent a gardener, James Harlow, to Jamaica, and the latter came home in 1692 with 20 cases each holding 50 plants.

Henry Compton, Bishop of London, who had once been a Cornet in the Horse Guards, was another collector who filled his garden at Fulham Palace with rarities and indeed suffered pangs of conscience towards the end of his life because of the large amounts of money he had spent on his garden. Apart from being a member of the Temple Coffee House Botanists' Club, he happened to be head of the church in the American colonies and was able to send out as missionary, John Banister, a young man who had shown a special interest in plants while still an undergraduate at Oxford.

Banister arrived in Virginia in 1678 and, within two years, he prepared a catalogue which, when published, provided the first printed survey of American plants. He drew figures of the rarer species and sent seeds to the English naturalist John Ray, as well as to the Oxford Botanic Garden.

One of his finds was *Magnolia virginiana*, with creamy scented flowers, the first of its genus to be successfully cultivated in Britain. There was also *Lindera benzoin*, the Spice Bush, a deciduous member of the laurel family, with dense clusters of greenish yellow flowers; and *Liquidambar styraciflua*, the Sweet Gum, with its show of red, crimson and orange leaves in autumn. *Cornus amomum* – a new species of dogwood, with blue fruits following on from its clusters of yellowish white flowers – came from him as well. Other plants credited to him include *Gleditschia triancanthos*, the Honey Locust Tree; *Mertensia virginica* called the Virginian Cowslip, but one of the borage tribe and a relative of our own native purple-flowered Oyster Plant, *Physostegia* (formerly *Dracocephalum*) *Virginiana*, the Obedient Plant – its mauve flower can be pushed into any position, *Echinacea* (formerly *Rudbeckia*) *purpurea*, *Chionanthus virginicus*, the Fringe Tree with its tassels of scented flowers and dark blue egg-shaped fruit, no longer much in cultivation; and *Rhododendron viscosa* with its alluringly scented pink-and-white flowers and its agreeable habit of flowering late in the season. But perhaps these plants did not at once meet with success, for the dates of introduction given in the Royal Horticultural Society's *Dictionary* are, in some cases, considerably later.

Banister would no doubt have followed up with many other plants but for his accidental death in 1692 while on an up-country plant hunting expedition along the river James. According to one account he died after falling from a cliff; another version has it that he was accidentally shot by a member of his party.

Meanwhile other expeditions had proceeded westward-ho, largely through Sloane's influence. In 1690 James Reed, who had already been to Virginia to collect plants for the King's Garden at Hampton Court, was despatched to Barbados by a syndicate of which Sloane was a member. William Sherard, who, like Sloane, had studied under de Tournefort, was able to raise 60 plants from the seeds sent home by Reed.

The next notable collector to visit the new world was Mark Catesby, who, partly because he drew the sketch from which Linnaeus named the so-called Bald Eagle, emblem of the US, is better known there than in England. He came from Castle Hedingham in Essex and first became interested in botany and ornithology through meeting John Ray, the naturalist, who lived nearby. Catesby's father, a magistrate, died when he was 23, leaving him enough money to guarantee his independence, and he decided to visit America where his sister and her husband, a doctor, were already established. He arrived there in April 1712 and stayed for seven years, sending home dried plants, seeds and a few living specimens in tubs to Bishop Compton, Thomas Fairchild, the Hoxton nurseryman and to Samuel Dale, a friend of John Ray. One of his discoveries was *Ceanothus americanus*, a deciduous species with dullish white flowers. Though long surpassed by other true blue spring and autumn flowering varieties, it is the co-parent of the popular frost-resistant border shrublet, *Ceanothus delilianus*, the so-called Californian Lilac. Another was *Porteranthus* (formerly *Gillenia*) *trifoliata*, a decorative member of the rose family with wayward thin long pointed pink or white petals. When Catesby arrived home in the summer of 1719, he found his reputation as a naturalist already fully established.

Sloane, the Duke of Chandos, and Dr Richard Mead, who had risen to be medical adviser to Sir Isaac Newton, to King George I and to Prime Minister Robert Walpole, promptly organised a new expedition for Catesby, finding him a post as attendant to the Governor of Carolina, with Charleston as its capital. He arrived there in May 1722 taking part in at least two expeditions into the Appalachian mountains where he discovered the Rose Acacia, *Robinia hispida*, though he was unable to bring back the seed.

This second visit led to *Coreopsis lanceolata*, that useful bright yellow daisy with the graceful leaves – a foil to the earlier *C. auriculata*, so called because of the ring of purplish brown surrounding the centre disc.

Another Catesby 'first' was the autumn flowering *Wisteria frutescens* with its lilac-purple blossoms each with a yellow spot. (The spelling of the genus deserves to be altered to agree with that of Professor Caspar Wistar of Pennsylvania University, after whom the plant was named; but my hopes are not high.)

A fine tree, *Catalpa bignonioides*, sometimes called the Indian Bean Tree, was one of Catesby's take-homes. It has heart-shaped leaves of a vivid green and white frilly flowers with orange centres and purple spots. The name commemorates Jean Paul Bignon, the President of the French Academy of Science, so this species was probably a capture rather than a discovery in Catesby's case. *Calycanthus floridus*, Carolina Allspice, was definitely a discovery undisclosed before Catesby's day even to the inhabitants of Charleston. It is a hardy shrub with strap-shaped petals of reddish brown, fringed with purple. *Callicarpa americana* – a member of the verbena family – was another Catesby shrub. It shows clusters of bluish flowers, with violet coloured fruit to follow. *Amorpha fruticosa*, the Indigo Bush, was another find. Catesby is also credited with two highly popular border plants, *Liatris spicata* and *L. squarrosa* – both purple bottle-brushes in appearance, but members of the daisy family. He finally left America in January 1725 returning home via the Bahamas, Eleuthera, Andros and Abaco. He is said to have brought back the original Jacaranda from the Bahamas, which Linnaeus named *Jacuranda* (sic) *coerulea* but its ancestry is uncertain. *Jacaranda chelonia* is at home in Paraguay and Argentina; *J. cuspidifolia* in Brazil and Argentina; *J. ovalifolia* in Brazil; and *J. jasminoides* in Mexico. But the name is Brazilian, rather than Mexican, which could be the clue to its family lineage.

Five years after his return Catesby produced the first parts of his *Natural History of Carolina, Georgia, Florida and the Bahama Islands.* To save money, he learnt to engrave his own plates, some of which are now in the Royal Library at Windsor. One of them shows a species of Witch Hazel, though not the *Hamamelis mollis* from the Far East most often seen in our gardens. The work was completed in 1743 and a follow-up, the *Hortus Britanno-Americanus* only shortly before his death in 1749. Meanwhile his plants and seeds must have been uncommonly useful to the Chelsea Physic Garden which Sloane had launched in the very year Catesby set out on his second expedition as well as to Christopher Gray in whose Fulham Nursery he worked.

British botanists were not the only ones to be stimulated by Sloane's successes. Louis XIV, the Sun King, was prompted to send Charles Plumier on three voyages to the West Indies – in 1689, 1693 and 1695 – and, in his work *Nova Plantarum Americanarum Genera*, published in 1703, Plumier gave the first description of a fuchsia. At the age of 16, Plumier had entered the religious Order of Minims, which aspired by suppressing all sense of self-

Common Gayfeather (*Liatris spicata*); although apparently a purple bottle-brush, this is actually a member of the daisy family

importance to live in and for God alone. All meat, eggs, milk, cheese and butter were forbidden, which might have been, but apparently was not, a handicap to foreign travel.

During one of his trips Plumier was able to discover that cochineal dye came from insects and not from the cactus in which they lived. He was also asked to go to Peru to bring home a live specimen of the tree which provided 'the Jesuits' Bark' used for treating fevers. The wife of the Spanish Viceroy of Peru had brought some quinine bark home in 1639 and John Evelyn had inspected a tree in the Chelsea Physic Garden in 1685, but because of its scarcity, strenuous efforts had been made by members of the Society of Jesus to keep its habitat a close secret. It was while waiting in November 1704 for a ship to take him on this mission that Plumier died, of pleurisy.

Behind him he left not only a book on wood turning which Czar Peter the Great translated into Russian, but more than 4,000 drawings of plants. He named more than 50 new genera, including some adopted by Linnaeus, and in use today. Of these lobelia and begonia are probably the most familiar. Begon had been Governor of the French colony of Santo Domingo – now Haiti – and was later Director of the Marseilles convict galleys. But he was also an enthusiastic botanist, and had first put forward Plumier's name to the King as a suitable person to collect specimens from the French Antilles. Lobel, we have already met. Leonhart Fuchs, Professor of Botany at Tubingen University in southern Germany, whose *De Historia Stirpium* galvanised German botanists, had died in 1566. But perhaps in this case, time was not the essence of the matter, for Plumier's fuchsia seems to have been lost for at least 80 years, if not longer, depending on whether the species he was describing was really *Fuchsia triphylla flore coccinea* as Plumier said, or *F.*

coccinea presented to Kew in 1788 by Captain Firth.

Another man of God, though of a very different nature, was George Wheler (spelt thus in the *Dictionary of National Biography*), an Oxford undergraduate, who was interested in collecting classical manuscripts and coins, as well as plants. Before taking his degree he went to Venice, and was fortunate enough to be able to join the party of an Ambassador who was bound for Constantinople, together with a friend. The journey was not uneventful, and at one time Wheler and his friend found themselves stranded by bad weather on an island without food, while their ship sailed away without them. However, they eventually got to Constantinople and Wheler, while on an excursion, came across *Hypericum calycinum*. It alone was worth the trip. He introduced the plant to us, and for years afterwards, it was known as Sir George Wheler's Tutsan. Its present name, the Rose of Sharon, is not nearly so appropriate as *H. calycinum* does not grow on Israel's western plain; a *Cistus* would fill the role much more effectively. Wheler also saw, and was impressed by, the Weeping Willow. It only remains to add that he duly published his *Journey into Greece* in 1682, was knighted largely in recognition, and went into the church spending the last 14 years of his life as Rector of Tyneside's Houghton-le-Spring.

Meanwhile, before Wheler's death in 1723, progress had been made towards providing gardeners with a more desirable Aster. A smooth-leaved *Aster novi-belgii*, first identified in 1687 by a Belgian botanist named Hermann, had been introduced into England in 1710. Most of the modern Michaelmas Daisies have been derived from it. Philip Miller in the 1733 edition of his *Gardener's Dictionary* gives three species which he says will flower till mid-November but the other species did not earn the name Michaelmas until after 1752 when England adopted the calendar which had already been established elsewhere in Europe by Pope Gregory XIII 170 years earlier. This change made on 2 September 1752, involved advancing the date by 11 days so that what would have been 3 September became 14 September. Thus the plants that would have been over on the feast of Michaelmas on 29 September would thenceforward be in flower.

Today, perhaps, now that some aster species have such a long-flowering season we should be thinking of another name. Indeed *Aster grandiflora* which Catesby introduced, flowers so late that it has already been called Christmas Daisy.

Two other introductions from across the Atlantic deserve to be mentioned here. One was the first tropical orchid, *Bletia verecunda*, to flower in England. The seeds were gathered by William Houston, a doctor in the service of the South Sea (Bubble) Company on Providence Island in the Bahamas. He sent supplies to both Sloane and Philip Miller. But the orchid flowered first in the stove house of Admiral Sir Charles Wager in Parsons Green. The plant was named after Don Luis Blet, a Spanish botanist.

The second development was the arrival of 1756 of *Halesia carolina*, the delightful Snowdrop Tree – more a bush than a tree in this country. Its bell-shaped flowers hang in rows beneath the branches like a shower of miniature ivory clothes' pegs. It was named after Dr Stephen Hales, a pioneer enquirer into plant physiology, and a spiritual trustee for the colony of Georgia.

But now, to catch up with what has been elsewhere, it is time to turn to the east.

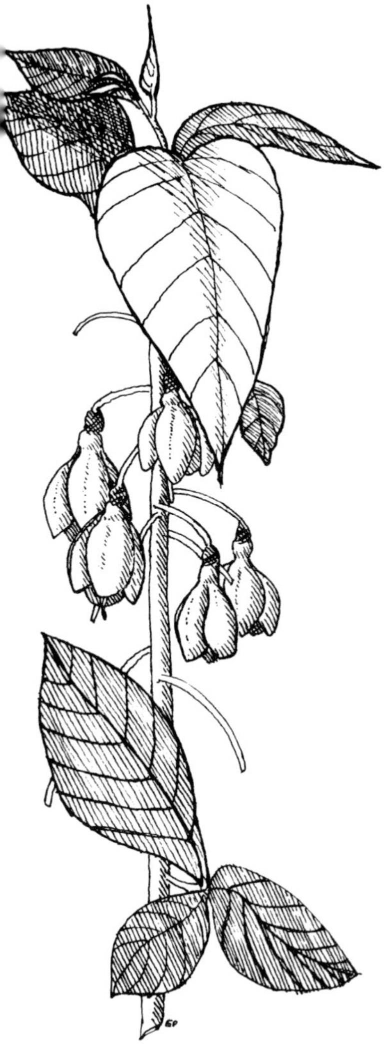

Snowdrop Tree (*Halesia carolina*), imported into Britain in 1756 for the first time, and named after Dr Stephen Hales, plant physiologist (1677–1761)

8 *From China to Peru*

John Evelyn, tree-fancier and diarist, wrote on 22 June 1664 'One Tomson, a Jesuit, shew'd me such a collection of rarities sent from ye Jesuits of Japan and China to their Order at Paris, as a present to be reserved in their repository, but brought to London by the India ships for them, as in my life I had not seene'.

There were rhinoceros horns, vests in lively colours, knives with edges so keen that it was dangerous to touch them, fans, and idols of 'monstrous and hideous shapes', and 'divers drougs that our drouggists and physitians could make nothing of, especially one which the Jesuits called Lac Tygridis'. (Could this have been the original version of the well-known Tiger Balm?)

Certainly the Jesuits, through their knowledge of medicine and other sciences, achieved a special status in both China and Japan, and were able to send home specimens and seeds overland in the caravan convoy which left for Europe once every three years – as well as by sea. One of them, Michael Boym, had already (1656) published a *Flora sinensis*. But, in sorting out what the Jesuits accomplished, we have to deal first with the confusion that has arisen over one of their order, George Kamel, after whom the Camellia was named.

Kamel was born in 1661 in Brunn in Moravia, now part of central Czechoslovakia, and joined the Society of Jesus in 1682 as a lay member concerned with the running of the Order's provincial Houses or Colleges scattered over the globe. Six years later he was sent to Manila in the Philippines where he set up a pharmacy from which medicines were handed out free to the poor. Kamel prepared a work on the shrubs, climbers and herbaceous plants growing on the island of Luzon, and, as we know from the *Philosophical Transactions* of the Royal Society, sent specimens and seeds to James Petiver, but the Camellia was not mentioned, and there is no evidence that he saw the plant before his death in Manila in 1706. Indeed the name Camellia was not chosen for the genus by Linnaeus until more than a quarter of a century after Kamel had died.

Meanwhile another explorer with a somewhat similar name had journeyed to Japan. He was Engelbert Kaempfer, born in north Germany in 1651, a physician who had studied medicine in Krakow and Königsberg and had travelled on semi-diplomatic missions to Russia and Persia.

In 1689 he was appointed Chief Surgeon to the Dutch East India Chartered Company's settlement in Japan and took up his duties the following year. Kaempfer was no Jesuit, but he suffered from the hate and distrust of foreigners stirred up by the previous efforts of Portuguese Jesuits to convert the Japanese to Christianity. All missionaries had been banished from Japan in 1639, and the treatment which foreigners could expect was well illustrated by the narrative of the captain of an East Indiaman, the Return, which approached the harbour of 'Nanguasacque' on Sunday, 29 June 1673. The captain was refused permission to trade because England's King Charles II had married a Portuguese Princess, Catherine of Braganza, and was ordered to leave if not immediately, then as soon as the wind changed to the north at the end of the monsoon.

'I asked whether we might wear our colours,' the Captain reported. 'They said we might wear any colours that had no cross in them, our cross being offensive to them for being nigh the Portugal cross.

Then asking whether we might return hither after the death of our Queen, they answered possibly we might if the Dutch and several Chinese did satisfy the Emperor, that we were not in amity with Portugal; but he could not assure us we should have admission, our surest way was not to come; for this Emperor's commands (according to the Japanese saying) were like unto sweat that goeth out of a man's hands and body, which never returned again; the Emperor's commands admit of no alteration.'

The Dutch company officials were little more fortunate. They were allowed a mission confined to Deshima, a small artificial island measuring 236 by 82 paces, walled around and connected by a closely guarded bridge to the mainland. The Japanese servants assigned to them were made to swear by treading publicly on the image of the Virgin Mary and of Christ on the Cross that they would never embrace the Christian faith.

The more senior Japanese officials dealing with the Dutch were made to swear an oath validated by some drops of their own blood, that they would never oblige the foreigners in any way. Only two Dutch ships a year were permitted to trade, and the Dutch were allowed on land only once a year when their Company was permitted to take to the Emperor at Jedo – the old name for Tokyo – a selection of presents.

Kaempfer's journey out to Japan seems to have been no more comfortable than the voyages of other botanists of his time. The ship's rudder broke loose in a storm and, after the ship had drifted helplessly for several days, the carpenter had to be lowered on a rope to make repairs. Then the hull sprang a leak and the ship, while still afloat, had to be canted on one side for more repairs. The poultry died, and the ship's company drank the last of the liquor, leaving none for the passengers.

Once ashore, though, Kaempfer made the most

of his opportunities. By giving a young Japanese assigned to him lessons in mathematics, astronomy and Dutch, he was able to procure specimens of plants growing on the mainland. As a physician, he could claim that it was necessary for him to go ashore to look for medical herbs, though when he did so he was accompanied by a magistrate and a body of Japanese officials who expected to be treated to an expensive meal at one or other of the temples.

Kaempfer was able to travel on two of the annual pilgrimages to the Emperor at Jedo, each of which lasted three months from March to May. He took with him a very large Javan box in which beneath the inkhorn, he concealed a mariner's compass covered with plants, flowers and branches from trees. He found the Bugjo or Commander in Chief of the party happy to find out for him the names of unusual plants and their uses, for, to use his words, 'The Japanese, a very reasonable and sensible people, and themselves great lovers of plants, look upon Botany, as a study both useful and innocent, which, pursuant to the very dictates of reason and the law of nature, ought to be encourag'd by everybody'.

But he could not help remarking on the fact that the Japanese rode their horses cross-legged, and protected themselves, the horse and their baggage from the rain with cloaks of double-varnished oiled paper; route-maps forbidden to Dutchmen, were habitually written on fans.

Kaempfer found 'an infinite variety of plants and fruits . . . (and) . . . numberless varieties of Feverfews, including some cultivated species, the size of roses, used as the chief adornment of houses and gardens' whereas most of the lilies were allowed to grow on waste ground. 'Nor hath nature been less kind with regard to the Narcissus, Flowers de Lys, Clove-Gilli-Flowers and the like. But one thing I cannot help observing, which is that these several flowers fall as short of others of their kind, growing in other countries, in strength and agreeableness of smell, as they exceed them in the exquisite beauty of their colours.'

Kaempfer left Japan in November 1692 and succeeded in bringing all his records with him. He was able to write an authoritative history of Japan, the English translation of which was completed in 1727. But his other treatise, usually referred to as the *Amoenitates Exoticae*, 944 pages long, written in Latin and first published in 1712, twenty years after his return, was far more important to botanists and gardeners.

The plants he described in it have been identified partly through Kaempfer's phonetic rendering of the Japanese names, both high-class and vernacular, together with illustrations supplied to Kaempfer by Japanese artists. Thus the classical name for 'Spiny Privet' was Kooki, the popular name Kuko 'though others called it Numi gussuri'. In many cases he also added the Japanese characters used irrespective of local dialects, throughout Japan, though the woodcut reproductions in *Amoenitates* sometimes lack precision.

This was especially the case with camellias, of which Kaempfer described more than 30 varieties.

His main success was with lilies. *Lilium speciosum* which Kaempfer was the first to describe appeared in *Amoenitates* as the Lily of Varied Colours 'with a flower of magnificent beauty, whitish pink with blood red spots, warty'. The first specimen to reach Europe was brought back more than 125 years later by Dr Philipp Franz von Siebold, a botanist and eye surgeon who was posted to Deshima in 1826.

Kaempfer also gave details of *Lilium tigrinum* (orange, spotted with purple and black), which he described as Devil Lily and *Lilium japonicum* (white trumpet-shaped fragrant flowers opening from pink buds). A scholarly study of Kaempfer's lilies by Professor W.T. Stearn appeared in the *Lily Year Book* of 1948 on which the above notes are based.

Kaempfer brought back notes of *Aucuba*, the shrub we now most often see with gold-splashed leaves; *Skimmia*, another conveniently slow-growing shrub which successfully resists city pollution; *Hydrangea*; *Chimonanthus*; and *Ginkgo biloba*, the giant ornamental tree with saddle-shaped leaves stalked at the pommel. The gingko is the only survivor of its genus from a race older even than the conifers. It was preserved with great reverence in Japanese temples having in all probability been taken along there with other plants by the Buddhist priests. Indeed it was not until the present century that it was found growing in the wild state. In the meantime a seedling was successfully raised in 1750 in the nursery run by James Gordon in the Mile End Road. A male specimen was planted at Kew in 1762 and is still there. The branch of a female was grafted on to it in 1911 and produced seeds eight years later.

Returning to the camellia, it should really have been no surprise that Kaempfer was able to describe so many. All were relatives of the tea tree which played such a large part in Japanese and Chinese social life. The first camellia to be seen in Britain was probably a dried specimen sent home by James Cunninghame, a surgeon in the service of the East India Company posted in 1702 to Chusan Island 150 miles south-east of Shanghai. Some 40 years later Lord Petre succeeded in procuring two live plants of the red single-flowered wild species which, to add to the confusion, is named *Camellia japonica*.

His lordship, a man of his time, considered that, as foreign and valuable plants, the camellias should be consigned to his stove-house at Thorndon in Essex, a procedure which, as the plants normally thrive in temperate conditions, ensured their demise. But all was not lost, for James Gordon, at that time still his lordship's gardener, took cuttings and succeeded in raising them in his nursery. The camellia shrub was on sale commercially in 1745. His house was then the last building on the left hand side of Mile End where he also raised the 'Great Melon Thistle' or cactus, and Loblolly Bay – *Gordonia lasianthus*.

Just 10 years later, the Chinese closed their borders to travellers, except for merchants confined to a settlement at Macao, and serious hybridisation of the plant did not begin in Britain until the 1820s when the camellia was taken up by the Chandler and Low nurseries.

In the meantime, however, another Jesuit-botanist had visited China with spectacular results. Pierre Nicholas le Chéron d'Incarville (1706–57) joined the Compagnie de Jésus in Paris at the age of 20, and, after completing his studies, served five years from 1730–35 in Quebec. In 1739 it was decided that he should go to Peking with the object of converting the Emperor Chien Lung to Christianity. D'Incarville had already studied astronomy and a craft closely linked to it – clockmaking. Now, hearing that the Emperor was interested in natural history, he took a six months' course in botany under Bernard de Jussieu, a member of the family which provided France with five of her most famous botanists. However, when he reached Peking in February 1742, d'Incarville found himself cast for a new occupation, namely that of Master Glass Maker to the Imperial Court – a post which, despite its importance, did not carry with it any freedom of movement. 'We have not the liberty of going where we please by ourselves,' he wrote, 'nor can we with prudence believe the reports of the Chinese.'

Nor was d'Incarville uniformly successful with the consignments of plants and seeds that he sent to the west. His first collection of plants was captured by the British; his second was shipwrecked. Pre-

Bernard de Jussieu (1699–1777), best known of a family of French botanists

sumably those sent to Paris went via the overland caravan train but d'Incarville expressed the fear that any publicity in Russia might damage his relationship with the Emperor. It was unfortunate too that a wave of persecution was besetting the Jesuit missionaries in other parts of China on whom d'Incarville was depending for specimens. Some escaped by disguising themselves as itinerant beggars, wearing pigtails and holding out begging bowls.

One of them, nevertheless, had already sent *Callistephus chinensis*, the Chinese Aster, to France, and some were successfully raised there. Red and white varieties were growing in the Chelsea Physic Garden in 1731. A blue variety though a single flowered one was received from the French in 1736 and seeds of the double red, blue and white came in 1753.

Many of d'Incarville's seeds were put on one side in Paris and were rediscovered many years later. One of these was *Viburnum fragrans* (now *farreri*), not cultivated until 1909.

D'Incarville had better success with the Tree of Heaven, *Ailanthus altissima*, the seeds of which arrived safely in Europe and were raised both in England and France – d'Incarville called it Frêne Puant – Stinking Ash. Another tree credited to him is *Koelreuteria paniculata*, the Golden Rain Tree sometimes described as the Chinese Willow-pattern Tree with handsome foliage and yellow star-shaped flowers – though other collectors also sent seed.

D'Incarville eventually managed to get on good terms with the Emperor by presenting him with two plants of *Mimosa sensitiva*. He was permitted to visit the Imperial gardens near Peking and was promised Chinese plants in exchange for European ones. Plants of the genus *Incarvillea*, named for d'Incarville at the instance of Antoine Laurent de Jussieu, cousin of Bernard, have deeply cut leaves and pink or red trumpet-shaped flowers. The species he sent back – *Incarvillea sinensis* – is a tender greenhouse plant and has since been superseded by hardier species. During his first year in Peking, d'Incarville discovered *Clematis macropetala* – nodding flowers with long narrow sharply-pointed lavender blue petals with deeper blue margins and petal-like stamens which suggest a double-flower. *C. macropetala* flowers in spring. Despite its striking appearance, it does not seem to have reached Britain before the early years of this century, after its re-discovery and collection by Reginald Farrer.

Meanwhile the circumstances in which the chrysanthemum came to Britain are almost as complicated as those surrounding the camellia. We should make a distinction at once between the not very exciting annual Corn and Marguerite Daisies and feverfews, which belong to the genus Chrysanthemum and the true chrysanthemums from the Far East, as described earlier by Kaempfer. These last have been cherished in China for 2,000 years, and Confucius writing in the fifth century BC singles out a dark-leaved, dark-flowered variety for special praise. Chrysanthemums in general were thought to bestow long life, and the dew from their leaves was collected and drunk. The Japanese took up the plant towards the end of the fourth century AD and it was adopted more than 1,000 years ago as the personal emblem of the Mikado, though the imperial standard in its present form, with the 16-petal flower, dates from 1871. It was the Japanese species that was first grown in Holland from seeds most probably sent by one of Kaempfer's predecessors. The plant – a cultivated variety – was named *Matricaria japonica maxima*; it did not, however, persist. A species with small yellow flowers, probably the wild *Chrysanthemum indicum* was, however, on show in the Chelsea Physic Garden in 1764 and Philip Miller declared that *C. indicum* was available in five other colours, namely straw colour, purple, lilac, copper-colour and brown. Though rarely grown today, this original wild yellow chrysanthemum was the ancestor of many of the modern varieties. The other dominant parent *Chrysanthemum morifolium*, a purple variety, was not seen here before 1793 but flowered in 1795 and was on sale commercially the following year in Colville's Nursery in the Kings Road.

Another Chinese speciality was the Moutan or Tree Paeony – *Paeonia suffruticosa*, which we know in this country as a shrub of about six feet with pale green leaves and large – six-inch – flowers which in the original wild form were white with petals blotched at the base with reddish purple. Other forms of *P. suffruticosa* are rose pink or magenta and there is a rather less impressive variety of this species known as *spontanea*. *P. lutea* can be brown, red or purple but is normally yellow. *P. potaninii* can be yellow, too, or maroon or white. At one time the plant was reserved for the imperial gardens and those of the mandarins, and most of those seen in Canton had been brought there from their natural cooler and drier home further west as dried roots and were forced as annuals in pots filled with unsuitable soil which left them too weak to be replanted.

There was thus considerable difficulty obtaining suitable seeds. A double-flowered pink form was procured by Dr John Duncan of the East India Company for Joseph Banks in 1789 and the first flowers appeared in 1793.

A popular variety of herbaceous paeony, the original cream-coloured *Paeonia lactiflora*, was secured in central Asia in 1784 by Peter Simon Pallas, the son of a Berlin surgeon, and himself a qualified doctor at 19, who accepted Catherine the Great's offer of the post of Professor of Natural Science at St Petersburg. He spent six years exploring the Urals, Siberia and the borders of Mongolia.

Doctor James Mounsey, a Scottish doctor from Trailflat, Dumfriesshire, was another medico-botanist at the Imperial Russian Court. He was in turn First Royal Physician and Privy Councillor to the Empress Elizabeth, Chief Director of the Medical Chancery under Czar Peter III and also served the Empress Catherine the Great. But in July 1762, a month after her accession, he asked leave to resign giving ill-health as the reason – though it was believed that his personal knowledge of the manner in which Catherine's husband, Czar Peter III, had died made it inadvisable for him to stay. He returned home bringing with him the seeds of *Rheum palmatum* which he handed to Dr Hope, Professor of Botany at Edinburgh University. This species, a hardy native of China, was the first true rhubarb to be grown in Britain. It still appears sometimes in gardens (if there is enough room) and displays purplish foliage and reddish bead-like flowers in June.

One man linked both East and West. He was a Quaker, Peter Collinson (1694–1768) – a wholesale woollen draper and gentleman's mercer, with a counting house in Gracechurch Street (postal address The Red Lion) and a country estate – Ridgeway House at Mill Hill, which later became the site of the school of that name. The Quaker philosophy with regard to gardens was that there should not be 'too great a superfluity of plants and too great nicety of gardens' and that 'all Friends in planting gardens should do it in a lowly mind and keep to plainness and the serviceable part, rather admiring the wonderful hand of Providence, in causing such variety of unnecessary things to grow for the use of man than in seeking to please the curious mind'. Collinson had a 'curious' mind and interested himself in such matters as air pressure, the resistance of solid bodies to fluids, sunspots and the enlargement of London Bridge.

And it is clear that, at times, Collinson found difficulty in resisting the delights of nicety in gardens, and even compared the planting of trees with contrasting shades of green to 'painting with living pencils'.

He received seeds not only from d'Incarville but also from another Jesuit, Père Jean-Denis Attiret, who was sent to China in 1737, became the Emperor's favourite painter, and remained in Peking until his death in 1768. Collinson, too, was in touch with Dr Mounsey (who sent him a hornbean from Persia) and with Georg Gmelin from Tubingen in southern Germany, Pallas' predecessor at St Petersburg. Count Grigorij Demidov, the owner of an ironmine and of some famous gardens in western Siberia, sent him in 1756 a lily 'as near to black as any flower' that Collinson had seen. The Iceland Poppy, *Papaver nudicaule* had been sent from Siberia in 1730 by J.H. de Heidenreich but further supplies came in 1759 together with *Fritillaria camschatcensis*, the species with delicate bell-like flowers of livid purple.

Collinson also corresponded with Dr Johann Ammann, the founder in 1736 of the Botanic Garden of the Imperial Academy at St Petersburg, and received from him *Delphinium grandiflorum*, a hardy perennial with violet blue funnel-shaped flowers, together with *Cornus alba*, more notable for its red stems than for its flowers, though it has given rise to a number of more decorative cultivars.

But equally Collinson was in correspondence with the west. He sent many 'English' seeds, cuttings and bulbs to John Custis, a pugnacious planter whose daughter-in-law, Martha Dandridge Custis married George Washington. These included tulips, carnations, auriculas, Crown Imperials, blue and white hyacinths, altheas, China Asters, Guernsey Lilies and the like. Collinson was a friend of Benjamin Franklin and shipped to the library founded by Franklin an apparatus which enabled Franklin to make his first experiments in the study of electricity. He was in touch with Catesby, asking him to search for a 'night bird called Whipper-Will if this can be shot and sent with its feathers, first bowelled and dry'd in a brisk oven, and then packed in tobacco leaves'. 'Pray observe whether it is a male or female,' Collinson added as an afterthought.

But by far his best correspondent was another Quaker, John Bartram (1699–1777), whose grandfather had migrated to America in 1682. John's father, William Bartram, owned a farm at Darby, about 10 miles west of Philadelphia, but some years after his wife died, he married again and moved to North Carolina (where he was kidnapped and murdered by White Oak Indians) leaving John in the care of relatives. John was educated at the local

Quaker school at Darby but does not seem to have profited greatly from it, for his spelling remained consistently unreliable. He married first Mary Maris of the Chester Monthly (Friends') Meeting, who died only two years after the wedding. His second wife, Ann Mendinghall, of the Concord Meeting, bore him nine children. Bartram was an excellent farmer and was able to enlarge his estate considerably by draining water meadows bordering the Schuylkill River at the bottom of his estate and, when he had to rebuild his house to accommodate his large family, he did so with his own hands, successfully splitting rocks 17 feet long in the process.

It was said that his interest in botany had been aroused during an afternoon of strenuous ploughing, when he took a breather in the shade of a tree and examined closely the structure of a daisy he had picked. He bought some books on botany and took a three months' course in Latin so that he could understand what was written in them. James Logan, Secretary to William Penn, presented him with Parkinson's *Paradisus* and he corresponded and later stayed at the house of Dr Alexander Garden of South Carolina, after whom the gardenia was named. Joseph Breintnall, a friend of Benjamin Franklin, first recommended Bartram to Collinson as a collector. Collinson offered Bartram five guineas for each box containing seeds of 100 different species and undertook to find him customers. Before long four Dukes, Richmond, Norfolk (for whom he collected pine cones), Bedford and Argyll, and the Earls of Bute, Lincoln and Leicester were among his customers, and eventually nearly 60 others subscribed to pay his travelling expenses.

In 1729 he started his own botanical garden, almost the first in America, and his list included *Mahonia aquifolium* – then a comparatively rare shrub – 12 different Evening Primroses and 13 asclepias.

It would be an exacting and laborious task to follow John Bartram on his journeys – lasting more than 30 years – often alone, along Indian trails and across the swamps and rivers of eastern America from Pennsylvania to Florida, sleeping often enough in the sheds or hovels 'little better than a hog-stye' grudgingly offered to a northerner by inhospitable fine old southern gentlemen. But many of his discoveries are alive today.

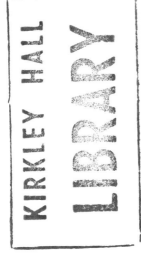

Thus in the 1730s he sent home *Rhododendron calendulaceum*, an azalea with brilliant orange or red flowers, the parent of many hybrids. It was lost and not recovered till 1806. His *Rhododendron maximum* is not often seen in modern gardens, but was, in its day, the first really large rhododendron to be cultivated. Two other popular shrubs which, like rhododendrons, grow well on acid soil, followed. They were *Kalmia latifolia*, the Calico Bush and *Kalmia angustifolia*, Sheep Laurel – both bearing rosy saucer-shaped flowers in lavish clusters. The evergreen *Magnolia grandiflora* he found at Bulls Bay, Southern Carolina. Its creamy white fragrant bowl-shaped flowers measure four to eight inches across and are well set off by the dark green glossy leaves. *Hydrangea arborescens*, one of the hardiest of the tribe if not the most decorative, was sent in 1736. *Lilium philadelphicum* – bright orange with a lower half of deep maroon – had been taken home by French colonists in 1675 but it was lost sight of until Bartram rediscovered it and sent bulbs in 1737 to the Chelsea Physic Garden. His *Lilium superbum* – orange with a red-spotted centre, red tipped petals and the stem tinged with purple – is still popular and easily grown. *Cimicifuga racemosa*, the elegant fragrant creamy white member of the buttercup family was new. *Hamamelis virginiana*, Witch Hazel, arrived in 1736 though it had been drawn by Catesby and may have been introduced still earlier. It was a September-flowering type and has since been displaced by the spring-flowering species. The English name was applied by Gerard and Parkinson to species of native elm and hornbeam.

Bartram played an important role in developing the Phlox family even if he was not, in every case, the first in the field. During the 1730s and 1740s he sent home *Phlox divaricata* (light blue), as well as *Phlox paniculata* (pale purple) which he called *Lychnidea folio salicino*, from which many of today's border varieties developed. He was certainly first with that treasure of the rock garden which he inventoried to Collinson in December 1745 as 'one

Magnolia grandiflora, found by John Bartram in Bull's Bay, South Carlolina. Its creamy white, fragrant flowers measure 4 to 8 inches across. From Pierre Joseph Buc'hoz' *Histoire universelle du règne végétal*, 1773

Scarlet Bergamot (*Monarda didyma*), found on the southern border of Lake Ontario in 1744 by John Bartram

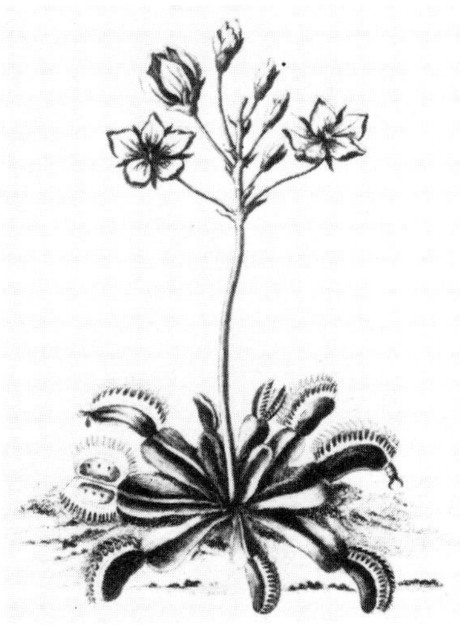

Venus Fly Trap (*Dionaea muscipula*), from Buc'hoz' *Histoire universelle*

sod of the fine creeping Spring Lychnis'. The plant was *Phlox subulata* – just two to four inches high. He also despatched *Phlox maculata*, a herbaceous border species with violet purple flowers, so called because of the spots on the stem. Smooth-leaved *Phlox glaberrima* was already being grown by Philip Miller in Chelsea in 1725.

In 1744 John Bartram sent back the seeds of *Monarda didyma*, the Scarlet Bergamot which he collected from Oswego on the southern border of Lake Ontario, where its fragrant leaves were used for making tea. *Monarda fistulosa*, the mauve-flowered hollow-stalked variety, collected a century earlier by John Tradescant Junior, had dropped out of cultivation, but Bartram's species with its mop-heads of scarlet (later, rose-pink or white) sage-like flowers is hardy enough to persist even in the average cottage garden.

Chelone obliqua, a hardy late summer border plant with spires of rosy flowers each with a lower lip showing from beneath an upper 'shell' was a Bartram introduction. During the 1750s he provided *Iris cristata* with lavender flowers and a cock's comb of white and orange – just about hardy in our climate. His *Stokesia laevis* with large one- to three-inch lavender-blue daisy flowers has proved its worth over the years; it is long-lived and long-flowering in late summer and early autumn. Bartram is also credited with *Aristolochia durior*, a hardy climbing species with Dutchman's Pipe yellow, brown and green flowers and heart-shaped leaves. It is sometimes used as a wall-cover.

Bartram also comes into the early history of *Dionaea muscipula*, Venus Fly Trap or Tippitiwitchet – the insect-eating plant with white flowers and spiny leaves that close up and trap any fly that settles on their surface. It was reported in 1760 by Arthur Dobbs, the Governor of North Carolina, and no doubt Bartram, too, found it in its favourite haunt in the wet pine barrens of Brunswick County. The introduction, however, has generally been credited to William Young, an American collector who became botanist to Queen Charlotte, wife of King George III. Young celebrated his appointment by bringing a live Tippitiwitchet to London in 1768.

In 1761, Bartram fell from a tree while picking holly berries, but it does not appear to have hindered his movements for, after visiting Southern Carolina the following year, he wrote home, 'I had the most prosperous journey that ever I was favoured with. Everything succeeded beyond my expectations; and my guardian angel seemed to direct my steps to discover the greatest curiosities'.

And to Collinson, about the same time he wrote, 'The variety of plants and flowers in our south western continent is beyond expression. Is it not, dear Peter, the very place garden of Madam Flora. Oh! If I could but spend six months on the Ohio, Mississippi, and Florida in health, I believe I could find more curiosities than the English, French and Spaniards have done in six score years'.

The expedition to Georgia and Florida did come off, the chief prize being *Franklinia altamaha* named after Benjamin Franklin and the Altamaha River. It is a tree 20 to 30 feet high, bearing white chalice-shaped flowers from late summer to late autumn. The last specimen of this tree in the wild was seen in 1803 near Fort Barrington, but thanks to Bartram, it has survived in cultivation.

Three things worried Bartram in later years. First, his son William, though a talented artist, was unable to settle down to a steady job. Secondly there were the Indians – barbarous and ungrateful as they seemed to Bartram. Collinson, writing from a safe distance, believed that the Indians were being exploited and as far back as 1763 had formulated 'Proposals for a lasting peace with the Indians', but Bartram told him, 'Those few Indians that profess friendship to us are watching for an opportunity to ruin us. Oh! Pennsylvania, though that was the most flourishing and peaceable province of North America are now scourged by the most barbarous creatures in the universe'.

Finally, though Bartram, through the good offices of Collinson, had been appointed botanist to King George III and actually drew a pension from the British Crown, the War of Independence, itself an affront to the Quaker philosophy, had broken out, and the Redcoats were advancing towards Philadelphia and Bartram's garden. The news was thought to have hastened his death in 1777.

Peacock Tiger Flower (*Pavonia tigridia*), from Mexico

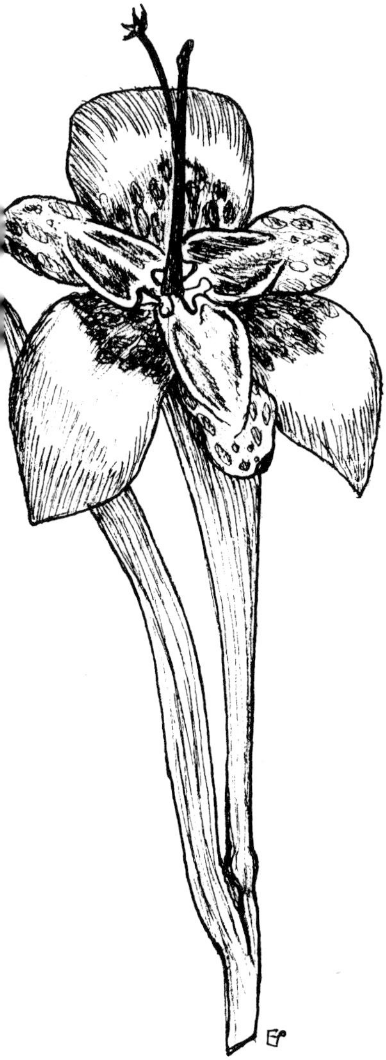

One or two other discoveries of the late eighteenth century deserve special mention. Claes Alstroemer sent Linnaeus the seeds of the Peruvian Lily named after him as *Alstroemeria pelegrina*, in 1753.

Then there was *Reseda odorata*, Sweet Mignonette, a native of Egypt for which the French had provided the name – meaning 'little darling'. It was sent to the Physic Garden in Chelsea in 1752 by Dr Adrian van Royen, one-time Professor of Botany at Leyden. Miller said it had a smell of fresh raspberries and warned gardeners against being fobbed off with de Tournefort's *R. phyteuma*, which had a larger empalement (calyx) and no scent.

The more spectacular finds came, however, from Mexico. One was the flamboyant *Tigridia pavonia*, the Peacock Tiger Flower, with its three large yellow or scarlet outer petals arranged like the blades of a propellor, and three inner smaller petals, red, spotted with yellow or vice versa. Another Mexican triumph was the zinnia. The seeds of an unspectacular species, *Z. pauciflora* were sent to Philip Miller in the Chelsea Physic Garden in 1753 but the species cultivated today, *Z. elegans*, arrived in 1796 when the seeds of a purple-flowering strain were sent together with those of *Cosmos bipinnatus* –

rose-coloured catherine-wheel daisies – by Professor Casimir Gómez de Ortega of Madrid to the Marchioness of Bute, wife of the British Ambassador to Spain.

That splendid adornment of the border, the Dahlia, arrived in the same way at about the same time, though its history goes back much further. It was mentioned in an illustrated 16-volume *History of Mexico*, completed by Dr Francisco Hernandez in 1577 but suppressed by order of the Spanish Council of the Indies, and destroyed in the fire at the Escorial in 1671. (A 10-volume work by Père Barnardez Cobo, the Jesuit priest who spent 45 years in Mexico and Peru and gave his name to the climbing cup-and-saucer wall plant, *Cobaea scandens*, was also suppressed.)

Another work by Hernandez dating from 1575 was, however, published in 1651, 83 years after his death, and in it, we see a drawing of a double dahlia with the name given to it by the Indians – cocoxochitl. Hernandez found two species of dahlia growing in sandy meadows near the Quauhnahauac mountains and recorded that the tubers were used for food by the natives. Eventually in 1789 Vicente Cervantes, who was in charge of the Botanic Gardens in Mexico City, sent some tubers to his friend, the Abbé Cavanilles, who was in charge of the Royal Gardens in Madrid, and in turn, some seed was brought by Dr Gómez de Ortega to the Marchioness of Bute. The first plants died out after a few years, but in 1804, Lady Holland procured the three species – *Dahlia pinnata*, *D. coccinea* and *D. rosea* – from which most of the modern dahlias except the 'cactus dahlias' have developed. Andreas Dahl, after whom the plant was named, was a pupil of Linnaeus. He believed, along with others, that the tubers might serve as a substitute for the potato.

But the Empress Josephine had other ideas, and in her garden at Malmaison the Dahlias became serious rivals to the roses painted so faithfully for her by Redouté.

9 *Recording the Image*

The origins of garden plants have been recorded, here and there, in portraits on all kinds of material from china, vellum, and wood to canvas, silk and paper.

The 1,400 or so illustrations which originally accompanied the Vienna Codex of Dioscorides' *De Materia Medica*, and which are believed to have been done in the early Christian era successfully captured the textual descriptions. But during the two thousand years that followed, when copying by hand still remained the only way of circulating written knowledge, artists were less successful – or took less trouble – over their work. The plants deteriorated into conventional symbols that were no more real than the lions of heraldry.

Standards in the west were probably at their lowest in the thirteenth century when respect for the authority of the church and for the Latin and Greek of the classics was greatest, and few if any artists took the trouble to draw their plant illustrations from life. When confronted with the task of illustrating a Latin or Greek text, they turned to a classical author, if one could be found, rather than to the living world.

The difficulty was to reconcile the vague and imprecise classical descriptions handed down to them with living plants that they could see. No botanic language existed which would allow writers to describe accurately the difference between one plant and another. It was a disability that could put lives at risk in cases where there were two similar herbs, one of which was poisonous and not to be taken, whereas the other would cure any complaint from swelling imposthumes to strangury.

The breakthrough, when it came, was due in part to the needs of the herbalists, but far more to that thirst for acquiring knowledge, at first hand, by direct observation which was so strong a characteristic of the Renaissance.

First signs that flowers were being drawn from life – and might therefore become identifiable – appeared as far back as 1475 in Konrad of Megenberg's *Das Buch der Natur* in which certain features of some plants were intentionally exaggerated in order to make them more easily distinguishable. A new departure was evident in the *Herbarius zu Teutsch* published in Mainz in 1485, for, in this case, there are signs that the anonymous artist was no mere recorder but was influenced by his admiration for and even affection towards the plants he was drawing.

Already, in 1530, examples of what might be called flower portraiture are to be seen in Otto Brunfels' *Herbarum Vivae Eicones*, as called for by its title *Living Images of Herbs*; and this work is notable for including a delightful study of the pasque flower even though as the author admitted, it had no medical properties. The artist, Hans Weiditz was a contemporary of Albrecht Dürer whose powers of observation and artistic good sense allowed him to make an attractive study out of the most insignificant weeds growing in a piece of turf. Leonart Fuchs gave even greater prominence to the illustrations in his work *De Historia Stirpium* (*Of the History of Plants*) published in 1542 and in his *Neues Kreüterbuch* (of German plants) which appeared the following year.

But the difficulties of the time were immense, for woodcuts were the only method of reproducing drawings. In Europe they were first used at the start of the fifteenth century for playing cards – about 700 years after they had been used in China for the more exacting task of printing Chinese 'characters'. Woodcuts were, of course, line drawings without half tones or even tinted shading. Shadows, where required, were represented by finely drawn parallel lines or cross-hatching.

When the artist had finished his original drawing, a second artist was needed to copy it on to the wooden block to be used for printing. A third craftsman had then to cut away from the wooden block all that part of it which would appear white in the illustration, leaving standing only the portions to be inked.

From Gerard's *Herball*

It was an operation performed with far greater accuracy and finesse on the continent than in England, which serves to explain why home-grown plants in Gerard's *Herball* had to be illustrated for the most part with foreign importations, which Plantin the printer had already used elsewhere.

Nevertheless, each advance in the technique of printing flower portraits, wherever it took place, helped to focus the attention of the well-to-do on plants which could add lustre to their possessions, particularly if the plants were uncommon.

As botanists increased their knowledge of plant structure and their skills in distinguishing one plant from another, the demand arose for artists who could more accurately be described as botanical draughtsmen – delineators who could have been asked to represent the coastline of Nova Scotia but who were equally prepared to tackle not only a plant and its flowers, but also its seeds in different stages of development, not to mention stamens, carpels, and other vital organs. This mattered particularly in the case of plants discovered by explorers abroad. People wanted to know exactly what was new about them.

But the draughtsman often had to reconstruct his drawing from a rough sketch made by the collector,

Armeria rubra latifolia.
Broad leaued Sweet-Williams.

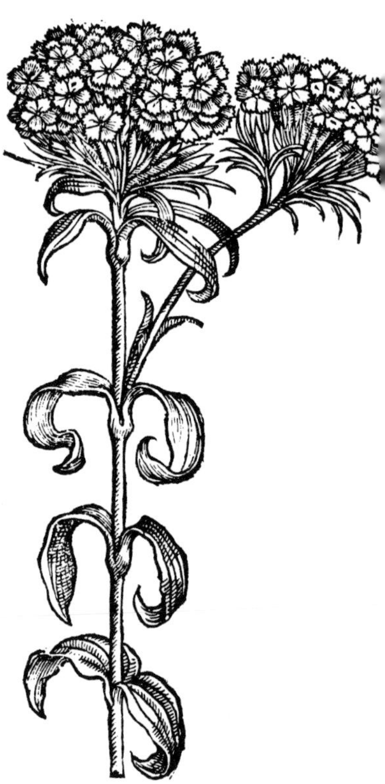

From Gerard's *Herball*

or from a pressed and dried specimen with a few words attached. Powers of deduction aided by imaginative speculation were needed and when drawing a plant even the most conventional draughtsman was obliged to try to create the impression that his illustration was not merely an arrangement of lines on a flat piece of paper but represented a three-dimensional living species with a distinctive character of its own.

Sometimes the other artists added realism to their flower paintings by including butterflies, birds, and even snails and by massing together flowers in the form in which they might have been selected from the garden to make a bouquet.

All cannot be mentioned, and the list of those selected must depend on the eye of the beholder and on whether he is a gardener, a botanist, a nurseryman, a craftsman, a poet, or an artist interested in the composition of the picture and the interpretation which it provides.

But I would follow those who praise the work of the anonymous artist who illustrated the herbal written for Francesco Carrara about the year 1397. This artist, a miniaturist, came from Padua and would presumably have benefited from the medical and botanical studies for which that city was already becoming famous. In his illustrations the leaves and flowers are drawn as nature made them with all their imperfections and blemishes and with a special finesse and delicacy, both in stem and leaf outlines and in the colours used, and, even in cases where the draughtsmanship is not sufficiently precise for identification of the exact species in modern terms, the character of the genus is delineated with reassuring fidelity.

This artist also seems far less inhibited by the limitations of the space allowed to him than other better known artists – among them Pierandrea Mattioli, the illustrator back in 1561 of an early tulip and one of a number of artists who apparently considered it necessary to compress a profusion of vegetation into each of their woodcuts.

The next two artists – though born in different centuries – both deserve special consideration not only because of their work but because of the unusual circumstances in which it was performed.

Jacques Le Moyne de Morgues went with René de Goulaine de Laudonnière, leader of the Huguenot expedition to Florida in 1564. His task was to map the territory and to make drawings of new discoveries – plants among them. But the Spaniards overran the area, massacred nearly all the Frenchmen and 'Le Moyne' was lucky to escape with his life.

Because of his religion he preferred not to return to France, and settled in England where he found a patroness in Lady Mary Sidney. His earlier water-colours can be seen in the Victoria and Albert Museum, his later ones in the British Museum. All show a genuine love of the flowers he chose to paint. His best known work, 'La Clef des Champs' was published in 1586.

Maria Sybilla Merian, born in 1647, was the daughter of a Frankfurt engraver who studied flower painting under her stepfather and, at the age of 17, married a fellow pupil, Johann Graff. After 19 years of marriage she parted from him and, persuaded by a friend, Anna-Maria van Schuurman, she entered a Dutch Labadist convent in Friesland.

While in the convent she became fascinated by a collection of butterflies assembled by a former Governor of the Dutch colony of Surinam (Guyana) and after 13 years sailed with her daughter Dorothea out to Paramaribo where she painted insects, tropical fruit and flowers with great insight and distinction, in a style which must have kindled lively interest in all who saw them. A volume of her flower studies is to be seen in the British Museum (Natural

History) in South Kensington, and other examples of her work are to be seen in the Royal Library in Windsor and in Leningrad.

Then there was the young artist, Claude Aubriet, who accompanied Joseph de Tournefort in 1700 on a tour to Crete and 33 islands in the Aegean during which de Tournefort hoped to discover new plants as well as those of the ancients. They went on to Trebizond in Anatolia where they saw *Rhododendron ponticum* in bloom. They finally reached and partially climbed Mount Ararat. The translation of de Tournefort's *Relation d'un voyage au Levant*, undertaken by John Ozell and published in 1718 is a colourful travelogue presented in the freshly minted English of an earlier age. De Tournefort's narrative did not confine itself to botany, and while on Samos he noted for the benefit of future travellers: 'The women of this island are very nasty and ugly and don't shift above once a month. Their habit is a vest after the Turkish manner with a red coif and a tassel, yellow or white, which hangs down their back as does their hair which most commonly they part into a couple of tresses at the bottom, whereof hangs a bunch of small plates of Block-tin or silver of a coarse alloy, for they have scarce any other in this country'.

Later de Tournefort's homesickness betrays itself for a moment as he writes, 'All the meadows round about Constantinople are fill'd with a beautiful sort of Crain's Beak . . . its root is like a cluster of French turnips'.

One of his discoveries in Crete was a close-growing rock plant with purple flowers, for which the French botanist Michel Adanson (1727–1806) chose the name Aubrieta (*not* Aubretia). Perhaps, in French, Oh-bree-ay-ta is lighter on the tongue than Oh-bree-ay-tia, and, though the name was tentatively modified to Aubrietia in 1821 by a French-speaking Swiss botanist, Augustin-Pyramus Candolle, the rule of priority for the names of plant species has not yet been relaxed to the point where the vernacular name for Aubrieta can become the official one.

Aubrieta deltoidea was likely to have been the species collected by de Tournefort and, by 1710, it was established in the Botanic Garden at Leyden; the improvements which have bestowed so much popularity on these plants were achieved only in the mid-nineteenth century.

Aubriet's somewhat severe and clinical drawings are not to everyone's taste but his powers of observation and mastery of detail are such as to satisfy the most exacting botanist; the first collection of his work was not, however, published until 1808 – 60 years after his death.

Throughout the eighteenth and part of the nineteenth century, the English still relied largely on artists from abroad to record the new plants introduced into their country from Europe and overseas.

George Dionysius Ehret, for example, was born in 1707 in Heidelberg and was originally employed by the Elector of that city and then by the Margrave of Baden, an eccentric with a magnificent garden at Karlsruhe, also in south Germany. Neither of these two aristocrats could have overpaid him, for when he left them to go to Vienna, he had to work his passage by helping to row a boat 300 miles down the Danube from Ulm to the Austrian capital. With help from a patron, Dr Christopher Jacob Trew of Nuremberg, he moved from Vienna to Paris, and then to Leyden where he received from Linnaeus himself a thorough grounding in the Linnaean system of classification. Thus when Linnaeus wrote his *Hortus Cliffortianus*, the first descriptive work based on the Linnaean classification, he asked Ehret to illustrate it.

In 1736, two years before the *Hortus Cliffortianus*

was published, Ehret visited London, met both Sloane and Miller, and decided to settle in England. There he found he was in great demand, both as an artist who could make accurate drawings of new plants that were then pouring into the country, and as a lecturer and a tutor to young ladies of good birth who wished to take up flower painting. His pupils included Catherine, Duchess of Norfolk, Mary, Duchess of Leeds, two daughters of Margaret, Duchess of Portland, three daughters of the Earl of Essex, two daughters of the Duke of Kent, two daughters of the Earl of Pomfret – (and so on). He was not only an expert draughtsman who made extensive use of the microscope to ensure accuracy but also a skilled engraver and etcher with a fine sense of colour. His talents were rewarded in 1757 when he was elected a Fellow of the Royal Society.

Perhaps the most successful of the great flower painters from the Continent to be employed by English collectors were two brothers, Franz and Ferdinand Bauer, born at Feldsberg near Vienna.

Ferdinand Bauer was chosen by Dr John Sibthorp, Professor of Botany at Oxford, as artist to accompany him on an expedition the object of which was to rediscover as many of the 300 or so plants which had been mentioned by Dioscorides but were still unidentified. Sibthorp, who had inherited a substantial fortune in 1780 on the death of his mother, had already been to Vienna and examined the Dioscorides Codex, and it seems likely that Bauer had been recommended to him on that occasion. At any rate they set out from Vienna in 1786 in a leisurely manner and visited Milos, Crete, Athens, Smyrna and Constantinople where they saw the 'Rose of Sharon' still flourishing in the very spot where George Wheler had found it more than a century earlier. After spending the winter in Constantinople, they visited some more islands in the Aegean and eastern Mediterranean, Athens and the area round it, and Salonika in northern Greece before sailing home from Patras in September. They arrived home in the second week of December, Bauer with sheaves of drawings and Sibthorp with dried specimens of some 2,000 plants – 300 of which were new, though few are cultivated today. Sibthorp died of a lung complaint at the age of 38 but he

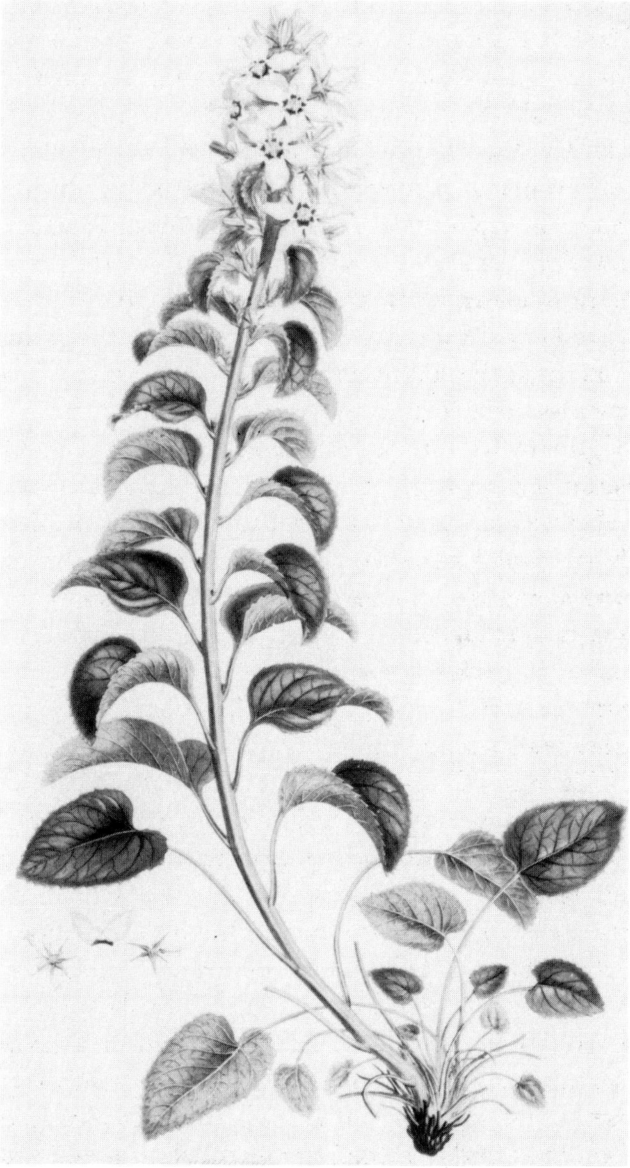

Campanula versicolor, from Sibthorp's *Flora Graeca*. John Sibthorp who found this flower died of an illness he contracted during his expedition to Greece

left enough money to finance the publication of Bauer's finished drawings in the 12-volume *Flora Graeca* which appeared in parts posthumously between 1806 and 1840.* One of the first flowers in Volume I was the *Salvia pomifera* which had so greatly impressed Rauwolf. *Iris tuberosa*, the green and purple Snake's Head Iris so vividly described by Gerard, was there too.

Bauer's next journey was as member of the expedition led by Matthew Flinders which sailed in 1801 to survey the coastline of New South Wales, Queensland and the Northern Territory. Bauer's work on this occasion was supervised by Robert Brown, afterwards librarian of the Linnean Society, and a noticeable improvement in accuracy and detail resulted. During the voyage home Flinders' small vessel, the Cumberland, had to put in to Mauritius for repairs and the French Governor held him captive there for more than six years.

Bauer and Brown, however, were released and Bauer started to illustrate Brown's descriptions of the plants they had found in 'New Holland' as New South Wales was then called. One of them was an orchid, *Cymbidium suave*, found at Port Jackson, the original name for Sydney. Bauer, like Catesby before him, took lessons in engraving in an attempt to reduce the costs of producing plates from his drawings, but the money could not be found, and Bauer returned to Vienna to live near the Palace of Schönbrunn where he completed his 236 drawings. Twenty-five of them appeared in *The Australian Flower Paintings of Ferdinand Bauer* by William T. Stearn with an introduction by Wilfrid Blunt (Basilisk Press, 1976). Others are to be seen in Vienna.

Unlike Ferdinand, Franz Bauer did not have to

* A copy sold by Sotheby Parke Bernet in New York on 1 October 1980 fetched the equivalent of £50,209.

travel in order to draw plants. They came to him and he was even more successful than his brother in his flower portraits. His eye for dramatic yet harmonious composition and for the unmistakable characteristics of each species he painted as well as his unerring success in conveying the texture and colour of each part of the plant has rarely, if ever, been surpassed.

His illustrations of strelitzias, the imperious crane

Helleboris officinalis, from Sibthorp's *Flora Graeca*

flowers from South Africa (1818) and of orchidaceous plants (1830) are in a class of their own.

English artists, however, were greatly encouraged by William Curtis, the founder of the *Botanical Magazine*, a mainstream of botanical illustration across two centuries. He was born in Alton in Hampshire in 1746, and is believed to have acquired his love of natural history from John Lagg, an ostler at the Crown Inn, Alton.

After serving his apprenticeship with his grandfather who was a local apothecary, he set up in London, but sold his practice in order to study plants grown in his garden in Bermondsey. In 1772 he was appointed Superintendent and Demonstrator at the Apothecaries Garden in Chelsea, and five years later began to publish his *Flora Londiniensis*, an account of the plants to be seen within 10 miles of the capital. It brought him much acclaim but, as he put it, 'no pudding'.

To remedy this he founded the *Botanical Magazine*, with financial aid from the Earl of Bute and Dr John Coakeley Lettsom, a Quaker physician. The first issue appeared on 1st February 1787. It sought to illustrate the plants which gardeners of the day could grow either on open ground or in a cool greenhouse, or in a glasshouse heated with a stove. The illustrations were hand-coloured line drawings, with descriptions in many cases, from Miller's dictionary though the caption to *Rudbeckia purpurea*, drawn by James Sowerby, one of the first plants to be shown, declared, 'This species differs from the other plants of the genus in the colour of its outermost petals, which are long narrow purple and pendulous and not inaptly resemble small pieces of red tape'.

Several new plants from South Africa were included in the first year, including a Yellow Mesembryanthemum stated to be hardy.

The earlier volumes of the *Botanical Magazine* appeared shortly before the rise to fame of Pierre-

Pierre-Joseph Redouté (1759–1840), the Belgian flower illustrator who painted lilies and cacti as well as roses

Joseph Redouté, the son of a Belgian interior decorator. He moved to Paris and became one of the protégés of the Empress Josephine, whose enthusiasm helped to bring variety and splendour to the grounds of her palace at Malmaison, making it one of the finest gardens of the day.

Redouté is best known for his paintings of roses, but he also produced eight volumes of studies of Liliaceae, and also studies of Cacti, where his skill in the use of perspective helped him to convey the solidity of the plants. He was one of the earliest and most successful exploiters of stipple effects, and by rubbing colours into different areas of his copperplate engravings achieved a form of simultaneous multi-colour printing.

Meanwhile records of new plants for European gardens were being made elsewhere in a very different style. The Chinese were, of course, several centuries in advance of Europeans in both painting and printing techniques. There, every child was taught to use a brush to reproduce the 20,000 or so characters which allowed the Chinese to communicate with one another irrespective of their local dialects. In their drawings the finest shadings could be obtained with a single stroke by loading less ink on to one side of the brush than on to the other. An almost invisible fine black line round the edges of leaves and petals set their plants into sharp focus and endowed them with extra vivacity.

Unusual colour effects were obtained by overwashing since the water-soluble colour pigments used by Chinese artists to allow drawings to be folded – as for instance on screens – could not be mixed together. Throughout eastern Asia, the whole philosophy of flower painters was distinctive. They saw each plant as a living organism with its own characteristics and perhaps even reticences, rather than as a specimen to be examined under the lens and physically dissected.

This approach was not that of explorers who sailed east in search of new species. Nevertheless it was obviously sensible for them to rely on local artists who could draw and paint plants while these were still in fresh condition.

One of the earliest collectors to do so was Van Rheede tot Draakenstein, the Dutch Governor of Malabar in south-west India at the end of the seventeenth century. The plants shown in his *Hortus Indicus Malabaricus* were drawn by a team of Brahmin artists from plants brought by local collectors to the Governor's headquarters at Cochin.

The East India Company, founded on the last day of the year 1600 AD, was another patron of the local artists, though in some cases Company officers had to curb their exuberance in gouache and impose on them the greater precision and restraint required for ink or water colour illustrations. Works of distinction were produced at various times by officers of the Company with the help of local illustrators. These included William Roxburgh's *Plants of the Coast of Coromandel* (1795–1819), Nathaniel Wallich's *Plantae Asiaticae Rariores* and Dr John Forbes Royle's *Illustrations of the Botany of the Himalayan Mountains* published in 1839.

There was also John Reeves, a tea inspector of the East India Company who worked during the tea season in Canton but lived and set up his garden on the island of Macao. Between 1812 and 1831, when he retired, he sent home not only plants collected and grown in his garden but drawings made by Chinese artists often under his supervision in his house. These drawings are to be seen in the British Museum and in the magnificent collection at the Lindley Library of the Royal Horticultural Society. In 1859 when the Society was in a financial jam, the collection had to be sold. It vanished without trace. Nearly 50 years later, however, Reginald Cory bequeathed to the Society his collection of botanical

Sulphur Rose, by P-J Redouté

works and memorabilia. They included some paintings of unknown origin which turned out to be Reeves illustrations.

The Chinese at this time were far ahead of the Europeans in the art of reproducing drawings and paintings. In the seventh century AD they had reached the stage of woodcutting complete pages of Chinese characters combined on the same block with illustrations. By the seventeenth century they had succeeded in printing in colour off wooden blocks.

An attempt at printing plants in colour from a single plate was made in Britain by John Martyn in his *Historia Plantarum Rariorum* published between 1728 and 1737; but for many years after this and even after the discovery of chromo- and photochrome lithography and colour photo-engraving, plant illustrations whether from engravings or lithographs, were coloured by hand with water-colour paints, which, it was felt, gave greater accuracy.

Certainly standards in 18th-century Britain were high, and soon to become higher still through the efforts of an enlightened and wealthy amateur who sailed round the world in search of new plants for English gardens.

Lilium superbum from Dr. Christophe Trew's *Plantae Selectae* (1750–1773). Native of eastern United States

Tab. XI.

Lilium superbum.
Sp. pl. 2. 434.

LILIVM *folis sparsis, multiflorum, floribus reflexis, fundo aureo, limbo aurantio, punctis nigricantibus, pedunculis singulis unico folio instructis.*

10 *The Great Banks*

As a schoolboy, Joseph Banks spent his summer holiday evenings fishing from a punt on the Thames near Chelsea with John Montagu, 4th Earl of Sandwich, drinking champagne and burgundy, and, when the holidays were over, it was to Eton that he returned, taking with him his mother's copy of Gerard's *Herball* which, as his tutor mournfully observed, was the only book he was seen to be holding when detected reading in his study.

Banks' special interest in botany developed one evening at Eton after he had gone swimming with a party of schoolfriends. Lingering behind, he was fascinated by the beauty of the roadside flowers in the setting sun, and when he fell in with a group of women picking herbs for the local apothecary, he arranged for them to collect plants for him – under contract. When he went up to Oxford to continue his education, he found that there was no one there to give him lectures in botany, so he imported an ex-student from Cambridge to do so.

In 1764, at the age of 21, he inherited a house in Chelsea and an impressive estate, Revesby Abbey, in Lincolnshire. At 23 he was elected a Fellow of the Royal Society of which he would eventually be President for 42 years.

Banks' first chance to shine had come in 1766 when, through the good offices of his friend the Earl of Sandwich, who by that time had risen to be First Lord of the Admiralty, he was appointed official naturalist on HMS *Niger* which was about to survey the coasts of Labrador and Newfoundland. His industry and enthusiasm during this expedition was

Iris kaempferi by Engelbert Kaempfer (1651–1715) from *The Genus Iris* (1913) by William Rickatson Dykes

such as to secure him a place aboard the converted collier *Endeavour* in which Captain Cook was to voyage round the world via Cape Horn and Botany Bay. The avowed object of Cook's expedition was to observe the transit of Venus over the disc of the sun on 3 June 1769, a conjunction the like of which, the Royal Society averred, would not recur for 100 years and which, if properly recorded, would greatly advance the science of navigation.

The French, the Spaniards, the Danes and the Swedes were, it was urged, making preparations to take similar readings, and the Empress of Russia had given directions for observations to be taken 'at several points in her vast dominions'. Obviously the Admiralty could not afford to be at a disadvantage.

Captain James Cook (1728–79), portrait by J. Webber

The Royal Society believed that somewhere not too far south of the equator would be the best location for the observation to be taken, and preferable to the alternatives of Spitzbergen or Hudson Bay.

But whatever might occur in the heavens, Banks' thoughts rested on the earth, and on the new forms of life to be found there. His personal entourage aboard *Endeavour* included two servants from Revesby, Daniel Solander, a Swedish botanist and pupil of Linnaeus who would classify and describe the new plants, an assistant botanist, Herman Sporing, a map draughtsman, Alexander Buchan and a natural history student, Sidney Parkinson who was to make rough sketches which could be worked up later into finished drawings.

Banks was not interested exclusively in plants, though he took with him a library of botanical works. He was also equipped with nets, trawls and drags for the sea bed, with an underwater telescope, with spirits for preserving the bodies of animals and with devices for catching and preserving insects.

His enthusiasm and enterprise were evident from the start. At Rio de Janeiro where the ship stayed for about a month to refit, the Portuguese Viceroy had given orders that no one except the Captain himself was to leave the ship, and even he was to be accompanied everywhere by a Portuguese officer. Nevertheless, Banks, Solander and Parkinson spent an illicit day ashore leaving the ship before dawn and returning after dusk. Banks bought a 'middlingly fat porker for eleven shillings and a muscovy duck for something under two shillings'. He shot and missed a hummingbird, bought some black market amethysts and topazes and collected an impressive number of plants. One of them was the *Rodriguesia rigida*, a member of the popular orchid family, though not generally cultivated today. Other specimens were met with in the fodder taken aboard for livestock or procured by special request as being suitable for salads.

A portrait of Banks at his most energetic is to be found in the narrative cobbled together by Dr (of letters) John Hawksworth who was commissioned to write the official account of the voyage:

'The date: January 1769 shortly before Cook rounded Cape Horn; the Place: the Maire Strait, Tierra del Fuego.

'Mr Banks and Solander, with attendants and servants and two seamen to assist, Mr Monkhouse the Surgeon and Mr Green, the Astronomer, set out from the ship with a view to penetrating as far as possible into the country and returning at night' the account says. 'The hills, when viewed from a distance seemed partly a wood, partly a plain and above them a bare rock. Mr Banks hoped to get through the wood, and made no doubt that beyond it, he should, in a country no botanist had ever

Sir Joseph Banks (1743–1820), portrait by Thomas Lawrence

visited, find alpine plants which would abundantly compensate his labour.'

But when the party reached the wood, they found it to be a pathless wilderness and the 'plain' turned out to be a swamp with bushes of birch 'so stubborn that they could not be bent out of the way'. Each step forward had to be made over a barrier three feet high and the ground was so soft that feet sank into it ankle deep.

About two-thirds of the way across this swamp 'one of Mr Banks' draughtsmen, Mr Buchan was unhappily seized of a fit' and the whole party had to halt. A fire was lit, and those most fatigued were left to warm themselves by it, while Banks, Solander, Green and Monkhouse went on and climbed the summit of the rock. 'As botanists, their expectations were abundantly gratified' recorded Hawksworth after his fashion, 'for they found a great variety of plants which with respect to the alpine plants of Europe are exactly what those plants are with respect to such as grow in the plains.'

Meanwhile, however, the delays on the way made it impossible to return to shore at the time originally arranged. It had grown much colder, and the prospect of having to spend a night in the open was a daunting one. Green and Monkhouse, therefore, were sent on ahead to find a sheltered spot where a fire could be lit. But while the others of the party were on their way to the rendezvous, the temperature fell still further, and the men began to suffer from exposure.

Solander who had had some experience of winter climbs in the Norwegian mountains declared with conviction: 'Whoever sits down now will sleep, and whoever sleeps will wake no more'. But he was the first to insist on lying down. Banks got him to his feet. Then Richmond, one of the black servants, said that he desired nothing so much as to lie down and die. Solander again insisted that he must have some sleep before continuing. Banks shook him awake and they stumbled on. It began to snow, and they had had nothing to eat except for a vulture which in the hope of devouring them, had incautiously come within range of their guns. Towards dawn, Richmond, together with another black servant, George Dorlton, and a seaman had to be left behind in the shelter of some trees. The seaman recovered, but the two black servants, who had been unwise enough to share his bottle of rum, perished.

But Cook's faith in Banks remained undiminished and indeed increased markedly after Banks succeeded in recovering a precious quadrant seized by a native chief in Tahiti before Venus had been observed. It was in Tahiti that Banks first tasted roasted dog with its entrails cooked in a coconut shell which he pronounced to be excellent – especially in comparison with the ship's biscuits which contained vermin and tasted 'as hot as mustard', though he could not promise that European meat-eating dogs would be as toothsome.

As a recipe for avoiding scurvy, he dosed himself with a mixture composed of one-fifth brandy and four-fifths lemon juice.

On his journey round the world Banks went ashore on New Zealand, where he collected 300 plants. They included the evergreen climber, *Clianthus puniceus*, known as the Glory Pea or Parrot's Bill. It is now scarcely to be found in the wild, but at that time it was cultivated as a sacred plant in almost every Maori settlement.

It was Australia next and there on landing he encountered almost at once that sensational shrub, *Telopea speciosissima*, the Crimson Waratah with its glories of colour, *Brachichyton acerifolia*, sometimes called the Flame Tree from its garish scarlet racemes, and various species of *Epacris*, an outsize heath-like plant. There were tree ferns and bottle-brush plants galore. He also noted that the Eucalyptus trees exuded gum and gave them the name all Australians use today.

It is sometimes assumed, from the fact that it took 200 quires of paper and a whole day to sort and dry the plants that Banks had by then accumulated, that he considered New South Wales, as it was to be called, a settler's paradise. This was far from being the case to judge by what he wrote six days after his arrival in a passage which Joseph Hooker saw fit to suppress when he edited Banks' journal: 'The country, tho in general well enough clothed, appeared in some places bare: it resembled in my imagination the back of a lean Cow, covered in general with long hair, but nevertheless where her scraggy hip bones have stuck out farther than they ought, accidental rubs and knocks have entirely bared them of their share of covering'. 'In every respect the most barren country I have seen' he added after four months cruising and careening up the east coast. It was a verdict confirmed by James Backhouse, Quaker and temperance worker in the convict settlements of Australia in the 1840s who affirmed that the soil of Botany Bay had to be turned two or three times to make it fertile.

Banks' best chance came when *Endeavour* rammed a jagged pinnacle of coral off the Barrier Reef and the crew saw her floor planks and false keel floating away in the sea. It took more than six weeks ashore for the repairs to be made, and Banks could botanise to his heart's content in the future state of Queensland. They made permanent repairs to the ship in Batavia and sailed home safe at last.

Counting Madeira and the other places they had visited en route, Banks accumulated 1,300 new species of plants, giving rise to 110 genera during his world tour.

One of the new plants was *Pernettia mucronata*, a white-flowered member of the heath family from the Straits of Magellan, with berries that persist and can still be used to enliven the winter flower-vase. The Australian flowers were more spectacular and some of the best belonged to the Protea family, whose showy flowers can resemble almost anything from the top of a maypole to a pin cushion, or even a rose. The red-flowered *Banksia serrata*, which lived up to its name by having leaves with a saw-like edge, was the first Australian plant to be raised in this country. It was cultivated by James Lee and Lewis Kennedy in their nursery, The Vineyard, set up in 1745 where the Olympia Exhibition halls now stand. The Vineyard nursery, which had formerly produced Burgundy-type wine, became sufficiently well known to be mentioned by name in Thackeray's *Vanity Fair* and, even when England and France were at war, John Kennedy, son of Lewis, was provided with a special document allowing him to travel freely to and from Malmaison, where he was helping to establish the Empress Josephine's rose-garden.

Lee and Kennedy also succeeded in raising *Lobelia refulgens* from seed taken in Botany Bay, and Kennedy's name is commemorated in *Kennedya*, the scarlet Australian Bean Flower. Their catalogue of 1774 offered the beautiful *Bauhinia acuminata* at least 30 years before it was generally distributed, as well as an early *Buddleia globosa* from Peru, and *Fothergillia*, a splendid bottle-brush shrub from America.

The seeds of two other Banksias travelled home on *Endeavour* – *Banksia integrifolia* with dark green leaves, silvery on their lower surface, and a sulphurous yellow cone of flowers, and *B. ericifolia* with spikes of yellowish red flowers decked with silky yellow strands. Banks' *Veronica (Hebe) elliptica*, an evergreen shrub with fragrant white purple lined flowers, is still grown.

Grevillea banksii, with sea-green foliage and a ruby cone of flowers, was also a Banks discovery though not introduced till 1868. It was dedicated by him to

Australian Bean Flower (*Kennedya rubicunda*), named after Lewis Kennedy, nurseryman, who sent David Burton to collect plants in New South Wales

his friend, the Hon. Charles Greville, one of the founders of the Royal Horticultural Society to be. Greville is also remembered as the promoter and builder of the port of Milford Haven and as the protector of Emma Hart, who as Lady Hamilton became Nelson's mistress. Some Grevilleas are hardy in the South of England.

James Lee, writing to Linnaeus after Banks' return, said 'It is the daily labour of many servants to paste them (Banks' plants) on paper, and Banks and Solander spend 4 or 5 hours a day in describing and re-arranging them'. Five artists were engaged to paint them in colours either from Parkinson's rough sketches or from the dried specimens. Eighteen top engravers, one resident in Banks' house, prepared the copper plates on which the drawings were to be reproduced, yet no collected account with coloured illustrations of the *Endeavour* plants was published until quite recently when Editions Alecto, with the encouragement of the British Museum began issuing their 34-part work, to include 738 plates taken from the original engravings, hand-coloured to match the original water colours.

Many of Parkinson's Australian plant sketches, and the completed hand-coloured drawings from them by artists such as John Frederick Miller and Frederick Polydore Nodder, are to be seen in the Botanical Library of the British Museum (Natural History) at South Kensington – together with notes in Banks' handwriting of where the plants were found – 'Lizzard (*sic*) Island', 'Endeavour River', 'Thirsty Sound' for example. The collected drawings serve to show how much of Banks' work went unrequited during his lifetime.

Looking at a sample volume, leaf by leaf, one sees with regret that many of Parkinson's sketches (showing the general structure of a plant and, in colour, a leaf and one or two flowers, plus a couple of lines of description) were never turned into finished illustrations. Moreover, the names suggested, presumably by Solander, have often since been altered beyond recognition: *Volkameria insectorum* becomes *Clerodendron floribundum*; *Pedalioides tribilus* becomes *Tecoma australis* . . . and so on.

Other plants were simply lost sight of or credited elsewhere. Thus we find no trace of *Josephinea grandiflora*, a stately plant with lanceolate leaves and pinkish foxglove flowers with impressively protruding scarlet lower lips. *Passiflora banksii*, a passion flower executed in a fine shade of dark red, did not live to appear in Aiton's *Hortus Kewensis* of 1812; it survives today presumably as a result of a reintroduction.

Actinotus helianthii, a member of the umbellifer or carrot family, though it looks more like a white pasque flower and is known locally as the Flannel Flower, also appears among the Parkinson drawings, but the date of its introduction is given as 1821 – 50 years after Banks saw it. *Darwinia fascicularis* – an intriguing heath-like plant with bare branches leading up to a terminal collar or ruff of pine-needle leaves and white flowers turning to scarlet fruits – was found in Botany Bay when Banks went ashore there, but the date of its introduction to Britain is given as 1820.

Other descendants of the Banks plants – reintroduced – can be seen at the Tresco Gardens in the Isles of Scilly, and at Inverewe in Rossshire where both *Banksia integrifolia* and *Clianthus puniceus* have been grown, but it must be confessed that few Australian plants, four-fifths of which are peculiar to Australia, really feel at home in Britain's climate.

The neglect which Banks' species suffered was due also in part to Solander's death in 1782 and to the new responsibilities which Banks undertook after his return.

The first of these was the establishment of His Majesty's Botanic Garden (now Gardens) at Kew.

In Charles II's time, Kew House had been a private estate owned by Sir Henry Capel, but in 1730 it was acquired on lease by Frederick, Prince of Wales, son of George II. Both he and his wife, Princess Augusta from Saxe-Gotha, were keen gardeners, and after Frederick's death in 1751, Augusta, with the encouragement of her good friend, the 3rd Earl of Bute (father of the 1st Marquis of Bute whom we have already met as Ambassador to Madrid) set aside nine acres of the estate as a garden for exotic plants. Her son George III was also a garden-lover. He had already inherited the Richmond estate next to Kew and on his mother's death in 1772 combined the two estates into one. On hearing of Banks' return from his voyage round the world, George III sent for him, and a warm friendship developed. The following year, shortly after Augusta's death, the King who had no great regard for Bute, dismissed him and appointed Banks in his place as Scientific Adviser on the Plant Life of the Dependencies of the Crown. Banks had inspired the King with the idea of turning Kew into an exchange centre through which those territories having valuable crops such as sago, camphor, and the mango should bestow them on other Crown lands where they were unknown. (The transfer of the Bread Fruit Tree to the West Indies in 1793, of quinine to India in 1860, and of rubber to Ceylon and the Malay peninsula in the 1870s were some of Kew's later achievements.)

Banks determined that, in addition, Kew should develop into the world's most advanced centre for botanic studies. William Aiton, who had trained under Philip Miller at the Chelsea Physic Garden, was in day-to-day charge of Kew. His *Hortus Kewensis*, the first edition of which was published in 1789, listed 5,535 species in cultivation at Kew. By 1813, the figure had nearly doubled.

Almost from the start, collectors were sent out to ensure that His Majesty's Botanic Garden would possess plants to be seen in no other garden.

'Directions for bringing over Seeds and Plants from the East Indies and other countries in a state of Vegetation' (meaning the plants and not the countries) – were formulated by John Ellis, Fellow of the Royal Society, and were published in 1770. Earth and moss, held together with pack thread, were recommended for plants, and paper wrapping for seeds. Collectors were recommended to test the seeds when buying them by cutting some to see that they were not dried out ones of the kind which 'crafty Chinese' were apt to unload on the unwary. Vapour from burnt sulphur was suggested as a deterrent to cockroaches and other vermin.

Francis Masson, one of the gardeners at Kew, was the first official collector to be sent abroad. He travelled to the Cape in 1772 with Captain Cook on the latter's second voyage, and spent three years in South Africa. From 1778 to 1782, Masson was in the Canaries and the Azores; from 1783–5 he toured Spain and Portugal, and from 1786 to 1795 he was once more in South Africa.

He was, of course, by no means the first in the field. Mary, first Duchess of Beaufort, had pioneered in the kind of flowers Masson later sent home. One of her brothers, Henry, who was created Baron Capel of Tewkesbury, we have already met as owner of the Kew estate. Her other brother, the Earl of Essex, was also a gardener, and when they came to arrest him for his complicity in the Rye House plot against Charles II, they found him gathering 'nutmeg peaches' in his garden.

The Duchess was also a friend of Sir Hans Sloane and sent him plants from her gardens at Badminton and at Chelsea, near Beaufort Street. (The latter was afterwards sold to Sir Hans for £2,500.) Some of her plants came to her from Richard Bradley, author of the first history of succulent plants which was published in 1717.

Ivy-leaved Pelargonium (*Pelargonium peltatum*), from the Duke of Beaufort's Book of Flowers, Badminton.

Everhard Kickius or Kichious who had illustrated Sloane's *Natural History of Jamaica*, went to Badminton to paint the flowers that were growing there in the years 1700–1705, and other plates were drawn there by Miss Henrietta London, daughter of George London, the principal founder of the 100-acre nursery set up where the South Kensington museums now stand.

These plates, carefully preserved in two flower books kept at Badminton, include the beautiful mauve-flowered plant clearly recognisable as *Pelargonium peltatum*, the Ivy-leaved Pelargonium in flower some seventy years before Masson went to South Africa. It was also to be seen in Caspar Commelin's *Praeludium Botannicum Plantarum*, published in 1703. There was also a pink zonal-leaved pelargonium at Badminton. *Pelargonium capitatum*, bearing rose-coloured flowers with purple veining, was in cultivation in Britain as far back as 1690 together with a somewhat similar species, *P. cucullatum*. A form of *Dimorphotheca*, the Star of the Veld, had reached England by 1752 and *Ornithogalum thyrsoides*, the white Chincherinchee which can travel 6,000 miles to Britain and still look fresh at journey's end, first arrived in 1757, though it seems to have been known a century earlier in Holland.

James Petiver, apothecary, collector and botanist whom we met earlier, is said to have been growing 100 different plants from South Africa around the year 1709. *Leonotis leonurus*, the Lion's Tail, was growing under glass in 1712; *Haemanthus coccineus*, the Blood Lily, was said to have reached our shores in 1731 at the same time as *Zantedeschia aethiopica*, the White Arum Lily, and an early *Crinum* was recorded in 1752.

Nevertheless Masson broke new ground. From his first visit he was credited with a dozen kinds of arctotis – brilliant asteroid daisy flowers, plus 40 of the 75 known stapelias (cactus-like plants with an indecorous smell and bizarre, mottled starfish flowers, some with hairy petals), plus 60 or so mesembryanthemums, of which 53 species were on offer in Kennedy and Lee's 1774 plant catalogue. One of these mesembryanthemum species known as the Kaffir Fig has escaped from the garden and grows wild on our south-west coastal cliffs.

One of Masson's proteas, *P. cynaroides*, which can be grown in a cool greenhouse, is pollinated by birds.

While in South Africa, Masson joined forces with the Swedish botanist, Carl Peter Thunberg, who was on his way to Japan to take up the post which Kaempfer had held nearly a century before. Between them, Masson and Thunberg discovered *Disa caerulea*, the startlingly sky-blue orchid, and the equally unusual *Ixia viridiflora* with six-petalled star-shaped flowers in bluish green with dark centres growing on wiry stems.

Masson also produced the spectacular *Sparaxis tricolor* with multi-coloured flowers varying between red, yellow and purple, and another tricoloured flower, *Lachenalia aloides* – yellow, red and bright green. His *Eucomis comosa* (formerly *punctata*) known as the Pineapple Flower because of its crown of leaves, appeared in the selection of rare plants drawn by Redouté while visiting England in 1786–7.

During his second expedition to South Africa, Masson set up his own garden near the foot of Table Mountain and his consignments to Kew were the better for it.

From the Canaries Masson extracted the ancestors of the cinerarias, those house plants with hollyhock leaves and starry dark red or purple daisy flowers. Cultivars and varieties in other bright colours were soon developed and they can now be bought in blue, white and coppery scarlet.

William John Burchell, the son of a Fulham

nurseryman, was another visitor to South Africa between 1810 and 1815. The Cape settlement had been occupied by the British in 1795, relinquished in 1803 and re-occupied in 1806, but Burchell received no assistance from the authorities, for his travels were up-country in territory untenanted by officials and unfamiliar even to the missionaries. At one point he reached what is now the border of Botswana. At Prieska, on the banks of the Orange River he picked up an object on the ground thinking that it was a small stone, and found that he had discovered *Lithops*, the Pebble Plant, which has only two leaves joined together to make a single body, and survives because it resembles nothing worth eating.

Pineapple Flower (*Eucomis comosa*), a member of the lily family from South Africa

In the same area, Burchell discovered South Africa's only native poppy, *Papaver aculeatum*. Then he returned to Fulham, ready to write his well known *Hints on Emigration to the Cape of Good Hope* (Hatchard & Son, 1819) and his even better known *Travels in the Interior of Southern Africa*. He brought with him the seeds of some 2,000 plants and nearly 300 bulbs. The bulbs appear to have included some of South Africa's most attractive exports: freesias and the crocosmias, members of the iris family.

The *Crocosmia* × *crocosmiiflora*, that we know as 'monbretia', is named after Antoine Conquebert de Montbret, one of the botanists who accompanied Napoleon in 1798 to conquer Egypt.

Burchell also saw *Clivia nobilis*, the amaryllis with a shower of red, orange-tipped tubular flowers springing from the top of the stem. It was named after Charlotte-Florentia neé Clive, wife of the 3rd Duke of Northumberland. Burchell brought home only a dried specimen of this plant which led very shortly afterwards to the introduction of a live example. He also introduced *Brunswigia orientalis*, a Spider-Lily, known in South Africa as the Candelabra Flower because of its coronet of flame-coloured flowers reaching for the sky.

James Bowie, a Kew gardener, followed Burchell in South Africa from 1816 to 1820 and has been credited with another early member of the *Brunswigia* genus. He had previously worked with a fellow Kew man, Allan Cunningham, in Brazil where they discovered the Gloxinia, now known as *Sinningia speciosa*, with large dark-green thick velvety leaves and two- to four-inch dark violet flowers. In South Africa, Bowie seems to have specialised in succulents and species of gladiolus.

Count Apollon Apollosevitch Mussin-Puschkin, former Russian ambassador in London, and tireless explorer, was another of Banks' contacts, and, on a joint expedition in the Caucasus between 1802–5

Rosa indica (Miss Willmott's indica) by Alfred Parsons, R.A. from *The Genus Rosa* by Ellen Willmott

with Baron von Bieberstein, he appears to have discovered *Nepeta mussinii*, Garden Catmint, *Gentiana septemfida*, one of the easiest to grow; *Scabiosa caucasia*, source of the larger garden varieties, and *Chrysanthemum (Pyrethrum) roseum*, parent of many successful hybrids.

They also secured *Lilium monadelphum* with yellow reflexed Turk's Cap petals spotted with purple; *Geranium ibericum* with showy dark blue flowers with purple veining; *Puschkinia scilloides* with pale blue bell-flowers striped with darker blue, and *Onosma tauricum*, a rock plant of the borage family with yellow flowers.

Banks himself would have liked to have gone with Cook on his second voyage which included the Pacific islands and the Antarctic, but the alterations which the great collector required to be made to Cook's vessel HMS *Resolution*, were too exacting for the Admiralty and according to Sir Hugh Palliser the comptroller of the Navy might even have jeopardised the safety of the ship. So, instead, a German naturalist Johann Reinhold Forster and his son Johann Georg Adam Forster took the place of Banks and Solander.

Cook did not find the Forsters as congenial as Banks and his party had been, but the botanical dividends were nevertheless worthwhile. They included *Clematis indivisa*, a winter-flowering species from New Zealand which has been known to produce 7,000 white stars, each two to three inches in diameter, on a single plant. *Howeia* – sometimes *Howea* – *forsteriana*, the Thatch Palm was found on Lord Howe Island – area five square miles – off Australia's eastern coast during this voyage. It has the special virtue of not exceeding six to eight feet in height, which makes it entirely suitable as a decorative plant for hotel lounges.

William Kerr, a gardener from Kew, was another Banks protégé. King George III agreed that he

Pelargonium peltatum, probably the earliest Ivy-leaved Geranium, painted by E. Kychicus for 1st Duchess of Beaufort, ca. 1703

should go as a collector for the East India Company in Canton with all expenses paid except for his £100 a year salary from Kew. He was thus the first resident professional collector whose full-time job was to assemble and dispatch seeds and plants, and he stayed in China from 1804 to 1812, when he left to take up an appointment as superintendent of the botanic gardens in Ceylon. He sent back many garden favourites including *Pieris japonica* with its young shoots of coppery red leaves and racemes of white flowers, and *Pittosporum tobira*, yielding creamy yellow fragrant flowers against a background of lustrous green leaves. His *Begonia evansiana* is still cultivated and is almost unique in being the only practically hardy species. He introduced, though he was not the first finder of, *Lilium japonicum* the white fragrant species with pink buds and also the hardier *L. tigrinum*. *Magnolia kobus* which was sent in one of his consignments proved to be the ancestor of *M. stellata* with its profusion of white star-shaped fragrant blossom; his *Nandina domestica* is better known as the Sacred bamboo though in fact it is a member of the Berberis family and his *Nymphaea pygmaea* is a delightful miniature Water Lily. He also collected a tall-stemmed yellow flowering plant, originally known as *Corchorus japonica*, but re-named in his honour *Kerria japonica*, to be seen today in many cottage gardens. The introduced plant was double-flowered. The single did not arrive till around 1835.

All these Far East plants were in addition to other valuable ones sent by Benjamin Torin, one of the supercargoes of the East India Company and a resident in Canton. In 1770 Torin sent *Saxifraga stolonifera*, Mother of Thousands, to Kew with *Osmanthus fragrans*, a shrub with white fragrant tubular flowers, and two greenhouse plants, *Cordyline terminalis*, known as the Dracaena Palm, although it is a lily, together with *Chalcas (Murraya) exotica*, the Orange Jessamine. In 1816 *Wisteria sinensis*, the species most generally cultivated, was brought to England.

Predictably Banks looked to Australia as a source of new plants for Kew, and, following a not too successful expedition by George Austin and James Smith, he sent George Caley, a hot-tempered, dispute-prone gardener, of whom he said, 'Had he been a gentleman he would long ago have been shot in a duel'. Caley had refused a job at Kew at a lower salary than he was getting at Chelsea but Banks paid his fare to Australia in 1800 and he sent back a number of interesting plants including *Epacris purpurascens*, a heath-like plant with white or rosy purple flowers, several new acacias, a Grevillea, some eucalyptus, an orchid, and *Platycerum bifurcatum*, the ornamental Stag's Horn Fern. In the Blue Mountains he discovered *Fieldia australis*, a woody perennial with creamy tubular flowers nearly 60 years before it was first grown at Kew.

Treasure Flower (*Gazania pavonia*), brought from South Africa

Banks did not, of course, have a complete monopoly of plant collection during his lifetime. Burchell, as we have seen, operated on his own and James Niven, was engaged by George Hibbert, a wealthy private collector who lived in Clapham, and after 1803 by a syndicate which included Lee and Kennedy and the Empress Josephine, to collect plants in South Africa over 14 years from 1798 to 1812. He specialised in Proteas, and heaths but also introduced *Gazania pavonia*, the Treasure Flower, a daisy-type with yellow flowers scalloped in the centre with brown and white. He also found *Nivenia corymbosa*, a cool greenhouse plant of the Iris family with clusters of pale blue flowers.

There was also James Main who, although briefed by Banks, was working for Gilbert Slater whose garden was in Essex and for the firm of Conrad Loddiges of Mare Street, Hackney. He returned from China in 1794 with *Chimonanthus praecox*, Winter Sweet, of which the yellow and purple flowers appear ahead of the leaves, and *Chaenomeles speciosa*, the Japanese Quince, more frequently seen than *C. japonica* (which to confuse matters still further is known as Maule's Quince).

Meantime Banks' stature continued to grow. He was elected President of the Royal Society in 1778, and was created a baronet three years later, and a Privy Councillor in 1797. He continued to live in simple style, with no appetite for the pleasures of fashionable society. He fished a little, and when opportunity served, drove out to his own garden at Spring Grove, Heston, Middlesex. He entertained and broke the ice for his guests by insisting on weighing them. He was happily married, though Lady Banks was rather more interested in the arts than her husband was. She collected china and was a friend of Sarah Siddons, the actress who gave recitations in private at Windsor Castle as well as to her guests in Upper Baker Street.

Banks was indifferent to discomfort and could not understand the reluctance of William Jackson Hooker who, as a young man, excused himself from joining a botanical expedition to Java. 'Let me hear from you how you feel inclined to prefer ease and indulgence to hardship and activity,' he wrote sarcastically. 'I was about twenty-three when I began my peregrinations. You are somewhat older (Hooker was 28), but you may be assured that if I had listened to a multitude of voices that were raised to dissuade me, I should now have been a quiet country gentleman, ignorant of a number of things I am now acquainted with.'

In Hooker's defence, however, it could have been pointed out that four years earlier, when Banks had induced him to join an expedition to Iceland, the ship loaded with tallow had caught on fire in mid-ocean and Hooker had all but lost his life. Banks, indeed may have taken this into account, for Hooker was eventually restored to favour and went on to serve as Director of the Royal Gardens at Kew from 1841 to 1865.

The Linnean (*not* Linnaean) Society was another project initially generated by Banks. At one of his famous philosophical breakfasts to which it was considered an honour to be asked – he received on the morning of 23 December 1783 a letter tipping him off that Linnaeus' wife Sara had put the great naturalist's herbarium and library up for sale following the death of her son. Banks had already tried to buy the herbarium and had been rebuffed, and he felt disinclined to re-open the bidding. So he tossed the letter across the breakfast table to a young medical student, then at Bart's, James Edward Smith, and suggested that he might persuade his father – a wealthy silk merchant – to put up the money. Smith was able to secure the herbarium and library for less than the £1,200 that Banks had offered for the herbarium alone.

The Linnean Society was founded in 1788 to preserve these treasures, and J.E. Smith, its first President, remained in office for 40 years. He was knighted in 1814 for his services to botany.

Banks also encouraged the formation of an organisation to be called the Horticultural Society, which held its inaugural meeting on 7 March 1804 in the house of Mr Hatchard in Piccadilly, on the site of the present bookshop. Its sponsors reasoned that, although many counties in Britain were already endowed with Agricultural Societies devoted to the improvement of farm husbandry and breeds of livestock, almost no attention had been paid to horticulture.

John Wedgwood was the prime mover. He was the eldest son of Josiah Wedgwood, the founder of the famous pottery firm and a friend of Erasmus Darwin, Joseph Priestley, and James Watt. John Wedgwood's sister, Susannah, married Erasmus

Darwin's son Robert, and so became the mother of Charles Darwin.

Banks himself read the paper setting out the aims of the new Society which was originally to devote its attention principally to the breeding, cultivation and forcing of 'useful' plants, as was evident from the profusion of fruit and vegetables displayed at its first Show, held in April 1805.

Ornamental plants were not, however, neglected, and the Dahlia was one of the first flowers to be discussed by the Society. Altogether six papers on flowers had been read by the end of 1809, the year in which a Royal Charter was obtained naming the body as 'The Horticultural Society of London'. In 1818 the Society received a slip of *Wisteria sinensis* from John Reeves which developed into a splendiferous climber 160 feet long and 11 feet tall.

Permission to use the adjective 'Royal' was granted to the Society in 1861 – by which time many a new flower had come to flourish in Britain – though with anything but help, as we shall see – from some of those who designed the gardens in which the new plants would have to flower.

11 *The Plight of the Flower Garden*

A major handicap to British gardening during the seventeenth century was the weakness of gardeners for copying the French. There were signs of the malady even under James I and Charles I, but Cromwell had put a stop to all that. Then with the Restoration, the fever returned. One Frenchman dictated the style of gardening not only in France but indeed throughout most of Europe, including England. He was Louis XIV's Master-Gardener, André Le Nôtre, who planned and laid out the gardens of Versailles, Chantilly, St Cloud, the Palais de Luxembourg and many other French châteaux and palaces.

Le Nôtre was the son of a Royal Master-Gardener and grandson of the Chief Gardener in charge of the parterres of the Tuileries. He was also a qualified architect.

His enthusiasm for projects of unexampled splendour, the meticulous accuracy with which he carried out those projects, and his outstanding organising ability commended him unreservedly to his royal master. Everything was conceived on the grand scale. Avenues stretching as far as the eye could see fanned out into the distance, the illusion of infinity being enhanced by a glimpse of water on the horizon. Estates were bejewelled with cascades, fountains, water gardens, obelisks, terraces, balustrades, and the like, often with classical associations.

Being an architect, he regarded the house and the garden as a single unit each complementing the other in a design imposed on the landscape so far as the climate and soil would allow. And, in so far as the garden could be regarded as an external wing of the house, its lines had to be regular. There were alleys with trees planted at regular intervals along each side, and they must be splendid alleys; broad enough to ensure that the trees when fully grown would not cast shadows on the statues which were equally important in garden design.

Shrubs were, of course, essential, for Le Nôtre held the well-established view that an open garden looked smaller than it really was. Flowers, except as patches of colour here and there, were of minimal interest, and indeed could be something of a nuisance at royal palaces, for the King could never be allowed to see them except when the blooms were in perfect condition, and on one occasion, when the King was visiting the Trianon, two million flower pots were used to ensure that the flowering plants he saw during his morning promenade were different from those on show in the afternoon.

As might have been foreseen, Charles II absorbed some of these grand ideas during his exile in France and the consequences for the English garden were unfortunate. Resources which might have been devoted to plants were squandered instead on masonry, plumbing and trees in a manner which could be emulated with advantage only by the comparatively wealthy owners of large estates such as Woburn and Melbourne Hall.

In England the firm of George London, Henry Wise and partners were the leading exponents of the French school. They re-designed not only the royal gardens of Windsor Castle, St James's Park and Hampton Court but private estates at Blenheim, Longleat, Chatsworth and Castle Howard. They favoured the clipped trees, corridor-hedges and flat parterre carpets on which the beds were arranged in geometrical patterns. There were other artificialities too. Celia Fiennes, the gossipy diarist, who travelled over much of the countryside on horseback in William and Mary's time, noted at Chatsworth an artificial willow that rained to order from every leaf, and at 'Bradby', Lord Chesterfield's house, a group of three fountains flanked by great statues. 'Each side on their pedistalls is a dial', she wrote, 'one for ye sun, ye other a clock which by ye water worke is moved and strikes ye hours, and chimes ye quarters, and when they please, play Lilibolaro on ye chimes. All this I heard when I was there.'

But a reaction against these enormities was to be expected. Some critics complained about the limited appeal of mere formality, a view discernible in the comment which poet Thomas (Elegy) Gray made after visiting Versailles, to the effect that he was impressed with the splendour when the gardens were filled with company and the water works were in full action.

Pope expressed the same view in a more pointed fashion after a visit to the Duke of Chandos' seat, Canons, in Middlesex:

> Lo, what huge heaps of littleness around!
> The whole, a labour'd Quarry above ground.
> Two Cupids squirt before: a Lake behind
> Improves the keenness of the Northern wind.
>
> His Gardens next your admiration call,
> On ev'ry side you look, behold the Wall!
> No pleasing Intricacies intervene,
> No artful wildness to perplex the scene;
>
> Grove nods at grove, each Alley has a brother,
> And half the platform just reflects the other,
> The suff'ring eye inverted Nature sees,
> Trees cut to Statues, Statues thick as trees;

With here a fountain never to be play'd
And there a Summer-house that knows no shade;
Here Amphitrite fails thro' myrtle bow'rs;
These Gladiators fight, or die in flow'rs

Unwater'd see the drooping sea-horse mourn,
And swallows roost in Nilus' dusty Urn.

My Lord advances with majestic mien,
Smit with the mighty pleasure, to be seen . . .

William Shenstone, also a poet, but a generation later than Pope, also criticised the straight-lined garden for its lack of surprise and urged that where an estate has a landmark or feature visible from afar, the visitor should be led to it not directly, but by a circuitous route so that its re-appearance close-to will be unexpected. There can be no joy in a garden, he insisted 'if the foot has to travel over what the eye has done before'.

Another more fundamental attack came from Joseph Addison who wrote in *The Spectator* of Wednesday, 25 June 1712: 'Writers who have given us an account of China [Note: Sir William Temple was certainly one of them] tell us the inhabitants of that country laugh at the plantations of our Europeans which are laid out by Rule and Line; because they say, anyone can place trees in equal rows and uniform figures. They choose to show a genius in works of this nature* and therefore always conceal the art by which they direct themselves. They have a word** it seems in their language by which they express the beauty of a plantation that thus strikes the imagination at first sight without

*Indeed the Chinese garden was intended to be viewed a piece at a time like an unwinding scroll.

** The word rendered in English as Sharawaggi was used by the Chinese to denote a pleasing state of disarray.

discovering what it is that has so agreeable an Effect.'

'Our British gardners, on the contrary, instead of humouring Nature, love to deviate from it as much as possible. Our trees rise in cones, globes, pyramids. We see the marks of scissars on every plant and bush.'

'I do not know whether I am singular in my opinion, but, for my own part, I would rather look upon a tree in all its Luxuriancy and Diffusion of boughs and branches than when it is thus cut and trimmed into a mathematical figure; and cannot but fancy that an orchard in flower looks infinitely more delightful than all the labyrinths of the most finished parterre.'

Behind these effusions lay a fundamental change of attitude in man towards the world around him. The role of Nature had been re-assessed. No longer was it a hostile environment on which the will of mankind had to be publicly imposed. Nature had become an ally in the search for beauty, and within an estate, it was believed that the site rather than the house should dominate the scene. Thus the easy curve was preferable to the straight line. Evidence of this new alliance can be traced in a proposal of Stephen Switzer who had been a pupil of London and Wise.

He suggested that on a large estate, it might be an improvement to do away with the boundary between the garden proper and the remaining parkland surrounding it, and in time this was duly effected by the device known at first as the Ah-ah, because of the expressions of amazement to which it gave rise, and later, more generally, as the Ha-ha. This was an artificial ditch or bank invisible from the house yet high enough to keep out inquisitive livestock. The idea has been credited to Charles Bridgeman, gardener to George II's Queen Caroline but it had already been used in a limited way in France.

However, this abandonment of the straight line and the visible boundary was at first of no great benefit to the ordinary plantsman, for in the designs of its chief exponent, William Kent, who exerted a powerful influence on garden design, 'Nature' was viewed through the eye of the artist. The aim was for a romantic landscape in which the countryside became the canvas, and the style favoured was that adopted by Claude Gelée of Lorraine, Nicolas Poussin, Salvator Rosa and others who had preferred to exercise their talents in Italy rather than in the stilted atmosphere of Louis XIV's court. Their landscapes associated ruined temples and palaces of classical Rome with the profusion of shrubs and trees of the Roman campagna – a combination still to be seen today on Rome's Palatine Hill and on the Via Appia Antica on the outskirts of the capital.

Paintings of this school were often designed to produce a particular concept or mood of exaltation, awe, wonder, reflection, melancholy, despair or even horror, as if the scene were being viewed through the mind rather than through the eye, and Kent, in his designs endeavoured to produce similar emotions, sometimes in sequence, with clumps of trees, and winding glades dedicated to Venus or some other symbolic character from mythology, but seldom, if ever, with flower beds. Crumbling ruins or funeral grottoes were frequently added to the scene for effect, bridges where there was no water and a shepherd's hut without any flock. Nature eventually turned to artificiality. 'I have the wilderness very much in mind,' lamented one gardener, 'but the soil is so excellent and I scarcely know how we shall make the land sufficiently barren.'

There was rather less mysticism about the man who followed Kent, as the leading improver of gardens, namely Lancelot ('Capability') Brown. His nickname came to him because of his habit on being consulted about an estate that was to be improved, of declaring that the property possessed 'great capabilities'. Brown was a Northumberland man, born of humble parents, and his first triumph was the construction of the magnificent lake at Blenheim which he contrived by damming a small river.

His services were soon in great demand and it was a rash owner who would consider making alterations of any consequence to his estate without consulting Brown. Brown 'naturalised' Bowood, Chatsworth, Chilham Castle, Harewood House, Luton Hoo, Sheffield Park and Petworth. He had an excellent eye for country and could visualise, after a comparatively short inspection, the cheapest way of creating the effects he wanted by clearing, planting or levelling – a faculty which allowed him to save money for himself and his employer. He relied on sub-contractors and supervised the work himself, carefully checking the costs. In time he became gardener to King George III and planted the Great Vine at Hampton Court.

Brown's respect for nature was so great that he brought the landscape right up to the house. The formal garden was banished from any position in which it would be seen from the windows; magnificent avenues were done away with because the trees had been planted in unnatural straight lines. At this point it must be confessed that these changes even at the highest levels did not proceed at the same rate or the same degree, yet the concentration of power and resources in the hands of the landowning classes were such that their whims even if not completely coordinated, were of considerable significance.

After Brown's death in 1783 – and following some excess by his disciples, a reaction began to set in. Critics complained that a house 'set in the middle of a meadow' in the way that Brown had favoured looked wrong. They unkindly suggested that Brown's style owed much to his early experiences as kitchen gardener to Lord Cobham at Stowe.

To Humphry Repton, the man who followed Brown as the most fashionable designer of gardens, we owe the restoration of the flower bed to its privileged position.

Repton's background was quite unlike that of Brown. He came of a prosperous family, was well educated with good connections, had travelled in Europe, and was happily married. But having lost most of his money in an unsuccessful business venture, he found himself, at the age of 36, with no professional training and a large family to support.

Almost on the spur of the moment he decided that he would take up garden designing. He was already an amateur botanist and knew which flowers would grow where. He was a close friend of James Edward Smith, who had even introduced him to Sir Joseph Banks, who would, no doubt, bring him to the notice of clients who mattered. He was an accomplished artist so that he could sketch the designs he wished to execute, and he was able to go into partnership with John Nash who supplied him with all he needed to know about constructional problems. He was thus well equipped to provide each of his clients with a Red Book, in which he sketched drawings of both the domain as it existed and of the estate as it would look after improvements had been carried out.

But this was not all. For if there was one other feature that distinguished Repton from earlier practitioners, it was his good sense. To aim at the picturesque when designing an estate was a mistake, Repton felt, if only because the artist when painting an effective landscape usually chose a limited and selective view covering a sector of perhaps 20 degrees, whereas the human eye embraces a field of 90 degrees.

Also, the artist sees his landscape from a fixed position, whereas the gardener is on the move. The artist can put a frame round his picture, a feat impossible in real life.

Furthermore, as Repton pointed out, there were practical difficulties in real life for strict followers of the picturesque school. 'How void of taste must that man be,' he reflected with sarcasm, 'who could desire a chimney or roof to his country house, when we are told that Poussin, and Paul Veronese, built whole cities without a single chimney and with only one or two slanting roofs.'

'This idea of deriving all our instruction from the works of great painters,' he continues, 'is so ingenious and useful, that it ought not to be confined to gardening and building. In our markets, for instance, instead of that formal and trim custom of displaying poultry, fish and fruit for sale on different stalls, why should we not rather copy the picturesque jumble of Schnyders and Rubens? Our kitchens may be furnished after the designs of Tenniers and Ostade, our stables after Woovermans, and we may learn to dance from Watteau or Zuccarelli; in short, there is no individual, from the emperor to the cobbler, who may not find a model for his imitation in the works of painters, if he will but consult the whole series from Guido to Tenniers.'

Repton also abominated 'ridiculous park lodges – small square boxes on each side of the gate, making, together, one comfortless smoky house of two rooms separated by a gate into the park'.

His reasons as to why the Nobleman's house and garden should be re-united were equally sound.

'In the execution of my profession,' he wrote, 'I have often experienced great difficulty and opposition in attempting to correct the false and mistaken taste for placing a large house in a naked grass field without any apparent line of separation between the ground exposed to cattle and the ground annexed to the house, which I consider peculiarly under the management of art.'

'This line of separation being admitted, advantage may easily be taken to ornament the lawn with flowers and shrubs, and to attach to the mansion that scene of "embellished neatness" usually called a pleasure ground.'

'The necessity of a fence,' he says elsewhere, 'to protect the house from cattle, seems to have been doubted by the followers of Brown, who generally used the ha! ha!, supposing that the fence ought to be invisible. On the contrary, it cannot surely be disputed, that some fence should actually exist between a garden and a pasture; for if it is invisible, we must either suppose cattle to be admitted to a garden – or flowers planted in a field; both equally absurd. . . . A magnificent palace ought not (like many that might be mentioned) to stand in a grass field, exposed to cattle, which are apt to take shelter near the building, and even to enter it where there is no fence to prevent them; but a terrace or balustrade marks the line of separation. The inside of the enclosure may be decorated with flowers; and we feel a degree of security for them and ourselves, by knowing that there is a sufficient fence to protect both.'

Without this, Repton complained, 'the character of a garden is now lost in the surrounding park, and it is only on the map that they can be distinguished; while an invisible fence marks the separation between the *cheerful lawn* fed by cattle, and the melancholy lawn kept by the roller and the scythe'.

'A large lawn, like a large room when unfurnished displeases more than a small one. If only in part, or meanly furnished, we shall soon leave it with disgust; whether it be a room covered with the finest green baize, or a lawn kept with the most exquisite verdure, we look for carpets in one, and flowers in the other.'

So towards the end of the eighteenth century, we

have got back our flower garden. Perhaps it had never vanished from the vicarages, the less-pretentious manor houses and many other small estates whose owners could not afford or were much too sensible to follow the fashions of the over-wealthy. But what, in the meantime, had happened to the flowers that formerly bloomed on the estates of the mighty?

Many of them were replaced by species grown under cover in some form of greenhouse, heated or otherwise, the design of which had been improved to meet the demand.

The portable 'sentry box' orangery was the first form of winter quarters and where there were several trees, this took the form of a wooden tabernacle erected over the trees, as in the case of those in the garden of Sir Francis Carew at Beddington near Croydon, in the reign of Queen Elizabeth I. In cold weather the trees could be warmed-up with the help of portable stoves, braziers or pans of hot charcoal, or even embers emptied into a hole in the ground.

The next step was to construct lofty buildings with doors or windows which could be opened to the south on sunny days or covered with mats when there was a frost.

In the 1690s John Evelyn designed a slightly improved hothouse in which fresh hot air was continuously circulated and fumes thereby greatly reduced. The stove and chimney were placed outside the house. The cold air to be heated was drawn from the floor area of the greenhouse by the draught of the furnace, and, as this air was removed from the hothouse, it was replaced by the air heated by the stove. One of the earliest wall thermometers appears in the drawing of John Evelyn's plan.

In parallel, a more efficient type of long-lasting hotbed had come into use from the 1720s onwards. In it, tanner's bark was used in addition to ordinary farmyard dung, and in cases where vegetables had to be forced, glass cloches were placed over the plants.

Then came greenhouses in which hot air was circulated through flues built into the walls, a system which reduced the risk of plants being scorched by direct currents of air.

Improvements were made to the glass; thinner panes were used with less green colour in them, a change which allowed more of the sun's light and heat to penetrate. More attention was paid to the angle at which the roof was pitched and to the problems of eliminating condensation which occurred at the edges of the panes and led to deterioration and breakages.

The various forms in which cast iron became available revolutionised the hothouse. Iron bars and pulleys made it possible for panes to be opened and shut as if by a drill-sergeant. Boilers came into use, and cast-iron pipes which could release the heat where it was most needed, though in the first quarter of the nineteenth century there was still some debate as to whether it was better to circulate hot water or steam in the pipes. Prince Potemkin's gardener, Mr Gould, had heated the vast conservatory of the Tauridian Palace in St Petersburg with hot-water pipes, and the same method had been adopted to a certain extent in England by a Mr Davies, a sugar-boiler in Essex. But others favoured steam because it could be carried further without danger of overheating or risks of blockages in the pipe. Moreover, no circulation pumps were needed, and the pipes carrying the steam could be of smaller diameter than those needed to circulate water. The Earl of Derby was one of the first to make use of steam which he installed in 1792 in his hothouse at Knowsley near Liverpool.

In the late 1820s some prejudice remained against using metal to frame the panes of greenhouses, it being alleged that metal frames were expensive, prone to rust, increased the number of broken panes and conducted away much of the heat.

'Great emulation now exists in this department of horticulture not only among country gentlemen but among commercial gardeners,' wrote John Loudon in the edition of his *Encyclopaedia of Gardening* published in 1828. Charles H. Turner of Rook's Nest, near Godstone, Surrey, had a stove and grapery 57 feet 2 inches long with a plain sloping roof and sashes opening at both front and back by means of racks and pinions, Loudon recorded. Messrs Sweets and Millers of Bristol, he noted, had invested in a greenhouse 40 feet long with a gothic span roof and folding doors, glazed on all sides; while T.A. Russell of Cheshunt Park, Herts, preferred a circular front with 'domical ventilator made to rise and fall at pleasure'.

The firm of Conrad Loddiges was renowned among the nurserymen for its palm house, 45 feet high and 60 feet wide, and for its planthouse 23 feet wide, 18 feet high and upwards of 100 feet long which stood without a single rafter or standard. The same firm, described by Loudon as 'those spirited cultivators at Hackney', received an award in 1817 from the Horticultural Society for its device consisting of a perforated pipe allowing showers of fine rain to be released at will from the roof of their palm house. The way was almost clear for Joseph Paxton whose giant water lily, a single leaf of which was strong enough to support the weight of his young daughters, flowered in 1849. The arrangement of the ribs on the underside of the leaf inspired Paxton with ideas for the structure of the Crystal Palace, the greenhouse to end all greenhouses. The plant had been discovered in Bolivia in 1801 and was formally named *Victoria regia* in 1838 as a compliment to the newly crowned Queen but re-named later – with more justification – as *V. amazonica*. The seeds that had been brought to England in 1846 germinated but did not flower.

Such a vast expansion in the number and size of hothouses went hand in hand with the arrival of semi-tropical and half-hardy plants – pelargoniums, begonias, cinerarias and the like – which needed to be sheltered indoors during the autumn and winter and could then be bedded out in the open when ready to flower. The nurserymen touring the great estates were able to suggest a continuous succession of plants which could be shown one after the other in the 'pleasure garden'.

Hardy herbaceous plants – either annuals sown each year or perennials which could be left in the ground but died down after flowering – were out of favour among the nobility and were more or less restricted to beds in the kitchen garden or on the edge of the shrubbery which surrounded so many stately homes.

Nevertheless, there is evidence that enthusiasm for gardening was not confined to the owners of large estates who would negotiate a private contract with the nurseryman of their choice, for, towards the end of the eighteenth century, nurserymen began to print catalogues showing, for the first time, the prices at which their plants and bulbs were for sale. In other words, they were looking for a wider public than could be reached with earlier unpriced lists.

John and George Telford, two third-generation nurserymen of Friars' Gardens, York, seem to have published a priced catalogue in England (1775) mentioned by John Harvey in his work *Early Horticultural Catalogues* (University of Bath Library, 1973), and their catalogue was closely followed by that of another Yorkshire family firm, William and John Perfect of Pontefract. In London, the first catalogue I have been able to examine with prices, at least for the bulbs, was that of Robert Edmeades, dated 4 April 1776. Little appears to have been written about him. Edmeades who described himself as a Seedsman and Gentleman's and Lady's Gardener, kept shop at No. 11 Fish Street Hill, opposite the Monument. He is mentioned at that address in Kent's *London Directory* from 1775 to 1782. In 1783 he appears in Baldwin's *New Complete Guide to London*, and the following year in Bailey's *British Directory*, by which time he had moved to No. 9 Fish Street Hill and had taken a Mr Roberts into partnership.

John Harvey writes that the partnership nursery was in Deptford. Edmeades' catalogue ran to 133 pages of print; and cost two shillings sewed or three shillings bound. It contained separate sections for tender annuals requiring a strong hot bed to bring them to perfection, for others needing a moderate hot bed, and for annuals, biennials and perennials which could be sown in open ground. Annuals needing a strong hot bed included *Solanum melongena*, the Egg Plant or aubergine from India – available in white or purple; *Gomphrena globosa*, Globe Amaranth (modern varieties survive in a cool greenhouse and yield everlasting flowers in red, purple, orange or white); and zinnias in red and yellow. 'Ten Weeks Stocks' and *Reseda odorata* were offered for the moderate hot bed. Annuals seeds for open ground included larkspur and lupin, both rose-coloured and blue; Scarlet Convolvulus; blue, purple or red 'cornbottle'; and *Nigella*, described as Devil-in-a-Bush.

A section for American Trees and Shrubs included three of Bartram's plants: *Magnolia acuminata*, described as deciduous, blue though in fact its colour is whitish; *Rhododendron maximum* interpreted as Large Rose Bay; and *R. nudiflorum*.

It is interesting to note that the 'Sweet Scented Pea' was already receiving attention. The plant grows wild in Sicily and was included by Father Franciscus Cupani in his *Hortus Catholicus* published in 1697. The first seeds to reach this country were sent by him in 1699 to Dr Robert Uvedale, Headmaster of Enfield Grammar School. Edmeades' catalogue lists five species: Purple – *Lathyrus odoratus purpureus*; Painted Lady – *Lathyrus odoratus zeylanicus*; White – *Lathyrus odoratus albus*; Tangier – *Lathyrus odoratus tingitanus* and the Winged Lotus – *Lathyrus tetragonolobus* – more akin to our semi-wild Dragon's Teeth, the greyish green sprawling plant with pale yellow pea flowers and a winged square pod.

Forty pages of the catalogue were devoted to bulbs, and hyacinths were evidently still the rage, though it was now many years since Madame de Pompadour had insisted they should be used in the French court for official internal decorations during the winter and spring months. Edmeades lists more than 1,200 varieties of hyacinth. There were double white with yellow eyes, or with scarlet eyes or violet eyes. A double flesh-coloured hyacinth was named after Admiral Byng who had been condemned to death and shot in 1757 for his neglect of duty in failing to relieve the island of Minorca from the French. Goldmine, a hyacinth cultivar, was available in bright red, purple and scarlet at £15 a bulb and *Flora nigra*, alleged to be black was offered at £21.

Ranunculus plants could be had in almost any number of combinations; black and coffee; black and violet; black brown and dark olive; white striped with crimson, orange and cinnamon, and in rose or flesh colours.

Both the hyacinths and the ranunculi were among the seven principal so-called shed plants which had been cultivated over the years in thousands of back yards, and formed the mainstream of local flower shows, particularly in the north of England around such centres as Burnley, Halifax and Manchester.

Two desirable plants from Sweerts' *Florilegium : Primula auricula*, red ; *Ramonda pyrenaica*, blue

Carnations, tulips, anemones, polyanthus and auricula were among the top-ranking shed plants, although they are perhaps more properly called

Florists' Flowers because of the rigid standards of perfection demanded in the blossoms.

Thus competitors are told that the auricula flower should be one inch and three-sixteenths across, the eye nine-sixteenths of an inch and the tube one-sixteenth. The pistil in the centre must not be visible. The body colour of the flower must be black or at least very dark, and the eye apparently covered by the floury meal-like substance known as farina. The farina is provided by the fine hairs of the plant each of which exudes a small drop of wax at the tip, and these hairs should be so closely packed in the centre of the flower that the eye looks to be covered with paste.

Equally exacting – some would say artificial – standards have been decreed for other florists' flowers.

But while the search for perfection continued beneath myriad potting-shed roofs, explorers were at work round the world hunting for new species of plants especially acceptable because of their ability to survive the winter outdoors, to the smaller gardener without a hothouse.

12 *Fortune and Misfortune*

The plant safaris which Joseph Banks instituted during his lifetime were soon followed up by the Horticultural Society of London. Until 1818 the Society had been obliged to farm out its plants to individual members to cultivate, but in that year it acquired its own walled garden of one and a half acres on the south side of Hammersmith Road, and three years later leased 33 acres from the Duke of Devonshire for an extended garden at Chiswick. Also in 1821 the Society sent George Don to the west coast of Africa, the east coast of South America and the West Indies, and John Potts to the Far East to collect new plants. Potts was to introduce 16 new cultivars of chrysanthemums from China.

David Douglas (1799–1834), son of a Scottish stonemason he became one of the Horticultural Society of London's most successful collectors on the American continent

But the Society's most successful collector was David Douglas. He was born in 1799, the son of a Scottish stonemason. At 11, he worked as a garden boy on the estate of the Earl of Mansfield at Scone Place near Perth. After an apprenticeship lasting seven years during which he tended outdoor plants, he moved to Valleyfield, near Culross, where he specialised in stove plants. His next post was in the Botanic Gardens in Glasgow and the Director recommended him to the Horticultural Society as a suitable collector.

Sent off to America at the age of 23, Douglas gathered seeds and plants almost without interruption for the next 12 years. He introduced 210 species, 130 of which were grown and cultivated, the remainder being regarded as interesting curiosities. He prospected for plants both in the eastern states of America and around the Columbia river on the west coast. He crossed Canada on foot from Vancouver to Hudson's Bay. He explored California in the days when it still belonged to Mexico, and met his death in the Sandwich Islands, as Hawaii was then called.

Douglas's first trip to north-west America yielded a clutch of useful introductions, among them *Gilia capitata*, a cousin of Jacob's Ladder with feather foliage, and lavender flowers in globe-heads. His *Godetia viminea* also had lavender flowers shading to deep purple at the base of the petals.

There was *Lonicera ciliosa*, the Trumpet Honeysuckle with yellow flowers tinged with purple, and *Gaultheria shallon*, which Douglas recognised from a dried specimen he'd been shown. It turned out to be a useful close-formation evergreen shrub producing sprays of pink flowers in early summer.

Douglas was responsible for popularising many flowers already known to botanists but inexplicably ignored by gardeners. The Red Flowering Currant, perhaps the most popular of all his plants, had first been discovered by Archibald Menzies in Nootka Sound in 1792. *Lupinus polyphyllus* – a stout perennial with (originally) purplish blue flowers, and one of the main ancestors of our border varieties, was an improved version of the perennial lupin sent home nearly 200 years earlier by John Tradescant Junior. *Eschscholzia californica*, introduced by Douglas, had been found by Menzies in 1792, was lost, then rediscovered by Adelbert von Chamiso, a member of Captain Otto von Kotzebue's expedition of 1815 to the Pacific. Chamiso dedicated the plant to Dr Eschscholz, a naturalist and physician attached to the party, and hopes were expressed that this might lead to Eschscholz's name being spelt correctly for ever more. (But it was not to be, for all too often, even today, an unwarranted 't' creeps in just before the 'z'.) Incidentally, Douglas came across the plant in Oregon, not California. Menzies' earlier voyage was also commemorated in another of Douglas's introductions: *Arbutus menziesii*, the Madrona Tree, a handsome dizzy-scented relative of our own Strawberry Tree; *Nemophila menziesii*, sometimes known as Baby Blue Eyes from its saucer-shaped sky-blue flowers, is also credited to Douglas, though it was not apparently discovered by him; likewise *Calandrinia menziesii*, a member of the purslane family with brilliant red-magenta flowers – showy but short-lived. Two other shrubs previously known but popularised by Douglas were *Cornus alba*, White Dogwood and *Mahonia aquifolium*.

Douglas also sent home two plants which had been named after earlier explorers, Merrywether Lewis and William Clark who had been commissioned in 1803 by President Thomas Jefferson to try to set up communications by water between the Pacific and the Atlantic Coasts. The Rocky Mountains put an end to that idea, but Lewis and Clark completed the east–west crossing in 1805, and assembled a collection of seeds and specimens. It included the first of the Lewisias – a genus of evergreen succulent perennial rock plants with showy flowers, some with striped petals. A Lewisia was later adoped as the official emblem of the state of Montana.

Clarkias, named after William Clark, are also showy, but hardy annuals, well suited to the border, in lime-free soils. Other Lewis-Clark plants introduced by Douglas include *Gaillardia aristata*, with yellow ray florets and red disc florets, the parent of many border varieties. There was also *Calochortus elegans*, one of the half-hardy Mariposa lilies related to the tulips and fritillaries; *Erythronium grandiflorum*, called Dog's Tooth Violet though it is a hardy lily, and *Holodiscus discolor*, a hardy flowering shrub with sprays of cream-coloured flowers and green leaves, white beneath. Some of the Lewis-Clark finds were grown in Philadelphia by an Irish-born nurseryman named McMahon whose name is commemorated in the genus Mahonia. One of McMahon's plants was the purple-flowered *Clematis douglasii* from the Rocky Mountains, re-introduced only in 1889, as was the bright metallic red *Delphinium cardinale* though this does not appear to have been established from the seeds sent by Douglas.

But his other successes remain undimmed. There is, for instance, *Limnanthes douglasii*, sometimes called the Fried Egg Plant because its saucer-shaped white flowers have orange centres. It is an attractive semi-rock plant, an annual which sometimes re-seeds itself. Even more distinguished is *Garrya elliptica*, the grey-green shrub with unusually long decorative catkins. Douglas named it after Nicholas Garry, Deputy Governor of the Hudson's Bay Company which consistently helped Douglas during his visits to North America.

He was a great admirer of the magnificent trees that formed the backdrop to the Columbia river. He brought back *Pseudotsuga menziesii*, known as the Douglas Fir; *Picea sitchensis*, the Sitka Spruce, and *Pinus ponderosa*, the pine with the outsize cones.

He secured the seeds of *Pinus radiata*, the Monterey Pine and of *Pinus monticola*, the Western White Pine.

But it was all done the hard way. The seeds of the Sitka Spruce which Douglas had secured during his first foray were lost and he had to make a second try; the seeds of *Sequoia sempervivens*, the Redwood tree were sent, but not established, and the cones of *Pinus lambertiana*, the Sugar Pine, second in height only to the Giant Redwood Tree were out of reach and had to be brought down by gun fire. Douglas was indeed seldom in luck.

On his very first visit to the eastern United States,

his guide ran off with his coat, his notes, his money, his vasculum and a copy of Persoon's *Synopsis Plantarum* which he had incautiously left on the ground while climbing an oak tree. Later, some of his specimens were spoiled because the rains never stopped for long enough for him to dry them; others were lost when his canoe was dashed to pieces in a rockbound whirlpool. A typical entry from his diary read: 'Morning: hung up my clothes to dry, and lay down and slept till 3 o'clock'. Once he fell into a ravine and lay unconscious for five hours, and, at one point, when food supplies failed, he was reduced to eating the berries he had intended to send home as specimens. Some Indians once exacted seven buttons from his coat and a handkerchief in return for a piece of sturgeon. Eventually his sight was affected by snow blindness; he lost vision in one eye and was compelled to wear smoked glasses. But even with this handicap, his powers of observation never faltered. The final tragedy occurred in May 1834 when Douglas was investigating the vegetation on the slopes of volcanoes in Hawaii. His body was found at the bottom of one of the pits concealed beneath branches and used for trapping the wild cattle descended from those left behind by Captain Vancouver. Douglas had been gored to death by a bull which had already been caught in the pit. He had previously been shown some pits and had been warned to look out for others, but he may have stepped too close to a crumbling edge. His small terrier was found nearby guarding his belongings. He was only 34 years old.

From then on, the number of collectors visiting North America tailed off to some extent. This was partly due to conditions there – in the west there was the conflict in the 1840s between the United States and Mexico for the possession of California, and the dislocation in communications caused by the Gold Rush of 1849, and in the east there was the American

Civil War. In any case the Americans were already becoming well equipped to do their own explorations.

Nevertheless, some plants still came – *Cupressus macrocarpa*, *Ceanothus rigidus* and *C. dentatus* collected for the Horticultural Society by Theodor Hartweg. He had already visited Mexico and Ecuador sending home 140 orchids, including *Cattleya maxima* which he was able to trace back after he had noticed one of its blooms decorating an Indian's hat. Hartweg's consignments of seed were so lavish that the Society was able to distribute 7,000 packets to its members. To Hartweg we owe the broad-leaved *Fuchsia fulgens*, one of the main parents of our garden varieties, and he was the first collector to mention the scarlet gentians growing in the Andes. He eventually retired to his native Rhineland and became Inspector of Gardens to the Duke of Baden at Schwetzingen, a locality noted for growing some of the best asparagus to be found in Germany.

Meanwhile, the prospects for collectors in China had improved in a sensational manner. As usual, the merchants arrived in the city centres ahead of the botanists. The British government had thrown open the field in 1833 by removing the monopoly of trade with China from the exclusive control of the East India Company. A sizeable English community had then grown up in Canton. In 1836, however, when the Emperor's Special Commissioner Lin Tse-hsu was endeavouring to halt the trade in opium, foreigners in Canton were besieged for six weeks and then expelled. The sequel was an expeditionary force sent by Lord Palmerston with orders to procure a commercial treaty or the cession of a small island on which British traders could live in freedom, and careen and refit ships. When Hong Kong was offered to Palmerston as being just such a port, he at first refused to accept it, complaining that it was 'a barren island with scarcely a house upon it'.

But his disappointment was assuaged in the Treaty of Nanking signed in 1842 by which the Emperor agreed to pay an indemnity and to open four other ports on the mainland, Amoy, Foo-chow, Ning Po and Shanghai to foreign traders.

Once the Treaty had been signed and ratified the Horticultural Society were quick to move. Their Far East Committee decided to send out Robert Fortune who had been in charge of the hothouse section of the Chiswick Garden since 1840; he was warned, however, that as far as the Society was concerned, the value of any plants he might send would decrease with the amount of heat needed to cultivate them. He should therefore concentrate on hardy plants, orchids, aquatic plants and others with particularly handsome flowers being the only exceptions to this rule. The Society also considered that a stick loaded with lead and known as a life-preserver would provide sufficient protection for their man in Shanghai and were persuaded, only with great difficulty, to give their permission for him to take with him a fowling-piece and some pistols. He was also equipped with a Chinese dictionary, and three of the new cases used for dispatching live plants through the tropics and across the equator. The new device had been discovered accidentally in 1829 by Nathaniel Bagshaw Ward, who had buried the chrysalis of a large moth in earth in a wide-mouthed bottle, sealed the mouth to protect the contents from dust, damp and draughts and placed it in a window. Some weeks later, he noticed that a fern and some grass had started to grow. They continued to prosper in the sealed bottle without extra water for more than three years. And so the Wardian Case, a portable closed greenhouse with carrying handles was evolved, and described first in the *Gardeners Magazine* in 1839 and later in a paper published in 1842 under the title 'On the Growth of Plants in closely glazed Cases'.

It saved the lives of thousands of plants. No longer was it thought necessary to air and re-pot the plants at St Helena on the way home (often a mistake as it caused them to develop prematurely); seeds that had only a short life if packed dry could now be safely planted in soil and shipped home in the new sealed glass-house. Plants sent by Fortune in Wardian cases assembled in China travelled home so well that some were shown by the Horticultural Society within three days of their arrival.

Fortune reached Hong Kong in July 1843 and arrived at Shanghai on the day the port was officially opened for trade by the British Consul.

Even before leaving Hong Kong he had found *Chirita sinensis*, an elegant plant with lavender purple foxglove flowers, which he later claimed were 'now to be found in many of the gardens of England' though in the long run the plant did not prove sufficiently hardy to succeed in the open. It is still grown under glass. Hong Kong also yielded *Enkianthus reticulatus*, a heath-type plant with bell-like flowers and brilliant foliage. In addition to Shanghai, Fortune visited the island of Chusan, Ning-Po, Canton and Foo-chow collecting new finds at each stop. On Chusan, *Wisteria sinensis* grew wild in the hedges, and near Tinghae he spied *Diervilla* (now *Weigela*) *rosea* in a mandarin's garden. The plant became one of Queen Victoria's favourites. Still on the same island, he collected *Daphne genkwa*, a species with lilac flowers, and *Buddleia lindleyana*, and he was able to send home specimens of *Chrysanthemum rubellum*, the Chusan Daisy and ancestor of the modern pompom chrysanthemums. In Shanghai he noticed *Anemone hupehensis*, the Japanese Anemone, originally a dark reddish-purple double flower growing in a Chinese cemetery and secured that as well.

And this was by no means all. By the time he returned to England four years later, Fortune had collected the first forsythia to be seen in western Europe; *Skimmia japonica*; two new viburnums – *V. macrocephalum* and *V. plicatum* (the Chinese Snowball Tree), and – at last – *Jasminum nudiflorum*, the real Winter Jasmine. It had been seen in Nagasaki by Andreas Cleyer, Kaempfer's predecessor at Deshima, but had never been introduced.

Fortune found *Lonicera fragrantissima*, a honeysuckle that flowered in winter; *Spiraea prunifolia*, a double-flowered species; and he reintroduced two plants which were already known but had been lost. One was *Dicentra spectabilis*, the showy Asian variety of the Locket Plant with inner white petals protruding from the red locket. Fortune correctly prophesied that it would become a great favourite in English gardens. Another reintroduction was *Platycodon grandiflorum*, a starry-shaped campanula, sometimes called the Balloon Flower because of the inflated appearance of the flower buds.

His *Rosa fortuniana* was to lead to many excellent hybrids.

Fortune's success in China brought him offers which the Horticultural Society could not match, and when he went out east again in 1848, he was working both for the East India Company and for Standish and Noble, the nurserymen. His main task was to secure bushes and seeds of the tea plant which would enable the East India Company to establish

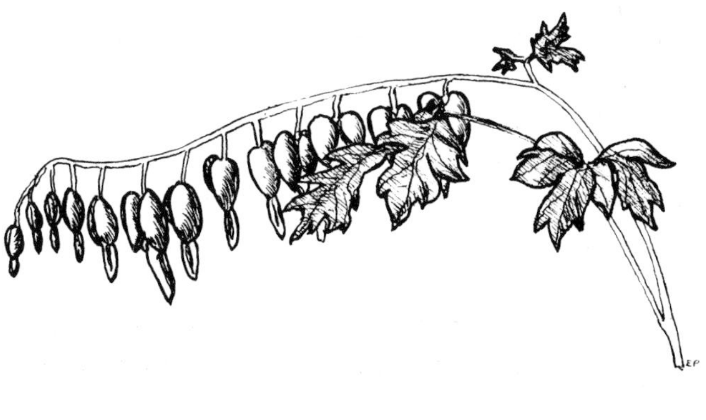

Bleeding Heart or Locket Plant (*Dicentra spectabilis*), which Robert Fortune rediscovered in China

their own gardens and tea factories in India. To achieve this he had to journey far beyond the 30-mile radius of a Treaty Port to which foreigners were still limited. Fortune got round the difficulty by shaving off his hair, wearing a wig and pigtail, and passing himself off as a Chinaman from beyond the Great Wall. And the further away he got from civilisation and the main trade routes where officials might have recognised him, the safer he felt. The bandits, like officials, hung around the big cities, and it was during a journey from Shanghai to Hong Kong during his first visit to China that his ship was attacked by five pirate junks. Fortune, down with fever, rose from his sick berth to beat them off with the help of his fowling piece. Even so, wherever he went, he travelled through territory where foreigners, known to the Chinese as 'quang-yang' were thought to bring bad luck, and if discovered, were likely to be run out of town or even set on and killed. In most towns and even at first in Shanghai, there were no European houses and Fortune, on one occasion, found himself in a farm house sharing a kitchen where he was to cook his meal with four other Chinese families. Most of the towns were fortified; the gates were locked every night and the keys given to one of the mandarin officials. Women, as a sign of elegance, still had their feet artificially cramped till they could no longer walk properly. Fortune met Buddhist priests so poor that they could not afford to burn a candle at night and were compelled to feed off water lily roots.

During this second trip and the one that followed it, he secured *Mahonia bealei* from a deserted garden; *Exocorda racemosa*, the Pearl Bush, a hardy shrub of the rose family, *Skimmia reevesiana*, with panicles of white flowers, *Clematis lanuginosa*, the parent of all the late flowering *Clematis jackmanii* varieties, a 'black' Moutan, *Paeonia atrosanguinea*; a new semi-double azalea, *A. amoena* which he said 'will be a great favourite in England when its merits are known', *Rhododendron vittata*, striped with pale blue or lilac lines, and *R. fortunei* endowed with a spicy scent.

Fortune was also full of praise for *Olea fragrans*, the greenhouse shrub with brownish yellow flowers 'most esteemed by the Chinese, one tree of which is enough to scent a whole garden. In England we knew nothing of the beauty of this charming plant,' Fortune complained.

He certainly saw '*Hamamelis chinensis*' (probably *H. mollis*) – the Chinese Witch Hazel but he either was unable to secure the seed or the plant failed. The same fate seems to have overtaken *Caryopteris mastacanthus* – (now *incana*), a member of the Verbena family with grey-green aromatic leaves and blue flowers.

Fortune was able to visit Japan in 1860 and discovered *Primula japonica*, a waterside species with magenta flowers in whorls;* *Deutzia scabra*, a shrubby species with white or pink flowers; *Euonymus radicans* sometimes used as a ground cover plant; and *Saxifraga fortunei*, a striking plant with crenulate leaves and white starry flowers with one petal longer than the others and pointing downwards like a spur; *Lilium auratum*, a glorious fragrant dazzlingly white lily with a golden ray and wine-coloured spots on each petal, also sent by John Gould Veitch. House plant lovers also owe something to Fortune for he also brought back with him the first male *Aucuba japonica*, thus making it possible for the female aucuba plants to bear those decorative red berries.

He also wrote home in praise of a 'hairy' Japanese type of chrysanthemum which after being coolly received at first, became popular among British growers.

* The seeds failed, and were re-introduced ten years later by Mr Keswick from Hong Kong.

Fortune was, of course, visiting Japan after the Government had agreed to foreign consulates being established on Japanese soil, but some plants previously reached Europe from Dr Philipp Franz von (more often 'van') Siebold, a Bavarian who was physician to the Governor of the Dutch East India Company and had been sent to Deshima in 1826. He found himself under the same restrictions from which Kaempfer earlier and Thunberg later suffered but he was an eye specialist, capable of performing operations to remove cataracts, and was therefore able to demand privileges which would not have been accorded to his predecessors. He even had a Japanese mistress. But after two years it was discovered that he had been procuring maps from the Court astronomer of the Japanese mainland and islands and was preparing to take them out of the country – an offence punishable by death. He was put in prison for a year and was expelled from the country, but was allowed to take with him plants and seeds, many of which came from his own garden on Deshima.

Among them were some Hostas – *H. plantaginea* with yellowish-green leaves; *H. albomarginata* (syn. *sieboldiana*) with white-margined leaves, some *Hortensia* (mop-headed) hydrangeas, *Corylopsis spicata* – a shrub which bears greenish-yellow flowers on the bare wood in early spring, and the sieboldia variety of *Clematis florida*, having white double flowers with contrasting purple stamens (or, to be more accurate, staminoids). *Magnolia sieboldii* has rather the same attractive contrast between pure white petals and red-wine stamens. Siebold also brought back *Fatsia japonica*, the evergreen shrub with handsome foliage and white flowers – hardy in southern areas; *Hamamelis japonica*, the yellow wood-shaving flowers of which are sometimes tinged with red; and *Deutzia gracilis*, the parent of many hybrids. Many of these he established in a garden at Ghent, pillaged to some extent by nurserymen during the war between Belgium and Holland but partially re-established in Leyden.

In 1859 after Japan had ended her policy of isolation he was allowed back but stayed for only three years before retiring to his native Bavaria.

This second visit of Siebold's produced among other novelties, *Hydrangea paniculata* – a species with a cone of flowers at the end of each stalk.

Meanwhile equally dramatic changes were taking place in South America with the collapse of the Spanish and Portuguese empires. Between 1816 and 1824 Mexico, Argentina, Chile, Brazil, Ecuador, Colombia, Peru, Venezuela, Guatemala and Costa Rica among others, achieved independence with Britain's blessing. The dead hand of Spanish and Portuguese bureaucracy which had proved such an obstacle to botanical discovery was thereby removed. Most Brazilian and other plants within 10 or so degrees of the equator required hothouse treatment, but Argentina, Chile and the mountainous areas of Mexico, Colombia, Peru and Ecuador offered tempting possibilities of new species capable of surviving outdoors in Britain and nurserymen were quick to take advantage of the fact.

Plants from Chile began to come in during the 1820s, forwarded to English growers by Francis Place, the friend of another Englishman John Miers who went to Chile in 1819 to set up a copper-refining and manufacturing plant. Early Chilean immigrants included the beauteous if not completely hardy *Schizanthus pinnatus* with fern-like leaves and orchid-like flowers coloured rose, purple and yellow. There was also *Calceolaria integrifolia* – an attractive shrub with its yellow slipper-flowers grouped at the end of long stalks. It, too, needs protection as does *C. corymbosa*, a herbaceous plant with yellow, red-lined flowers. *Eccremocarpus scaber*, the Chilean Glory Flower, an evergreen climber with orange to scarlet tubular-bell flowers, though susceptible to frost, will thrive in our milder western counties.

Dr John Gillies was another successful collector in the same general area during the 1820s. He established himself at Mendoza, a city in the foothills of the Andes on the Argentine side of the border with Chile. He discovered *Salpiglossis sinuata*, an attractive half-hardy annual with funnel-shaped flowers now obtainable in deep violet, crimson, scarlet, pink, gold, yellow and white. He also sent home *Verbena rigida* (synonym *venosa*) – a near-hardy species with purple flowers; and also the scarlet-flowered *Verbena peruviana*, the name of which suggests that Gillies was not the only collector to find it. Gillies saw, but did not introduce, *Ipheion uniflorum*, the attractive star-like lily with flowers ranging from white to violet blue and a smell borrowed from the garlics.

Escallonia rubra, apparently the first in the field of these decorative hedge-shrubs, and *Geum chiloense*, the parent of many orange and scarlet hybrids, both came from Alexander Cruickshank, another part-time collector in South America during the 1820s.

The white-plumed Pampas Grass, *Cortaderia selloana*, so popular in Victorian gardens came from James Tweedie, former head man in the Edinburgh Botanic Garden who emigrated to South America to set up there as a landscape gardener. He visited Argentina, Brazil and Patagonia travelling more than two thousand miles on foot and sent home seeds up to within a few years of his death in 1862 at the age of 86 in Santa Catalina near Buenos Aires.

Tweedie introduced the Ipheion that Dr Gillies had reported earlier. Travelling up the coastline of Brazil and Uruguay in company with the Envoy Extraordinary, Henry Stephen Fox, who had just been posted from Argentina to Brazil, he discovered *Verbena phlogiflora*, the brilliant fiery scarlet species and added two more species, *V. platensis* and *V. incisa* to help swell the choice of hybrids. He dedicated the Argentine Jasmine *Mandevilla suaveolens*, a fragrant white-flowered greenhouse climber to H.J. Mandeville, British Minister in Buenos Aires. *Bignonia unguis-cati*, the Cat's Claw Bignonia was another of Tweedie's greenhouse climbers, with bright yellow flowers. But his own favourite must have been *Tweedia caerulea* (now *Oxypetalum caeruleum*) the flowers of which turn from pale blue, to greenish, then purplish and finally to lilac.

Tweedie did much to inspire the cultivation of Petunias and if he was not the very first to send home *Petunia violacea*, still cultivated as a species, he introduced many others that led to the attractive cream red and white and violet-striped hybrids now planted out in tubs, baskets and window-boxes.

But perhaps the most successful collector in this part of the world at that time was William Lobb. He was the first of the twenty-two collectors sent out by Veitch, the famous firm of nurserymen. John Veitch 'the first' came south probably around 1792 from Jedburgh in the Scottish border country to take up landscape gardening in the west of England. He set up his first nursery at Lower Budlake on the road from Exeter to Cullompton and later in 1832 at Mount Radford, Topsham Road, Exeter.

John Veitch's son, James, was taken into partnership with his father, and he in turn took his son, James junior, into partnership in 1838. James junior had worked in London for two years at Chandler & Son, a well known nursery in Vauxhall and also with William Rollisson who specialised in both heaths and orchids at his nursery at Tooting. It was there that the younger Veitch was inspired with the idea of building up a collection of orchids, to be assembled by the firm's own collectors. William Lobb and his brother Tom, two young brothers from Cornwall who had learnt their trade in Veitch's nursery, were chosen to collect for the firm. Thomas Lobb went to the Far East and William Lobb to Brazil in 1840; from there he went south to Argentina and then travelled overland to Chile where he procured abundant supplies of Monkey Puzzle seed, previously available only in small quantities. From this and a later visit to Chile he sent back plants which are still a joy to gardeners.

Abutilon vitifolium, the climber with pale blue flowers, a fine example of which has been grown outdoors at the Wisley Gardens of the Royal Horticultural Society, was scarcely known before he sent back the seeds, and he helped to establish *Berberis darwinii*, first discovered by Charles Darwin in June 1834 on the island of Chiloe off the coast of Chile about midway between Cape Horn and Valparaiso.

William Lobb also sent back supplies of *Embothrium coccineum*, the Chilean Fire Bush which can be grown in milder counties of Britain; and other plants of startling beauty though in need of protection; *Crinodendron hookerianum*, the Lantern Tree with scarlet urn-shaped flowers suspended singly on long stalks; *Mitraria coccinea*, the Mitre Flower with scarlet trumpet flowers; *Lapageria rosea*, the Chilean Bell Flower, a climbing lily with three-inch blush pink flowers; and its more modest relative *Philesia magellanica*. He also helped to introduce *Desfontainea spinosa*, the compact spiny shrub with one-and-a-half-inch scarlet and yellow waxy tubular flowers – named after René Desfontaines, the nineteenth-century French botanist.

Lobb sent two Tropaeolumns from Chile: *T. speciosum*, the Flame Creeper with brilliant scarlet petals which eventually open out flat, and *T. azureum*, a tuberous rooted blue-flowering species which can be raised in a cool greenhouse.

Another very lovely plant from Lobb was *Strepto-*

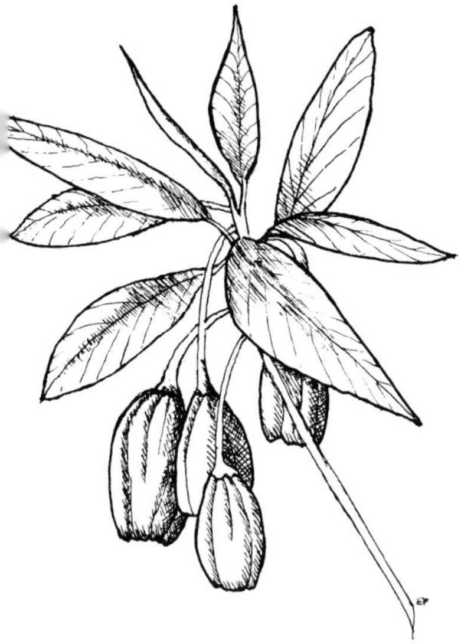

Lantern Tree (*Crinodendron hookerianum*), found by the Cornishman William Lobb on an expedition to Chile in 1840

solen jamesonii, a wall shrub with brilliant orange flowers, each a wide-mouthed trumpet, massed together in long drooping panicles.

Lobb also paid two visits to California but when he first arrived there in 1849, found great difficulty in organising transport. The guides, drivers and ship's crews had all been swept away in the Gold Rush.

Eventually he was able to send the seeds and live plants of the Giant Redwood Tree and two more winners, *Delphinium nudicaule*, an attractive scarlet-orange variety, though more loosely flowered, perhaps, than some would like; and *Fremontia californica*, a lustrous climber with large chalice flowers of rich yellow, each petal delicately spiked at the outer edge.

Many once-in-a-lifetime introductions came throughout the nineteenth century from amateurs, travellers, officials and holiday-makers who seized their chances where they saw them. Thus amateurs as well as collectors sent back the seeds of *Salvia patens*, the sage with the clear blue flowers and mid-green pointed leaves native to Mexico, and also those of *Salvia splendens*, the scarlet species from Brazil.

There were also semi-professional collectors, who for one reason or another secured only one or two memorable plants. Among these was Thomas Coulter, the adventurous and likeable Irish physician and mine manager who, during a trip to the southern part of California, discovered *Romneya coulteri*, the shrub with frilly white flowers four to five inches across and a golden pompom of anthers in the centre. Coulter was in Mexico about the time that *Choisya ternata*, the medium size shrub with aromatic leaves and clusters of white fragrant flowers, was introduced here; and it could have been among the 50,000 plant specimens he brought home with him. It was named after Jacques Denis Choisy, a noted Swiss botanist whom Coulter probably met when studying botany under de Candolle in Geneva.

Then there was Thomas Bridges who set up as a brewer in Valparaiso in 1828 in order to get the resources to collect plants. He botanised in Chile, Argentina, Bolivia and Brazil and it was there, while on his way down the Amazon en route for Trinidad that he found and collected the seeds of the giant Water Lily, *Victoria amazonica* which he brought back to London in 1846 packed in wet clay. But only two of his seeds germinated and no flowers were produced. It was introduced by Robert Schomburgk, and flowered four years later at Chatsworth.

Another Thomas, Thomas Drummond, a friend of Douglas, introduced *Phlox drummondii*, the best of the annual species with large trusses of flowers now cultivated in maroon, salmon, cream and other attractive shades. It came from Texas.

A third Thomas Nuttall, an impecunious printer from Liverpool arrived in Philadelphia in 1808, pioneered in the Missouri–Mississippi region of North America and in the Middle West, and at one time latched on to one of John Jacob Astor's fur prospecting parties. But not until he crossed the Rockies in 1834 did he find the plant by which he is most remembered, *Cornus nuttallii* – the Western Dogwood, one of our most striking hardy shrubs. The green buds of next year's flowers are visible in the preceding summer and the free-flowering display starts in spring when large creamy petal-like bracts reminiscent of a clematis or even magnolia unfold around the cone of greenish fragrant flowers.

In 1841 Nuttall inherited the printing business of his Uncle Jonas to which as a young man he had been apprenticed, on condition that for the rest of his natural life he spent nine months in each year in England. *Cornus nuttallii* hardy in our climate, must have been a consolation to this dedicated botanist who felt compelled to renounce overseas botanical exploration for good.

But there were many others ready to take his place.

13 *From the Himalayas and the Jungle*

Kew Gardens had languished during the final years of Banks's life. Seeds received there remained unsown. Orchids were potted in ordinary garden soil and left near panes of glass unprotected from scorching by the sun or the chill of the night frost. Plants, if grown, were not distributed, for they were royal property. Giving them away without prior permission would have been presumptuous, and even an above-board sale would demean the Crown.

It needed two generations – father and son – to put the matter right. William Jackson Hooker was the father. He came of a Norwich family and attracted the attention of leading botanists, including J.E. Smith (founder of the Linnean Society), in 1805, when at the age of 20, he discovered a new (to Britain) species of moss growing near Sprowston, a village less than a mile from the centre of Norwich.

A year later he was elected to the Linnean Society. Though interested in most branches of natural history, he specialised at first in illustrating an exhaustive work on the history of British seaweeds by Dawson Turner, a local Norwich banker, whose daughter Maria, Hooker was eventually to marry. He also prepared a study of a tribe of non-flowering plants, the liverworts.

In 1809, as we have seen, he visited Iceland, but his plants and most of his notes were lost when his ship caught fire and sank. In 1815 on the death of his father he inherited a share in a brewery, but nothing would make him renounce his ambition to make a career in botany.

In 1820, mainly through Banks's influence, he

William Jackson Hooker (1785–1865), by Thomas Woolner, 1866

was appointed to the Chair of Botany at the University of Glasgow, and achieved an almost instantaneous success. His plant-hunting excursions and his botany lectures, illustrated with dramatic and effective wall diagrams, drew spontaneous applause from the students. Their numbers increased, and so did the number of plants in the University gardens, as also the esteem in which Glasgow was held in other European botanical centres.

While still in Scotland, Hooker discovered Walter Fitch, an apprentice calico pattern-drawer, and turned him into one of the most accomplished plant illustrators of the century. In 1836 Hooker was knighted for his services to botany, but it was touch and go as to whether he would get the appointment on which he had set his heart – the top job at Kew.

There was even some doubt about whether Kew Gardens would continue to exist, for the Royal Steward, Lord Surrey, launched a determined attempt to suppress Kew altogether. He even offered to divide up the Kew plants between the Horticultural Society and the Royal Botanic Society whose garden in Regent's Park had been established in 1839, a proposal scornfully rejected by both learned bodies. Then he gave orders to the kitchen gardener to throw Banks's plants out of the Botany Bay glasshouse on to open ground where many of them died. Plants in the Cape of Good Hope House were to be treated with even less respect. They were to be destroyed.

There was a public outcry when the news leaked out, and within a few days, Kew was removed from Lord Surrey's control. Already in 1838 a committee of experts had been appointed to look into the management of the Royal Gardens and after the latest scandal, Lord Melbourne felt he had to act. Kew was removed from the Crown and transferred to the Department of Woods and Forests. Kew would be taken over by the State and become a garden worthy of the nation, a world famous centre of learning for the study of plants of all kinds. Lord John Russell, Secretary of State for Home Affairs, was deputed to see Hooker and find out on what terms he would accept the post of Director.

Hooker took over in 1841, and that very year four more acres were added to the gardens, bringing the total to 15 acres. The following year another 40 acres were added and in 1846 the total was increased to 650 acres by the incorporation of the Richmond Old Deer Park, though not all was used for horticulture.

Since Kew Gardens now belonged to the nation, it was decided, though with considerable misgivings, that it would be possible to allow the public to see their new inheritance from dawn till dusk as of right and in 1844 Hooker received permission to prepare an official Guide Book. In 1847 the total number of visitors reached 64,000.

Hooker doubled the size of the Cactus House. He installed new hot water pipes for the orchids. More room was found for tropical plants and the great Palm House, 362 feet long and probably the most beautiful of its kind, was completed in 1848. Queen Victoria visited Kew three times that year.

More important for gardeners was the fact that Kew was ready to send out collectors to search for new plants. The first two collectors, with part of the expenses paid by the Duke of Northumberland and the Earl of Derby, set out in 1843; William Purdie, a Kew gardener, to Jamaica, and Colombia, and Joseph Burke to north-west America.

Then came Joseph Hooker, second son of Sir William who became in effect the explorer that Joseph Banks had wanted his father to be. At the age of 22 he sailed to the Antarctic with Captain Ross to discover the position of the earth's south magnetic pole, and later wrote an authoritative two-volume work on the flora of that area. After a spell at home he wanted to prospect for plants in the Pacific or the Himalayas.

His interest in the Himalayas had been awakened by the success of the East India Company's Botanic Garden in Calcutta, founded in 1786. It had long been both a resettlement area for species discovered in China and Japan as well as a forwarding depot for plants and seeds from India and the Far East that were to be sent home to official and private collectors. William Roxburgh was in charge of the garden for nearly a quarter of a century and by the time he retired in 1813, he had compiled a list of more than three thousand species grown there. He employed native artists to keep records of his treasures. His successor, Nathaniel Wallich, a Dane, went further and employed local collectors. He sent

Joseph Hooker (1817–1911)

two gardeners to Nepal in 1813, and visited Katmandu himself in 1820. Wallich's introductions included *Bergenia ligulata*, probably the most beautiful of all this genus belonging to the saxifrage family: *Houttuynia cordifolia* with red stems, heart-shaped bluish leaves and mop-heads of white flowers; the popular *Geranium wallichianum*, ground-hugging species with blue-purple flowers and *Morina longifolia* a member of the teazel family with pinkish tube-flowers and spiny leaves.

The East India Company also had another garden at Saharanpur, in the Punjab, giving access to the more westerly sector of the Himalayas, and Dr John Forbes Royle who was in charge of the garden during the 1820s was able to collect mountain plants such as the moisture-loving *Primula denticulata*, which presents lilac globes of closely packed flowers on drumstick stalks rising from rosettes of 'floury' leaves, and *Leycesteria formosa*, sometimes called Job's (or is it Elisha's?) Tears, a plant of up to six feet, with drooping stems from which hang white tubular flowers set off by reddish bracts.

Royle also collected *Polygonum vaccinifolium*, which sends up rosy spires of flowers from its mat of evergreen leaves; it is widely used as a ground cover plant for inhibiting weeds. Royle's name was originally commemorated in the pink-flowered Himalayan Balsam, the Policeman's Helmet, and survives in his work on the flora of Kashmir, published in 1839.

In 1827, while Royle was still in Saharanpur, Lord Amherst, India's Governor General, visited Simla, then totally un-Europeanised, and stayed there for 10 months. Lady Amherst and her daughter, Sarah, were both keen botanists and sent home seeds of *Clematis montana*, the early free-flowering species and also those of *Anemone vitifolia*. Other plants secured by collectors from Saharanpur included *Androsace lanuginosa*, the so-called Rock Jasmine with silver green leaves and small pinkish flowers and *Pyracantha crenulata*, the first of the Asian Firethorns to reach this country; a variety of this plant, *P. rogersiana* is still a popular garden wall shrub yielding snowballs of foaming white blossom succeeded by bright orange-red berries. It was named after Mr Coltman Rogers who first showed it at Vincent Square.

Meanwhile Wallich had visited Burma, and in 1835 went with his successor Dr William Griffith to Assam, a province which the Burmese Government had ceded to Britain in 1826. Griffith, acting as physician to the Pemberton mission of 1837, also visited the State of Bhutan lying to the north of Assam.

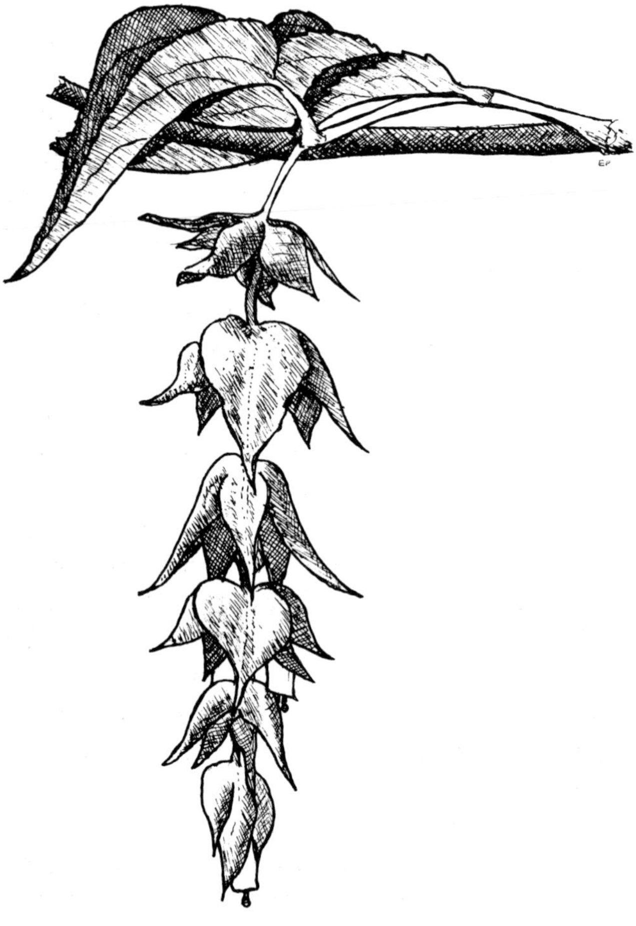

Job's (or Elisha's) Tears (*Leycesteria formosa*), collected by Dr John Forbes Royle for the East India Company's garden at Saharanpur in the Punjab

Other amateur expeditions unconnected with the East India Company were mounted. The Duke of Devonshire sent one of his gardeners, John Gibson, to India to obtain a live specimen of *Amherstia nobilis*, the spectacular red-flowered leguminous tree which Wallich had discovered in a neglected monastery garden on the Salween River. (Like its close relative, the Flamboyant, this tree had hardly ever been found in the wild state.)

In addition, military men serving with the army and civilians in the Indian Civil Service made their own contributions. Lt Strachey sent the first bulb of *Nomocharis oxypetala*, a lily species, the flowers of which are yellow, marked with violet in the throat. Major Vickery found *Amphicome arguta*, a member of the bignonia family, which produced pink or red funnel-shaped flowers, and is still cultivated today. Captain Munro sent *Cyananthus lobatus*, a rock plant related to the campanulas, with bright blue periwinkle flowers. Captain Hardwicke's find in 1796 was *Rhododendron arboreum*, the evergreen tree as high as a house, and Major Madden introduced *Cardiocrinum giganteum* – a six-foot lily, greenish white with streaks of dark purple, and *Abelia triflora*, a small tree with fragrant pink flowers.

It was named after Dr Clarke Abel, the physician who had accompanied Amherst on his unsuccessful mission to Peking in 1816.

This then was the situation in 1848 when Joseph Hooker, now 31, landed at Calcutta. Bengal, of course, had been British for nearly a century, but the buffer states of Nepal, Sikkim and Bhutan, though subject to British influence, were self-ruling, and the smallest of the three states, Sikkim, wedged between Tibet in the north, Nepal in the west and Bhutan in the east, had never been explored and was not even officially surveyed until 35 years later.

So Sikkim was selected as Hooker's main project. The Rajah of Sikkim owed his position there to the

British, who had protected him from attacks of his next door neighbours, the Gurkhas, but his Dewan, or Prime Minister, was from Tibet, and was as suspicious of foreigners as the Chinese themselves. At first no permission for Hooker to visit Sikkim was forthcoming; then, under pressure, it was granted with numerous 'ifs' and 'buts' and restrictions on freedom of movement. So Hooker had to spend six months in Darjeeling, the hill station in northern Bengal. Nevertheless he found many new plants there. One of them was a rhododendron afterwards named after Lady Dalhousie – a magnificent white, lemon-scented species. It was shown as the first plate in Hooker's most famous work, *The Rhododendrons of the Sikkim-Himalayas*. Other rhododendrons found near Darjeeling included R. *argenteum* with silvery leaves beneath its white flowers; R. *barbatum* with rich red flowers and pinkish grey bark and R. *falconeri*, a tree with creamy bell-like flowers marked with purple in the throat.

Meanwhile the ruler of Nepal to whom Hooker had also applied made no difficulties, and offered him an escort of Gurkhas to take him to any part of the kingdom he wished to visit. So Hooker decided to travel north through Nepal and then to allay the fears of the Dewan of Sikkim by entering Sikkim only on his way back to Darjeeling.

But this was to be no ordinary expedition of the David Douglas type. It was far more in Banks's style.

Hooker himself carried a telescope, knife and digging tool. Also he took with him eight thermometers, two barometers, two chronometers, three compasses, plus compass stand, a sextant and an artificial horizon and a geologist's hammer. He had his own personal servant, a Portuguese half-caste and eight coolies to carry his tent and equipment, his bed, his clothes, his books and papers and his drying paper and stores. The coolies were in charge of a headman, Nimbo, who also had his own private coolie. Hooker's interpreter also had his own coolie. Three Lepchas, natives of Sikkim, were needed to climb trees, to arrange Hooker's finds and to change the papers in which they were to be dried off. Hooker was accompanied by Brian Hodgson, zoologist and former Resident at the Nepalese Court who was to record the wildlife of Sikkim, and he brought with him an animal collector, a shooter, taxidermist and four more coolies. The Rajah of Nepal had provided Hooker with a guard of six men plus two officers and a corporal, and they brought four coolies with them. Fourteen Bhutan porters were needed to carry the food stores and cooking equipment, as food was likely to be scarce.

Hooker was, to be sure, setting out to map an area of great complexity in which elevations, accurate measurement of gradients and latitude and longitude were essential. 'During the greater part of my journey,' he wrote to his father, 'I saw not a single known object, and had to observe with the sextant. No map contains the name of a single place I have visited! That I was poking about in and out over the western base of Kinchin is all I can confirm.'

And nothing could ensure that this journey would be without discomfort. Mist could restrict the visibility to 10 yards. The Bhutan porters stole the food, mutinied and decamped. There was a profusion of leeches, and Hooker's only protection against snow blindness was a veil given to him by Mrs Campbell, wife of Archibald Campbell, the British Agent to the Rajah of Sikkim. Those for whom there was no veil shielded their eyes with pieces of paper, a yak's tail or their own long hair pulled down over their foreheads.

But when Hooker returned to Darjeeling from this first foray, there was plenty to show and he was able to send off 80 man-loads of plants by coolies, carts and water transport. Discoveries included two of our best-known rhododendrons: *R. campylocar-*

pum (yellow flowers, leaves dark green above, blue-white beneath) and R. *thomsonii* with rather similar leaves but blood-red flowers.

On his way back from this first expedition, Hooker had crossed into Sikkim, and got a renewed undertaking from the Rajah to allow him to return the following year. But when he did so early in May 1849 it was evident that the Rajah or his Dewan had changed his mind. Visits to this or that mountain were refused on the pretext that there was holy ground there and that the gods would be angry if it was disturbed. Delays were requested on the excuse that the road ahead was impassable in its present state and would need to be repaired before anyone could use it. Tree trunks had been drawn across the paths, stepping stones taken away from the streams, and the fastenings of the bridges removed. It was even suggested that the Rajah wanted the whole expedition to be postponed because his son (with whom he was on less than good terms) had recently died. But Hooker insisted that he would take orders only from the British agent, Archibald Campbell. He pressed on northward through Sikkim and reached and crossed the frontier into Tibet. He even climbed to a height of 19,300 feet up the Donkin mountain in the north of the country.

And this second trip was even more successful than the first. On it he learned to like brick-tea and curds, and to use a hole in a rock or a shed of leaves as his residence for days at a time. He also learnt the difference between a fowl and a chicken. 'Of the latter I eat bones and all; of the former I cannot.'

During this second journey he saw the great amphitheatre of rock and snow under Kinchinjhow, walled in with precipices and an ice face of 4,000 feet 'a great big curtain reaching from heaven to earth broken only in places where icicles ran along in lines like organ pipes – and beneath cones of snow rising above the rocks like gouts of fire from some volcano that had been turned to ice.' Among the well known (but new-at-the-time) rhododendrons encountered during this second trip were R. *triflorum* with lime green flowers; R. *glaucophyllum* with aromatic leaves, mid-green above and slate-coloured beneath, setting off rose-pink flowers; R. *wallichii* with lilac flowers, pink spotted; R. *maddenii* with a pinkish blush; and R. *aucklandii* (later *griffithianum*) with some of the largest flowers known in the genus. Miniature species included R. *pumilum*, a three-inch plant with pink flowers, and R. *nivale*, the Snow Rhododendron rising but two inches from the soil, with woody branches 'as thick as a goose-quill' and purple flowers smelling of eau-de-cologne. Hooker found it growing at an elevation of 19,000 feet and rated it as the world's top altitude shrub. One of the toughest too, since it had to survive the mountain-scorch of the sun, plus snow and ice and, at times, local whirlwinds. Till then R. *catawbiense*, the lilac and green-flowered shrub introduced from north America in 1809 by John Fraser had been awarded the first prize for hardiness.

Altogether 36 rhododendron species were collected, 28 of them new, though Hooker was content to leave his father to determine this at Kew and even to provide the names, except for a few reserved for his friends.

Botanising however came summarily to a halt at one point in November 1849 when Hooker, and Campbell who had joined him, were forcibly seized by order of the Dewan of Sikkim in an attempt to impose a new treaty on the Governor General, Lord Dalhousie. The two travellers were confined in a hovel, half-starved and, in Campbell's case, maltreated. They were released only on 23 December after troops had been hurried up to Darjeeling and an ultimatum sent to the Rajah.

The rhododendron was by no means the only flower to interest Hooker. He introduced *Primula sikkimensis*, 18 or more inches high, with pale green leaves and cowslip type flowers; *P. capitata* with blue flowers; *Meconopsis nepaulensis* similar to the Welsh Poppy but with three-inch purple or red flowers, and *Vanda caerulea*, the tall blue orchid; Hooker and his men collected seven men's loads of this orchid though few plants reached England alive.

Hooker returned to England in 1851 to marry his patient fiancée, Frances, daughter of the Rev. John Steven Henslow, Professor of Botany at Cambridge. By this time, Hooker rhododendrons were already flourishing in Cornwall, Wales, Devon and Argyllshire – and some had been sent to Queen Victoria at Osborne. In 1855 Joseph Hooker was appointed Assistant Director at Kew; and became Director 10 years later on his father's death. He was knighted for his services to botany, received the Order of Merit on his 90th birthday, wrote many other books on botany, and was still classifying the balsams 'deceitful above all plants' four days before his death at the age of 94.

Hooker made many friends during his long life and one of them was Charles Darwin. Darwin had found a real winner from the Straits of Magellan in *Calceolaria darwinii*, the Tobacco Pouch Flower which was striking blossoms of orange flecked with reddish brown, with a white band, a yellow stigma and green sepals,* but Hooker regarded him as a friend rather than a botanical collector. He strongly supported Darwin's theory that species, whether of flowers or animals were not immutable but evolved through a process of natural selection, and he encouraged Darwin's researches into the genetics, the mechanics of orchid pollination and the movements of climbing plants. Darwin in his will reciprocated by bequeathing to Kew the money

Tobacco Pouch Flower (*Calceolaria darwinii*), which as its name suggests was discovered in the Straits of Magellan area by Charles Darwin

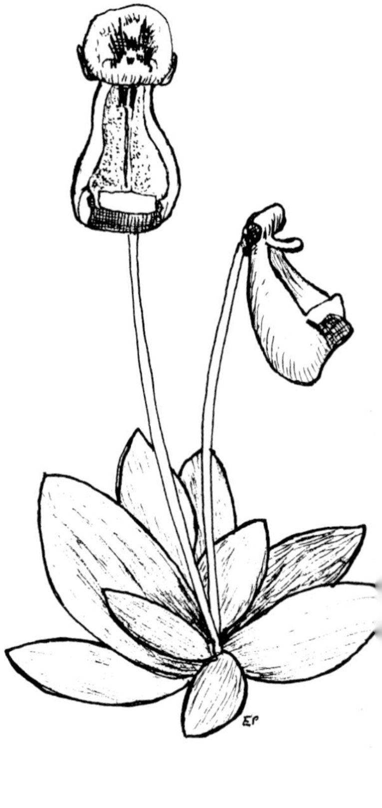

*It grew happily on the island of Chiloe but was not successfully introduced until 1894 60 years after Darwin's visit.

needed to initiate the *Index Kewensis*, a list of all flowering plants from the time of Linnaeus onwards, the number of which is now put at a minimum of 250,000. (Hooker, incidentally, abandoned the Linnaean classification in favour of something more natural.)

Meanwhile at a time when the first volume of *Index Kewensis* was still in preparation, other collectors were finding species to be added to succeeding volumes.

The Veitch nursery was still among the most active in the field. Their collectors were of all kinds. Gustav Wallis, a German who collected successfully in Brazil and tropical South America, had been deaf and dumb up to the age of six. James Henry

Charles Darwin (1809–1882)

Chesterton was valet to a widely travelled gentleman and became a collector to Veitch after writing to ask advice on how to bring orchids safely home. He collected for Veitch in South America between 1870 and 1878. David Burke, who collected in the Philippines and New Guinea in the 1890s lived with the natives as a native, and Veitch & Co. heard of his death only by chance from a German commercial traveller. A.R. Endres who collected in the 1870s in Costa Rica and succeeded in sending home *Miltonia endresii* – a spectacular white, yellow and rose orchid – was a half-caste. Charles Curtis on the other hand, who was despatched to Borneo about the same time to collect *Nepenthe northiana*, one of five new exotic species discovered and painted by a Miss North,* went on to become superintendent of the Botanic Gardens at Penang, and retired in 1905 to Barnstaple.

The firm sent Richard Pearce to the Argentine, Bolivia, Chile and Peru, on two three-year contracts lasting, with a break between, from 1859–66. In Chile Pearce secured *Eucryphia glutinosa*, a large shrub, hardy in the west, with dark green glossy leaves, and two-and-a-half-inch paper-white flowers tufted with upstanding yellow stamens.

Pearce also sent two other attractive plants, both Chilean, and in need of some protection: *Mutisia decurrens*, a climber of the daisy family with starry orange blossoms; and *Berberidopsis corallina*, another climber with coral red flowers. His white-flowered *Escallonia virgata*, though overtaken by hybridis-

* Marianne North an elegant, well-connected and talented traveller had painted flower pictures in most tropical countries including Jamaica (where she hung up an enormous bunch of bananas – chandelier style – in her living room and ate her way down as they ripened), Brazil where she saw a spider as big as a sparrow and America where she dined with General Grant who she found 'had much talent for silence'. Her paintings can be seen in the gallery which she built and presented to the Royal Botanic gardens.

ation, has given inherited strength to many a garden hedge. His *Hippeastrum leopoldii*, a large flowered brick-red species has added to the size, if not to the delicacy of many *Amaryllidaceae* hybrids.

But Pearce is best known for the choice tuberous begonias that he introduced: *Begonia boliviensis*, a large scarlet-flowered species; *B. veitchii* with well-formed scarlet flowers; and *B. pearcei* – with marbled leaves, also from Bolivia and the only tuberous species with yellow flowers in general cultivation today.

John Gould Veitch, the great grandson of the founder of the nursery, went personally to Japan in 1860 to take advantage of the fact that British nationals were now allowed to visit certain ports and to circulate within 10 miles of them. Despite these limits Veitch was able to get a good selection of plants from nurseries, temples and private gardens. His Asiatic version of the Virginia Creeper, originally named *Ampelopsis veitchii*, but now *Parthenocissus tricuspidata*, proved an immediate success, and became far more popular than the original 'true' Virginian plant. Veitch went on to Australia and the Pacific Islands where he collected a number of useful stove and house plants before returning to England in 1866. He married in 1868, and a son, James Harry Veitch was born; two years later, aged 31, he died of tuberculosis.

The Veitch nurseries continued meanwhile to prosper. James Veitch, the father of John Gould Veitch, had opened the Kings Road, Chelsea, branch of the firm, known as the Royal Exotic Nursery, in the 1850s with highly profitable results. In 1877 it was decided to send Charles Maries, one of the Veitch foremen, to collect plants in China and Japan. He sent home *Hamamelis mollis* which has since become the most popular of the Witch Hazels; *Primula obconica*, a close-growing early flowering lilac pink species; *Enkianthus campanulatus*, with creamy, red-veined bell-heather flowers followed by fiery autumn foliage; *Viburnum tomentosum var. mariesii* which produces trays of white flowers along its horizontal branches; and a white variety of *Daphne genkwa.* The two then proceeded to plant-hunt together in British North Borneo.

Thomas Lobb had already prospected the area for Veitch, and other plants had been sent home from Sarawak by Hugh (later Sir Hugh) Low who became secretary to Rajah Brooke and lived on the nearby island of Labuan for 28 years. Burbidge succeeded in introducing two giant pitcher plants, *Nepenthes bicalcarata* and *N. rajah* which Low had found but had not been able to get home alive. The size of these plants can be gathered from a paragraph in Spencer St John's *Life in the Forests of the Far East* published by Smith Elder & Co. in 1862 which read: 'This morning, while the men were cooking their rice, as we sat before the tent enjoying our chocolate, observing one of the followers carrying water in a splendid specimen of Nepenthes rajah, we desired him to bring it to us, and found that it held exactly four pint bottles. It was nineteen inches in circumference. We afterwards saw others which were much larger, and Mr. Low while wandering about in search of flowers, came upon one in which was a drowned rat'.

There was another more vivid rat episode when a large grey-tailed Norwegian-type rat was found in the cave where they were sheltering. It was killed and promptly eaten by the guides. Later they ran out of water and had to rely on the larger pitcher plants for supplies, and just before they started for home, one of the servants upset a kettle of scalding water over Burbidge's foot and he had to ride home on the back of a (female) buffalo.

But few people enjoyed the life of a collector more than Burbidge.

As he sailed on a trading steamer from one island

off the coast of Borneo to another, he paints a delightful picture of the Far East in the days before Somerset Maugham and Noel Coward wrote of it. He tells of dinner at Government House, of spiders with webs strong enough to pull your hat off, of the days when a looking-glass was payment for a night's lodging, when the curry arrived cooked in coconut lamp oil, and of boar-hunting with the Sultan of the Sulu archipelago.

But the scene was already changing. Of Labuan, Burbidge wrote, 'The whole island is tolerably flat, and at one time was entirely covered with forests, yielding fine timber. Of late years, however, jungle fires have been frequent during the dry season; and at the present time but little old forest remains. The climate is now generally supposed to be drier and more healthy than formerly; but the flora has suffered much, many orchids and other rare plants, formerly found here in abundance, being now quite extinct'.

Abbé Armand David (1826–1900), a French missionary, whose adventurous spirit took him into the remote regions of Inner Mongolia and up the Yangtze River

Meanwhile just when Veitch's collectors were concentrating on tropical plants, a flood of new hardy plants were coming out of western China and were particularly welcome in England at the time when there was a growing demand for Chinese paintings, tiles, textiles and porcelain.

John Pierre Armand David was one of the most influential of the new collectors-at-large. He was born in 1826 in Espelette, a small town in the Basque country 16 miles from Biarritz – the son of a doctor. At an early age he decided to become a priest, and when he was 22 he enrolled in the Lazarist Order of St Vincent de Paul, which was dedicated to foreign missionary work. He was ordained a priest in 1851 and, the following year, pressed to be allowed to go to China, believing, as he said, that God had called him to this task.

It was 10 years before his wish was granted. In 1862 he was sent with three other priests to set up a school for 100 boys in Peking.

David, who had always shown a marked interest in both plants and animals, was to teach natural science to the pupils, while the three other priests concentrated on mathematics, physics and music. Some specimens which David sent back from Peking to Paris were, however, so well presented and interesting that in 1866 he was given leave to go on a research mission to Inner Mongolia far to the west of where Fortune had been working. Indeed, it was an area so remote that the Chinese were still battling with the Mongols for control over it.

Fortunately David kept a diary of his travels and this has been translated and sympathetically edited by Helen Fox for the Harvard University Press. From it we learn that in the more settled areas, David and his party had been able to find inns where even foreigners were allowed a place on the brick platform under which smoke from the hearth was allowed to pass to warm the clientele sleeping on it. But sometimes because of the noise, the Abbé David preferred to sleep beneath a tent in the inn courtyard on a bed of dried dung and stones rather than join the noisy throng in the communal dormitory.

Where no inns existed, it was a case of camping out, and on one occasion Abbé David and his three companions, Brother Chevrier, a guide and a young Christian Chinese assistant, pitched their tent near the celebrated lamasery of Wu-t'ang-chiao in a rugged mountain area frequented by wolves. 'Hence for fear of these animals, we take the donkey into our tent, though its presence there is not without inconvenience,' David recorded.

Three years later Abbé David undertook a far more ambitious journey from Peking to Shanghai, up the Yangtze River past the famous gorges and through the rapids to Chungking on to Chengtu, the capital of Szechuan and then on into one of the independent principalities, a round trip of at least two thousand five hundred miles. Food consisted for most of the time of tsamba, a flour made from pre-cooked beans and barley having the appearance of a reddish dust. This flour was then mixed with hot or cold water and rolled by hand into balls which David said, 'must be eaten with courage'. The mixture was almost without taste and the Abbé found it 'capable of defying all but the most ravenous hunger'.

It was on this expedition that David, who was a zoologist as well as a botanist, saw his first Great Panda – first the skin of an adult, then a young cub which the hunters took alive but had killed on the way home so that it could be carried more easily, and later the skin of another adult. Later still, David was brought another live panda. 'This animal does not look fierce, and behaves like a little bear. Its paws and head exactly resemble those of my white bear. Its stomach is full of leaves,' he wrote. A live panda was sent to Paris and also the progenitors of the herd of Père David's Deer still to be seen at Woburn but extinct today in the wild.

Abbé David also contributed to the living world with his botanical discoveries even if he did not himself introduce the best of them. The most well known of all is *Davidia involucrata*, the Handkerchief Tree, so called because of the pairs of white bracts of various lengths – up to seven inches – which almost completely conceal the yellowish-green flowers, giving the tree the appearance of being decked with paper handkerchiefs.

Then there is *Buddleia davidii*, the Butterfly Bush, with its spikes of fragrant purple flowers, the most popular and easily grown of the family – too easily some might say. The name Buddleia commemorates another man of the Church, the Reverend Adam Buddle, botanist and Vicar of Fambridge on the river Crouch in Essex who had died in 1715 almost exactly a century and a half earlier.

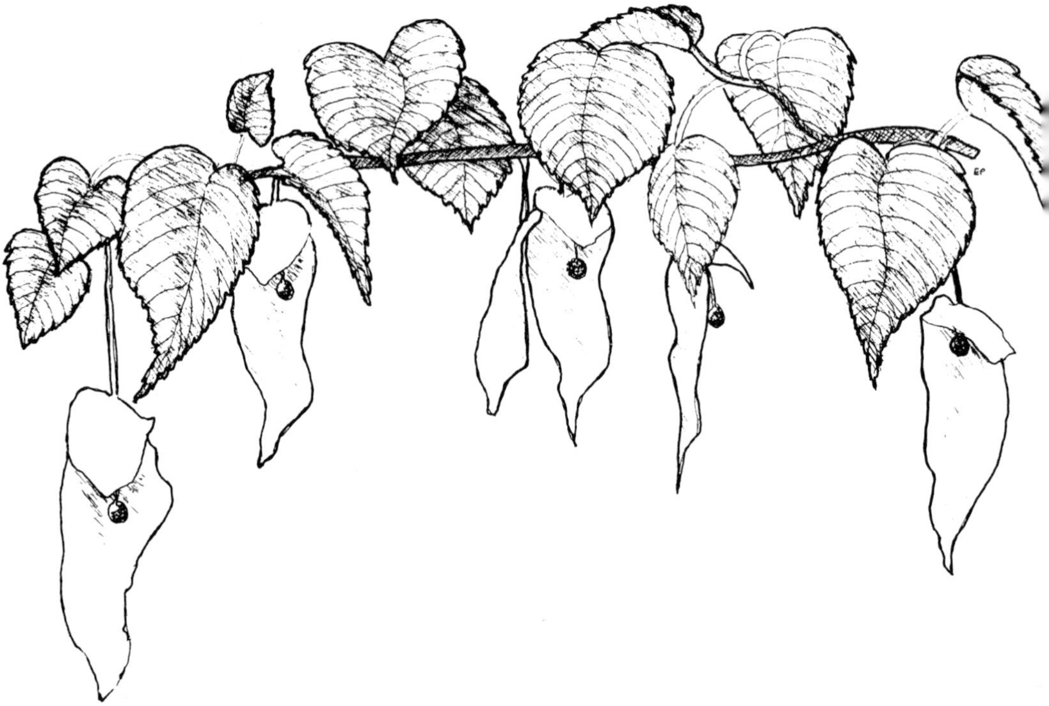

Handkerchief or Ghost Tree (*Davidia involucrata*), one of Père David's discoveries

Père David's name is remembered in two clematis species – *Clematis armandii*, the evergreen with dark green leaves and small fragrant waxy cream-coloured flowers and *C. davidiana* – a herbaceous type with blue hyacinth-like flowers. It is now usually represented by *C. heracleifolia*. *Astilbe davidii* is a distinctive member of the Saxifrage family; its feathery leaves have a bronzy look when young, and the spires of rose-pink flowers are set off by bluish anthers.

In all, David discovered 250 new species of plant, and when he returned to Paris in 1874, he set up his own museum and helped to train young candidate missionaries. He lived to be 74.

Abbé David was followed by other French missionaries, notably Jean Marie Delavay, who made most of his discoveries during the 1880s in Yunnan, the province of south-west China bordering on Burma and Indo-China. He introduced

Deutzia purpurascens, one parent of the popular hybrid *D. elegantissima*; *Paeonia lutea*, a fragrant yellow single-flowered species; the Rhododendron called *racemosum*, though its flowers are not invariably at the end of a branch; *Incarvillea delavayi*, a fine back-of-the-border plant with deep rose flowers and deeply cut foliage; *Primula malacoides*, an indoor species with reddish purple flowers and the mauve-flowered *Thalictrum delavayi* often mistaken for its near relative, *D. dipterocarpum*.

He also discovered *Meconopsis betonicifolia* (synonym *baileyi*) generally called the Himalayan Blue Poppy, though first found in Yunnan. Selective breeding has helped to sharpen up the colour of its petals to the shade of blue we now enjoy.

Clematis armandii, an evergreen with dark green leaves and small fragrant, waxy, cream-coloured flowers

Delavay sent back some 200,000 specimens, including perhaps 1,500 new species, but the resources of the French Natural History Museum were unable to cope with such abundance, and many packages were discovered years later unopened. Later French botanists sent their seeds to the nurseryman, Maurice de Vilmorin, with happier results; de Vilmorin succeeded in raising the first seedling of the Handkerchief Tree, though not before the seed had apparently failed to germinate and had been thrown away and afterwards recovered from a rubbish heap.

Jean André Soulié, yet another medical missionary, was responsible for introducing – as distinct from discovering, *Buddleia davidii* near the Tibetan border; he was one of the unlucky collectors and was seized and killed by bandits in 1905.

A stream of hothouse plants continued to come from Australia, in particular from James Drummond, who had been selected in 1829 to establish a botanic garden in the newly established settlement of Western Australia. Among these were *Anigozanthos*, the Kangaroo Paw and *Brachycome iberidifolia*, the Swan River Daisy.

Two winners, one hardy and one fairly hardy, came from Ronald Gunn who went to Tasmania also in 1829, as Assistant Superintendent of Convicts. These were *Eucalyptus gunnii*, a species often grown in England, with silvery pink shoots turning to blue-green leaves on maturity; the other plant was *Olearia gunnii*, one of the Daisy Bushes.

New Zealand with its more temperate climate also made contributions. Richard Cunningham who visited the country in 1834 at last found *Clianthus puniceus* in the wild more than half a century after Banks had discovered the cultivated specimen. Cunningham also discovered *Fuchsia procumbens*, one of the most interesting species of the genus and highly suitable for a hanging basket. The flower has no petals and consists of a cream-coloured tube with recurved sepals of green and purple. Cunningham also found some interesting Hebes including *H. speciosa* with purplish flowers, and *H. salicifolia*. Like most of their tribe they are resistant to wind and salt, if not to frost.

Other new plants came from here and there: *Galanthus elwesii*, the Green Snowdrop came from the Smyrna area in 1874, followed, three years later by *Chionodoxa lucilae* which has light blue flowers with white centres. George Maw, a tile manufacturer interested in soil as a raw material, who afterwards became a specialist in the genus *Crocus*, collected this plant in the same area.

Dr John Kirk, British Political Agent in Zanzibar, sent *Impatiens sultani* which shares the name Busy Lizzie with its near relatives.

Finally *Polygonum baldschuanicum*, the Russian vine, was discovered near the Russian-Sinkiang border by a German, Albert Regel, son of Edward Regel, Director of the St Petersburg Botanic Garden. It was said to have been named after Baldschuan on the banks of the River Wachsch in Bokhara where it was found – a locality, however, too insignificant to be marked on normal scale maps. Regel also found *Tulipa kaufmanniana*, an early flowering species, the white flowers of which, tinged with red and yellow, open wide to form a six-pointed star. It is sometimes called the Waterlily Tulip, but is at its best in a sunny spot in the rock garden – an area to which more significance was coming to be attached.

14 *The Specialists*

The Rock Garden had a very respectable history. William Forsyth, who succeeded Philip Miller as Curator of the Chelsea Physic Garden, assembled his own rockery in 1774, using 40 tons of stone rescued from the roadside outside the Tower of London, together with flint and chalk, and some lava brought back from Iceland two years earlier by Sir Joseph Banks. In the following year, Dr John Fothergill, the Quaker physician, and his friend Dr Pitcairn of Warwick Lane, London, sent Thomas Blaikie (whose *Diary of a Scottish Gardener* records his experiences in Paris during the French Revolution) to Switzerland to hunt for Alpines – a class altogether apart from the ordinary run of rock plants. From the Swiss Alps and the Jura (where he was fascinated to see the mountain cowherds using one-legged milking stools secured with straps to their backsides), he sent home 430 parcels of plants, many of which he first planted in the garden of Paul Gaussen at Bourdigny near Geneva. The new alpines collected by Blaikie are presumably those credited in Aiton's *Hortus Kewensis* to Drs Fothergill and Pitcairn as having been introduced in 1775. They included *Ranunculus glacialis*, described as the Two-flowered Crowfoot; *Campanula cenisia*, Mont Cenis Bellflower; *Trifolium alpinum* with sizeable pink flowers; *Veronica bellidioides*, Daisy-leaved Speedwell; and *Hutchinsia alpina*, a neat little Rock Cress.

It must be admitted, however, that for many years, stretching even into the twentieth century, the rock garden was regarded as a scenic attraction rather than as a well-planned sanctuary for rock plants. Thus Lady Broughton's rock garden assembled in the 1830s at Hoole House near Chester was intended to represent the valley of Chamonix with all its hair-raising defiles, precipices, and Mer de Glace. Marble chips did duty for the snowfields. Some attempt had been made to reproduce the stratification of the rock, but the effect was rather spoilt by the fact that some perfectly normal trees had been allowed to take root and grow near the glacier. The Backhouse Nursery at York showed a comprehensive range of alpines and rock ferns in their well-known rock garden built in 1859, but it was not until 1882 that Kew established a rock garden worthy of the name.

By this time, to judge by the catalogue of the day, there was a ready demand from the general public for rock plants. Few private gardeners realised, however, that alpines succeed only where nothing else can survive, that some rock plants prefer limestone, others sandstone – or perhaps granite; that some are tolerant of shade and others intolerant and that cavities holding water, and clefts through which the soil can drain away, are equally unacceptable.

Horticultural know-how was also badly needed in cities where lack of space compelled householders to concentrate on a very different style of garden. An attempt to tackle the problem had been made as far back as 1722 by Thomas Fairchild, the nurseryman of Hoxton, who dedicated his treatise *The City Gardener* to the Honourable and Worshipful Governors of the Hospitals of Bethlehem and Bridewell, pointing out that for 30 years he 'had been placed near London where I have raised several thousand plants both from foreign countries and the English growth' but that everything will not prosper in London 'either because the smoke of the sea-coal does hurt to some plants or else because those people who have little gardens in London do not know how to manage their plants when they have got them'.

He put forward a list of plants and shrubs (holly and privet for example) that would grow in London squares, courtyards, 'close places' and even on balconies, and particularly commended the greenery around the fountain at Plummers at the upper end of the Haymarket, and the vine at the Rose Tavern in Temple Bar.

But a more influential writer on the subject of city gardens came to the fore during the first half of the nineteenth century in John Claudius Loudon (1783–1843), who succeeded amongst other things in demolishing the wall which cut off Kensington Gardens from public view. He was the son of a Cambuslang, Lanarkshire (now Strathclyde) farmer, but trained himself to be a capable draughtsman as well as a linguist and horticulturalist. His *Arboretum et Fruticetum Britannicum*, published in eight volumes described and illustrated all the known trees and shrubs, native or introduced, growing in Britain. In 1826 he established the *Gardener's Magazine*, the first of the really popular weekly periodicals, and also completed a comprehensive *Encyclopaedia of Gardening*. These accomplishments were all the more remarkable because of the fact that at the age of 23, Loudon was partially crippled by an attack of rheumatic fever following a night journey he was obliged to make on the outside of a coach, and the surgeons who treated his complaint only made it worse.

At the age of 47 he married Jane Webb whom he had met following a review he had written of her imaginative and witty novel, *The Mummy* which forecast the life-style of the twentieth century. Jane was 24 years younger than her husband, but they worked together as a team and, after Loudon's collapse and death in her arms, she continued to write attractive and readable works on gardening for women, even though until her marriage, she had known nothing about plants. The Loudons had their own London garden at 3 Porchester Terrace, and Loudon, both in his *Encyclopaedia of Gardening* (from 1822) and in his *Suburban Gardener and Villa Companion*, published in 1838, paid special attention to would-be gardeners for whom the elaborate designs and landscape adventures of the past were totally inappropriate.

In his *Encyclopaedia*, Loudon suggested that the suburban house with a carriage entrance should have a forecourt varied by shrubs and a few trees with a central circle of turf ornamented with baskets of flowers or roses. In the middle of this should be set a statue, sundial, fountain, small pond or evergreen tree.

Nearer the centre of London, Loudon had proposals for the Citizen's Villa – which was clearly superior to the suburban house. Loudon thought, however, that it was unlikely to have more than an acre of ground, and that in this case it would be better to dispense with the kitchen garden altogether since better fruit and vegetables can be got 'from that first of all gardens, Covent Garden'.

The flower garden of the Citizen's Villa, Loudon suggests, should consist mainly of lawn with only the most select flowers, trees and shrubs, principally evergreens, around it. His design shows the paths around this garden disposed to conform to the wish which he realises some owners have of avoiding having to talk to the gardener – especially if he should be a mere jobbing gardener – during their walks. His design also accords with the disposition of the scholar. 'Easy turnings in walks are also a great luxury to studious persons,' Loudon wrote. 'For this reason an author if he can afford any other garden than a pot of mint should surround his plot with an open path, that he may walk on without end, and without any sensible change in the position of his body'.

Loudon had no specific suggestions for the 'common front garden' except to say that 'it is of great importance to the advancement of gardening that the art should be displayed to as great a perfection as possible in those gardens which are most universal, which are continually under the eye of a large city population; seen by the whole country's inhabitants when they visit towns; and which chiefly come under the eye of foreigners'.

More important for gardeners was Loudon's recognition, towards the end of his life, of the attractions of the gardenesque style. By this phrase he meant 'the production of that kind of scenery which is best calculated to display the individual beauty of trees, shrubs and plants in a state of nature; the smoothness and greenness of lawns, and the smooth surface, curved directions, and firmness of gravel walks; in short it is calculated for displaying the art of the gardener. . . . All the trees, shrubs and plants in the gardenesque style are planted and managed in such a way as that each may arrive at perfection and display its beauties as if it were cultivated for that purpose alone'. There was thus a new respect for the individuality of plants and a realisation that the plant must be sited where it will grow best in preference to a less favourable spot where it might suit the designer. Clearly Loudon would have agreed with the Rev. Henry Nicholson Ellacombe who followed his father as Vicar of Bitton, near Bath, and maintained that you should always proceed round a garden facing the sun, because only in this way could the veining and reticulation of leaves of plants be seen to the full advantage.

It did not follow from this that Loudon approved of experimentation for its own sake or of giving prominence to novel specimen plants simply because they were new or uncommon. Indeed he advised against it, quoting from Maria Jackson's *The Florist's Manual* published in 1816, to the effect that 'the fashionable novice who has stored her borders from the catalogue of some celebrated name with a variety of rare species; who has procured innumerable rose trees, chiefly consisting of old and common sorts brought into notice by new nomenclature; who has set aside a portion of ground for American plants, and duly placed them in bog soil, with their name painted on large-headed pegs, becomes disappointed when, instead of the brilliant glow of her more humble neighbour's parterre, she finds her own distinguished only by paucity of colour, and fruitless expenditure . . . and the cause of the general failure in this particular is the prevalent solicitude for rarity and novelty in preference to well-blended quantity; as without frequent repetition of the same plant, it will be vain to attempt a brilliant flower garden as the art of procuring it consists in the judicious mixture of every common colour. Hence the foundation thus laid, the solicitude of those who wish to complete the superstructure must not be for rare species, but for new colour, so that the commonest primula which presents a fresh shade of red, blue, yellow, &c. ought to be esteemed more valuable than the most rare American plant which does not bring a similar advantage'.

Good advice such as this may not have led to immediate introductions of new plants but served to recruit new gardeners which in the longer term was probably more important. But whereas, in the past, the difficulty had been to find space enough on the estate for a flower bed, now that the flower bed was there, competition had built up between the multitude of plants available to fill it.

Specialist gardens of the kind we have mentioned, however helped to siphon off some of the pressure and, in addition to the rock garden, there was the fernery. The Victorian conservatory with its display of foliage plants and ferns was placed often enough next to one of the living rooms which were no longer situated on the first floor. Interest in semi-tropical foliage plants such as the Aralias and Gunneras was stimulated in the 1860s by James Shirley Hibberd, an authority on species of ivy, editor of the highly successful periodical, *Floral World*, and of the re-constituted *Gardener's Magazine*. Hibberd was also the first editor of *Amateur Gardening*, established in 1884, and author of *New and Rare Beautiful-leaved Plants*, published in 1869.

The conservatory also harboured some of the flowers needed for the formal decorations and flower arrangements for so many Victorian dinner parties and soirées. Improved heating systems opened the drawing-room door as it were to more house plants. In houses without a conservatory, the fernery sometimes took the form of an enlarged Wardian case, within which the Victorian parent could demonstrate to his children how moisture taken up during the heat of the day would condense at night on the roof of the case and would thus moisturise the plants before dawn, just as happened in a real rain forest.

Outdoors there were new types of specialist garden. Classical and other gardens were restored with historical accuracy; there were Italian gardens, and towards the end of the century, the Japanese garden, an example of which led the Japanese ambassador to remark 'Magnificent. We have nothing like this in Japan'. There were spring gardens, autumn gardens and winter gardens; there were municipal gardens. There were even garden cities.

Technical advances helped to extend the area of garden which could be cultivated. One was the cylinder mowing-machine designed by Mr Edward Budding around 1830. The inspiration for it came from the apparatus used, in the Stroud cloth mill where he worked, for imparting a high quality finish to the cloth used for military uniforms. Larger lawns meant that flower beds need no longer be a restricted border but could float like an island amid a sea of turf.

Another advance came with the arrival in the mid nineteenth century of the India-rubber hose. No longer was it necessary to trundle the cumbrous iron tumbril known as the water-barrow to and fro over rough ground to the outermost corners of the estate. Water could be taken to the most remote bed by turning on a tap, and by 1895, Harrods' catalogue offered Wrinch's Dew-Drop Revolving Lawn Sprinkler with nickel-plated head, gun-metal body and tapered union for hose, for one shilling and ninepence halfpenny. And the well-endowed property owner, (clearly not an author) could contemplate his good fortune in a swing hammock chair 'so arranged that the occupier may recline at any angle by a simple motion with the foot against the footrest'. It cost twenty-one shillings and ninepence.

There was, however, one early nineteenth-century practice which threatened to deprive gardening of its universal appeal, by turning it into a rich man's hobby. This was the habit of filling up precious outdoor flowerbeds with cosseted plants brought forward under glass. This abuse had been encourage by the discovery around 1822 of a method superior to the one in use since Roman times for drawing glass. The new sheet glass was soon made dutiable by an observant government but the 'tax on light' was withdrawn in 1845 and wider and still wider greenhouses were the result. The Tom Thumb Pelargonium which could be counted on for a long flowering season was an especially popular greenhouse plant and was supported by other low growing plants such as the scarlet alonsoas, the *Cuphea ignea*, the scarlet, purplish-black and white Cigar Flower, together with foliage plants such as the iresines. The routine followed mechanically year after year provided labour for the gardener but contributed little to the progress of horticulture and nothing to the enjoyment of gardening.

It was against carpet bedding that the nurseryman, traveller and writer, William Robinson, raised his standard. He was an Irishman with the Irishman's love of a fight, and held strong opinions on most subjects, which were expressed freely in his writings, the most famous of which was *The English Flower Garden.* This was published in 1883 and by 1956 had run to sixteen editions. Robinson had many prejudices. He detested gardens designed by 'builders and wallpaper merchants'; he was against 'statues which destroyed repose', and against wooden 'rustic' bridges across ditches when a drain covered by earth would have done as well. He had no love for Italian gardens decorated with marble which perishes in our climate. He hated standard roses, first seen by Kennedy at Malmaison, and launched in Britain in 1818; and to him the elm was 'a short-rooted tree without dignity often blown down wholesale . . . which may kill us on a fine summer day'. He deplored what he called 'fountain mongery' and contrived grass slopes which he rates as 'embankment gardening' and was opposed to most forms of artificiality, complaining that 'in Vienna may be seen men perched on ladders fifty feet high endeavouring to clip Hornbeam and Beech into hideous shapes'.

Beds cut into geometrical shapes were to him 'pastry-cooks' work'. But above all he was against 'carpet bedding' – the practice of filling beds with a single species taken from the greenhouse, a shameful imposture in his eyes, and one degrading to the individual plants. Indeed when he established himself in 1884 at Gravetye Manor, a magnificent estate in East Sussex, his first care was to demolish its greenhouses.

As Robinson saw it, the garden should reflect the outer world of natural beauty which existed beyond its boundaries. Indeed, in his book *The Wild Garden* published in 1894, he proposed to blur the lines between wilderness and cultivation in a style still followed today. Exotic plants, he said, should be established in a site where they can take care of themselves – as for instance the Winter Aconite under native trees, the Lily of the Valley and Solomon's Seal in the woods, and the daffodils in the orchard. Short grass could form an excellent background for paeonies, and a yew tree for a starry white clematis. Thus instead of 'nature' driving out the garden as it had in Lancelot Brown's time, here was a garden spilling over into the countryside. Many plants, Robinson pointed out, did better in the rough than in the flower bed, and moreover the absence of blooms after their flowering season was over, was less noticeable against the tapestry of the wild garden, than it would have been in a flower bed.

Apart from his book, *Alpine Flowers for British Gardens* (1870) which he wrote after a walking tour in Switzerland, Robinson did not aim to introduce many new bedfellows to English gardeners, preferring to concentrate particularly on the hardy herbaceous species which he knew from experience would suit the positions in which he suggested they should be planted. But the delight which amateurs derived from the new natural style of gardening helped to ensure a wider public interest than ever before.

Robinson's policy was strongly supported by that remarkable woman, Miss Gertrude Jekyll (the name rhymes with 'treacle').

Her first outside commission came, it is said, in

the form of a letter from a factory lad in Rochdale who wrote to ask how to grow as many different species as possible in a small window box, but it was not until after 1889 when she met Edwin Lutyens, then a young architect in his early twenties, that commissions began to flow. Lutyens, who was eventually to design the Viceroy's Imperial Palace in Delhi and the Cenotaph in Whitehall, was, like Gertrude Jekyll, a great admirer of local country-style vernacular architecture. Together they explored the Surrey countryside in a pony cart drawn by Bessie, studying cottage gardens, and learning, as Miss Jekyll put it, the importance of simplicity, of not being in too much of a hurry and of doing one thing at a time.

She had the artist's sense of colour, and noted the success of the impressionists who, in their paintings, achieved the appearance of a single colour from touches of many quite different shades. Some of her critics suggested that her style amounted to outdoor upholstery. But the cascades of foliage that soften the outline of a garden wall and the pincushions of saxifrage peeping from the dry walls at eye level as one walked down stone steps – invariably broad and

Gertrude Jekyll, portrait by William Nicholson, 1920

with a gentle gradient – served to emphasise the structural solidity of the garden in a highly agreeable manner and even offered in some ways a hint of cubism.

She was a friend of Mrs C.W. Earle whose views first expressed in *Pot Pourri from a Surrey Garden* published in 1897 could well have influenced her and of George F. Wilson whose wealth came from trade with Czarist Russia and from an invention which allowed high-grade candles to be made from low-grade tallow. Wilson was an unorthodox but highly successful gardener and in 1878 bought land at Wisley which was acquired on his death by Sir Henry Hanbury and presented to the Royal Horticultural Society. Wilson was a lily specialist, but Miss Jekyll's own preference was for Mediterranean plants such as lavender, cistus and the sages which she had learned to love during visits to the South of France, Asia Minor and Greece. Like Robinson, however, she was happy to find a place for wild plants such as Wall Pennywort, Stitchwort, Yellow Toadflax, Welsh Poppy, Wood Sage and Red Valerian; hazel bushes, she said, made a very attractive contrast to *Primula denticulata* near the water garden.

She was also a rosarian, with a particular affection for *Rosa alba* which she saw mainly in cottage gardens and accepted as a traditional feature, surviving over the centuries. And so it was.

But the mere mention of roses, so dear to us partly, perhaps, because they grow wild only in the northern hemisphere, and their history stretching back for more than two thousand years, leads us inevitably to a subject that can no longer be ignored, namely that of hybrids as a source of garden plants. Whole books could be, indeed have been, written about the subject.

Many of our best loved roses are hybrids – even among the older European strains familiar to the

Primula, new species, by Leen King, from *Chinese Drawings*

運
Primula.
(42)

Greeks and Romans. Thus *Rosa alba*, the White Rose of York, was a hybrid between the wild Dog Rose and the sweetly scented *Rosa damascena*, the Damask Rose, to be seen on frescoes dating from the middle of the sixteenth century BC at Knossos, Crete.

The Damask Rose, in turn, was a hybrid. One of its parents was *Rosa phoenicea*, a climbing rose with single white flowers; the other parent was *Rosa gallica* known twelve centuries BC in Persia and afterwards as *Rosa officinalis*, the Apothecaries Rose. It was later adopted as the Red Rose of Lancaster. To add to the confusion it is sometimes known as the Rose of Provins (*not* Provence) from the locality near Paris where it was extensively cultivated.

The Moss Rose so beloved by the Victorians was developed from *Rosa centifolia*, the Cabbage Rose or Rose of Provence which was itself a cross between *Rosa alba* and *Rosa moschata*, a species from Western Asia.

Rosa gallica also combined with *Rosa moschata*, to produce another hybrid, the Autumn Damask Rose – *Rosa damascena bifera*, believed to have been referred to by Virgil in the Georgics.

Then, towards the end of the eighteenth century, Joseph Banks introduced a new element. His rose was a hybrid between two Chinese species. One parent was the crimson-flowered *Rosa chinensis*, described as remontant because of its ability to flower more than once in a season. The other parent was *Rosa gigantea*, with petals which unroll from an attractively peaked centre – with a scent reminiscent of the delicate perfume of freshly crushed tea-leaves. In fact it was called the Tea-scented Rose. Banks' hybrid was known as Parson's Pink China because of the fact that it flowered in the garden of a Mr Parsons at Rickmansworth in 1793.

Two yellow chrysanthemums, from *Chinese Drawings*

Hybridising between *Rosa chinensis*, *Rosa gigantea* and other cultivated roses gave rise to a strain known as Chinese Hybrids which were both long-flowering and fragrant but somewhat vulnerable to the rigours of the English climate.

Final success was achieved through the medium of the Bourbon Rose from the Île de Bourbon (now Réunion) in the southern Indian Ocean.

The Bourbon was itself a cross – an accidental one between two roses growing in neighbouring beds. One of these was the Autumn Damask and the other Parson's Pink China. When the Bourbon was back-crossed with a hybrid derived from *Rosa chinensis* and Autumn Damask, a hardier race of roses known as Hybrid Perpetuals was evolved, the French being the first in the field with their Rose du Roi (Louis XVIII) produced in 1816.

The Bourbon Rose reached these shores in 1825; and *Rosa foetida*, a native of Persia and source of many yellow roses, arrived here in 1838, in the form of a variant popularly known as the Austrian Briar.

The Hybrid Perpetuals held the field during most of the nineteenth century and they were one half of the equation which led to the modern Hybrid Teas. The remaining half of the equation came from the Tea Rose. The Tea Rose was a cross between the Bourbon Rose and a 'Chinese' hybrid known as Hume's Blush Scented Rose from the fact that it had been imported to England by Sir Abraham Hume in 1809. The Tea Rose possessed qualities lacking in the Hybrid Perpetuals, namely a peaked centre and a strong fragrant scent.

When these two strains, namely the Tea Rose and the Hybrid Perpetual were crossed, the modern Hybrid Tea Rose emerged to gain unsurpassed popularity in its particular field. Once again the French were first in the field with La France, a rose with silvery pink scented blooms which first appeared in 1867. But Britain was not far behind, and the Reverend Samuel Reynolds Hole, later Dean Hole, fox-hunter, bon-viveur and originally Vicar of Caunton, Nottinghamshire, and his fellow cleric, the Reverend Henry Honywood d'Ombrain helped to stage the first National Rose Show held at St James's Hall, Piccadilly, in 1858, and to form in 1876 the National Rose Society (now the Royal National Rose Society).

It will be seen nevertheless from this oversimplified account of one sector of the genus Rosa (we say nothing about Floribundas introduced in 1924, Climbers, Miniatures or Rambler roses) that hybridisation can be a lengthy, expensive, complicated and chancy business.

The first attempt at intentional hybridisation had taken place back in 1717 when Thomas Fairchild, testing out the theories of Dr Nehemiah Grew on plant structure and fertilisation, applied the pollen of a carnation to the stigma of a Sweet William. Fairchild's 'mule' had the structure of a Sweet William but larger double flowers in red. But, as the mule was infertile, little came of the experiment. Early in the following century, however, William Herbert, who rose to be Dean of Manchester, ignoring any strictures he might have received for interfering with the course of nature, became an enthusiastic hybridiser and regarded hybridisation as 'an endless source of interest and amusement'. From 1808 onwards, he devoted a considerable amount of his time to *Gladioli*, the *Ericas* and the *Amaryllidaceae*, about which he wrote a book. New hybrid delphiniums, lobelias and night-scented petunias sprouted copiously in the 1820s and 1830s and hybrid verbenas from Peru, Brazil and Uruguay in the 1840s.

Some of the most conspicuously successful hybrids were, like the Bourbon Rose, produced accidentally or at least unheralded. *Magnolia soulangiana*, one of the most popular of all the magnolias, appeared in 1826 by chance in the garden of M. Soulange-Boudin at Fromont near Paris, and was an accidental hybrid between two other species, the pure white *M. denudata* and the mulberry coloured *M. liliiflora*. *Caryopteris × clandonensis* occurred by chance in 1930 in the garden of Mr A. Simmonds at Clandon, near Guildford.

The old-fashioned garden hybrid pink, Mrs Sinkins, was raised in the workhouse by the Master of Slough's Poor Law Institution and was shown by the Royal Horticultural Society in 1880; the flower was incorporated in 1938 in the coat-of-arms of the Borough of Slough.

Sometimes new species from abroad helped. A new boost to the cultivation of the gladiolus came when S.F. Townsend, the Resident Engineer supervising the construction of the bridge over the Zambesi at Victoria Falls, sent home in 1902, four corms of *Gladiolus primulinus*, the small-flowered primrose and red species which flourished in the spray of the Falls and was prepared to do the same at Kew, Edinburgh and Cambridge. Hybrid gladioli with thin but strong stems, and hooded flowers with slashed petals, followed in a large range of colours.

Towards the end of the nineteenth century, another amateur, Sir Michael Foster, Professor of Physiology at Cambridge, took the trouble to get new species of the Bearded Iris from the Middle East which produced larger flowers than *Iris pallida* and *Iris variegata*, the two species then generally used for breeding. (*Iris germanica*, *I. florentina*, and *I. albicans*, are all sterile clones which have to be propagated by division, and are useless for hybridisation.)

Foster's work was carried on in the present century by W.R. Dykes, appointed Secretary of the Royal Horticultural Society in 1920, by Sir Arthur Hort, the Harrow School Housemaster and by George Yeld, master at St Peter's, York and first President of the Iris Society (now the British Iris Society) founded in 1924.

One of the most famous of all garden hybrids is a clematis, the large dark purple *Clematis × jackmanii* which appeared in Jackman's nursery in 1860 though it was not named till 1865.

But until comparatively late in the nineteenth century, many nurserymen and amateurs alike were pollinating with great enthusiasm but limited knowledge, learning little from their failures or their successes.

A more scientific approach was adopted by the Royal Horticultural Society whose researches into plant breeding were eventually linked to those of the Royal Society into the general questions of heredity and genetics. An international conference on hybridisation was held in London in July 1899, and papers read there drew attention for the first time in this country to the conclusions of Gregor Mendel, the Abbot of Brunn, whose observations on the varying characteristics shown by successive generations of peas of different sizes, though written more than thirty years earlier, had been largely disregarded. (Mendel himself died a disappointed man after experimenting with unsuitable plants which failed to support his theories.)

Moreover, even after it had been generally realised that the main structural characteristics of each plant recur in every germinating cell of that plant, scientists had yet to discover that, attached to the nucleus of each male or female cell were a number of elongated bodies known as chromosomes (because of the fact that they are most clearly seen when stained with chromatic dyes). These chromosomes determine the structural character of each plant. Most cells have at least two sets of chromosomes, one inherited from the father, the other from the mother plant. Thus in a single cell there might be two sets each of two chromosomes, and we can think of A and B as representing one set, inherited from the male parent and A′ and B′ as the other. A and A′ are similar and can be regarded as a pair. So can B and B′. But neither pair resembles the other. As the plant grows, each cell and each chromosome undergoes a process known as mitosis, splitting in two, and you then have two half-cells, each of which, in our example, would have four half-chromosomes. The half-cells and their half chromosomes then develop into two full-size cells each containing four full-size chromosomes, and with the same characteristics as before. The process is then repeated – with variations – until the plant reaches maturity.

But when mating time comes, and a male pollen cell has to fertilise a cell in the female ovule, a different kind of operation has to take place. For the male pollen cell has to join up with a female germ cell, and instead of one cell becoming two, two cells will become one. But if this merger were to take place between a male and a female cell, each having the characteristic number of chromosomes for that plant, in our example four, the fertilised cell would be a monster with eight chromosomes, twice as many as its parents possessed. And the cells of the next generation would have sixteen chromosomes. And so on ad infinitum.

To avoid such calamities a reduction process known as meiosis must take place, during which the number of chromosomes in the sex cells to be mated – both male and female – is halved.

At an early stage in this process each set of chromosomes within each sex cell forms a separate chain or necklace – two chains, each with two beads, in our example.

These two chains become attracted to each other and each chromosome unites with its pair in a 'matching up' process, A with A′, and B with B′, so that, instead of two chains, there is only one.

Then the chain and each element in it divide lengthwise and the two half chains twine round each other, breaking and re-joining in places, so that an exchange of material takes place between A and A′ and B and B′.

At the end of this process, known as 'Crossing Over', each 'bead' in the chain possesses an inheritance of both male and female elements.

Both the cell and the chain now divide in two so that we now have two half-cells each with two 'half-beads' or chromatids, to give them their proper name. Each half-cell will grow into a full-size cell, and each chromatid, now no longer linked in a chain, grows into a full-size chromosome.

Then, when fertilisation takes place between male and female cells, each having two chromosomes, the result is a fertilised cell, with four chromosomes, which, if all goes well, produces a seed capable of germinating, and so providing a new generation of plants. But where the two plants are hybrids there is no certainty that they will behave in the same way. Sometimes the reduction process fails in one hybrid because the pairs of chromosomes are not compatible, and in this case the germ cells of that plant will have twice their quota (eight in our example). If fertilisation then takes place with another hybrid with a normal count, the resulting ovule will have three sets of four chromosomes instead of two sets – and is known as a triploid. It in turn will not be fertile because the normal pair-to-pair matching process at the start of meiosis cannot take place.

In other cases, where two sets of chromosomes can be matched and paired off, the splitting up which should follow takes place irregularly or incompletely, and no seedling develops.

Earlier hybridists could not understand the reason for these mishaps, and even today it is not possible to avoid them altogether.

Another problem is that, attached to each chromosome, are chemically active, living and self-reproducing substances known as genes. They are too small to be seen, but their influence on such things as the colour of petals, leaf formation, and other features can be unmistakably detected. Some genes are effective only in combination with others and may react differently if the combination is varied. When two plants are crossed an exchange of genes also takes place. Some genes – perhaps because they are present in larger quantities – have a dominating influence over the next generation of plants. Other genes, present in smaller quantities, are recessive – and their influence is smaller – indeed may not normally be detectable at all in the first hybrid generation and, theoretically, may appear in only a small proportion of plants of the second generation. Plants of later generations will, on the law of averages, include some plants with no dominant and only recessive genes and these will, if crossed, breed true. A proportion of 'dominant' hybrid plants on the other hand can be expected to pass on a recessive streak to the next generation, thus failing to breed true, a fault which may have to be corrected by back-crossing.

Earlier hybridists, not realising this, threw away many potentially good plants of the first generation. They had also to contend with the fact that some plants had more than one recessive gene and would not breed true unless all were present. There was also some uncertainly as to which of two species in a proposed hybrid should be the male and which the female parent.

Faced with these obstacles, it was hardly surprising that many growers preferred to rely on selective breeding of varieties of established species for their new plants. Variations in the structure or appearance of an established species often occur accidentally, as for instance when a gene is misplaced during the 'crossing' operation during meiosis and, by breeding from these 'freaks', a new strain can be established. Apart from this, there will be variations in size of individual plants with some more vigorous than others.

The pansies and violas of today resulted originally from selective breeding of *Viola tricolor*, the wild flower known as Heartease. Lady Mary Bennet started collecting seedling plants in 1812 and had them planted in the figure of a heart. Her near neighbour, Lord Gambier at Iver, started a similar collection in the following year and asked his gardener, William Thompson – afterwards a successful nurseryman – to develop them.

Thompson's outstanding success, namely a flower with a dark patch in the middle (the mark then thought to distinguish pansies from violas and violettas) came accidentally from a plant cast out on to the rubbish heap. For many years pansies and violas were florists' flowers, cultivated for the show bench with strict regulations on ground colours and the shape and edging of the petals, but these limits were disregarded by Dutch and Belgian breeders and by the average gardener who looked for and eventually got, a more compact and erect plant sufficiently decorative to feature in many a cottage garden. Towards the end of the century, pansies, violas and violettas were artificially hybridised and in some hybrids even the rays which served in the original species to guide insects to the nectar, were bred out.

Shirley Poppies were developed around 1880 entirely by selective breeding from the original corn poppy by the Reverend William Wilks of Shirley, Surrey, who happened to notice one wild plant with flowers having a white edge. He marked the plant and collected the seed. Today Shirley Poppies are available in rose, crimson, salmon pink, scarlet and even orange.

The Sweet Pea was another species in which natural variations were relied on to produce new shapes and colours, at any rate during the first half of the century. In some ways, it was an ideal species for the nurseryman, since being an annual, it could be expected to yield seed during its first season and was popular enough to grow in large quantities on the chance of a a freak occurring. The Sweet Pea also has the additional virtue of being self-pollinating. That is, if you get a single flower of an unusual colour or shape, you can be almost sure that the seed you get from that plant will not have been cross-pollinated from another plant. This is not the case, for instance, with the primrose, which produces two different forms of flower, the pin-eyed with short stamens and a long style and the thrum-eyed with long stamens and a short style. As if to prevent in-breeding, no seed is produced unless pollen from a long stamen is transferred to a long style or vice versa. Henry Eckford's is probably the best-known name in the world of Sweet Peas. At Wem in Shropshire, he succeeded in increasing both the length of the stem and the number of blossoms on it – formerly two – to four. W.J. Unwin produced the first frilly sweet pea from his cottage garden.

George Russell, the York allotment holder who founded a dynasty of lupins from the perennial *Lupinus polyphyllus* and the annual *L. hartwegii* between the years 1911–37, relied on natural selection to provide improved plants but he profited also from random natural pollination of his different strains by insects. In that way, perhaps, there were fewer mis-matches.

There was, however, one man who believed that new species rather than selective breeding or hybridisation offered the best chances of development even in the case of such a well known genus as the narcissus. Peter Barr, born at Govan, Clydeside, in 1826, was the seventh of 12 children and, when he left school, it was to take a job as a draw-boy in the shed of a muslin-weaver. He joined the Glasgow nursery of James Thyne, and already at the age of 20 was in charge of the firm's seed department. After a struggle in the provinces, he set up his own business in London and specialised almost at once in bulbs, including tulips and lilies. But narcissi – both the daffodils with their trumpets and the narcissi proper without, were his first favourites. He had been able to buy the whole collection of a talented amateur, William Backhouse, a banker who had been breeding new hybrids since 1856. Barr followed this up by forming a syndicate of five partners to buy the collection of 24,000 bulbs belonging to another narcissus fanatic, Edward Leeds, a Manchester stockbroker.

But new species of narcissi were what interested Barr most, and it became his chief ambition to rediscover those described by famous gardeners of the past – including John Parkinson, many of which had since been lost. From his friend, Alfred Tait who lived at Oporto and bore the title of Baron de Sontellinho, Barr had learnt that the miniature daffodil, now officially listed as *Narcissus triandrus albus*, but more popularly known as the White Mosquito or, if you prefer it, Angel's Tears, was still to be found growing wild. So at the age of 61, he turned over the running of his business to his son and set off on his sentimental journey into the past. Apart from Angel's Tears, he was looking for the cyclamen-type narcissus with completely reflexed petals, as well as for *N. moschatus*, a miniature white daffodil which like Parkinson's 'early straw coloured Bastard daffodil' had not been seen in England for more than 250 years.

Barr spoke no foreign lingo – and his English was concealed behind a thick Glasgow accent which even his grandchildren found hard to penetrate, but he pursued his expeditions over the mountains of Spain and Portugal with great success, showing pictures to the peasants of the species that he wished to find, and when his shoes were burnt to a cinder in an effort to dry them, he carried on in wooden sabots. A photograph in Mea Allan's *Plants that Changed our Gardens* shows Barr looking somewhat farouche, bearded, and with wire-rimmed spectacles, surmounted by a Basque beret.

He was one of the last group of plant hunters to prospect for new species in Western Europe; but other stalwart explorers were still ready and eager to try their luck further afield.

15 *The Turn of the Century*

It was by a happy chance that the opening years of the new century coincided with the success of a British collector, who became renowned on both sides of the Atlantic for his achievements as well as for his modesty about them.

Ernest Henry Wilson, eventually nicknamed 'Chinese Wilson', was born in 1876 in Chipping Camden, one of the most attractive of Cotswold villages. After leaving school, he trained first at Hewitt's nursery in Solihull, south of Birmingham, and then at the Birmingham Botanical Garden in Edgbaston. There, after the day's work was over, he studied Botany at Birmingham's Technical College, and carried off the Queen's Prize awarded for botany by the Board of Education. Still under 20, he was snapped up by Kew, and made his mark there both as a lecturer and as a gardener. A year later he was thinking of joining the Royal College of Science as lecturer, but an unusual set of circumstances led him to become one of the world's best-known collectors, the discoverer of at least 1,000 new species.

It happened that Augustine Henry, a doctor from Ireland, was serving in the Chinese Imperial Maritime Customs Service, which, at that time, was operated by the British on behalf of the Emperor. Henry was originally stationed at Ichang in the province of Hupeh which, although more than 800 miles up the River Yangtze-Kiang, still ranked as a maritime port. Henry had made a detailed study of herbal drugs used by Chinese doctors, and studied botany in order to distinguish between the plants that provided them. Impressed by the number of unusual species around the famous river gorges and the neighbouring provinces which he was unable to identify from their local names, Henry got in touch with Kew and asked if they would like to see some. He became a part-time collector for Kew. Between 1881 and 1900 he sent back some 15,000 dried specimens, including more than 500 new species. Some of his consignments included bulbs and seeds as well as specimens. Repeatedly, however, he warned that hundreds of plants which were still to be found in Szechuan and Yunnan further south were in danger of becoming extinct through the ravages of Chinese woodcutters and charcoal burners.

Whole forests near the Chinese Vietnam border were disappearing. Kew, unaided, could do nothing to halt the destruction. Nor had they the resources to send a collector to bring home the plants to be cultivated in Britain.

So Henry sought help in the United States. He wrote to Charles Sargent, who was in charge of the Arnold Arboretum attached to Harvard University. Sargent was sufficiently interested to ask Henry to estimate the cost of a life-saving expedition, and after considering it, said he would find the money if Henry would lead the expedition. But Henry at 38 had suffered enough exile – he had already decided to settle at home and afterwards became a successful forester.

In the meantime, however, another lifeline had been rigged. While at Ichang, Henry had found a single specimen of the Handkerchief Tree originally discovered by Père David, and his description inspired (Sir) Harry Veitch, grandson of the founder of the firm, with the idea of sending out a collector whose principal task would be to collect Handkerchief Tree seed and bring it home. Young Ernest Wilson was picked for the job, and was given six months' training in the Veitch nurseries. There he learnt something of the plants they already grew and those they hoped to grow in the future. On his way to China, Wilson called in at the Arnold Arboretum. There he was given a crash course in the latest techniques used for plant collection and transport.

His instructions from Veitch were to go for the 'big one' i.e. the Handkerchief Tree and not to wander about spending money on searching for other plants. For Veitch had already sent Charles Maries to Ichang with only moderate success, and assumed that 'very probably almost all the worthwhile plants would have already been introduced to Europe'.

Unfortunately for Wilson, Henry had recently been promoted to Acting Chief Commissioner for Customs with the official status of Mandarin, and had been transferred to Szemao, in south-west Yunnan near the border with Burma, more than 1,500 miles away from where the Handkerchief Tree had been found. And he was shortly to leave China for good. Moreover, it was nearly 12 years since Henry had seen the tree. Nevertheless Wilson had to make sure of seeing Henry before he left China. He reached Szemao in October 1899 under the protection of an armed escort having crossed Indo-China to get there. While en route he had been imprisoned for several weeks as a spy, suffered bouts of fever, and barely escaped shipwreck in the notorious Red River.

Ernest Wilson, imprisoned as a spy during his voyage of rediscovery of the Handkerchief Tree in China

Henry raked his memory and prepared a sketch map of the area to be searched with as many landmarks as he could recall. Shortly before sailing for home, Wilson established himself in Ichang where he lived on a houseboat, unmolested despite the Boxer Rebellion promoted against foreigners by the Society of Patriotic and Harmonious Fists. From talks with local collectors, he was able to pin down the place where the tree should be growing, and set off on a ten-day march in time to reach it in April, when it would be in flower and therefore conspicuous. Alas! When he got there, he found that there was nothing to be seen. He was indeed on the right spot, but the tree had been cut down the previous year to form part of a house. And the nearest known *Davidia* would now be the one seen much earlier by David, in the city-state of Mupin hundreds of miles to the west.

Wilson, however, was undeterred, and was able to discover a whole grove of trees locally from which he secured not only seed but also photographs taken from a precarious perch on the four-inch branch of a neighbouring tree 200 feet from the ground. The first Handkerchief Tree flowered in England in 1911.

Even during his first year, Wilson did not take too literally Veitch's instructions not to wander about searching for new plants. From his first series of expeditions based on Ichang, he introduced 'live' many of the best plants which Henry had discovered and sent home as dried specimens; and he re-introduced others of which Henry had sent seed.

They included *Clematis montana rubens*, the starry pink early flowering species, and *Clematis armandii* with evergreen shiny leaves and fragrant waxy flowers; *Actinidia chinensis*, Wilson's Gooseberry, so called from the form of its fruit; two honeysuckles, *Lonicera pileata*, a small shrub useful as ground cover, and *L. tragophylla*, a showy and vigorous climber with dark green leaves, white below, and whorls of golden three-inch flowers at the end of its branches; a close relative of the honeysuckles, *Kolkwitzia amabilis*, the Beauty Bush, unusual in that family for its wide-mouthed yellow-throated pink flowers produced in early summer. He also introduced two *Ligularias* (with golden daisy-like flowers, and large strap-shaped leaves), *Rodgersia pinnata*, a saxifrage with reddish purple flowers;

Erica conspicua, from *Delineations of Exotick Plants* by Franz Bauer, 1796

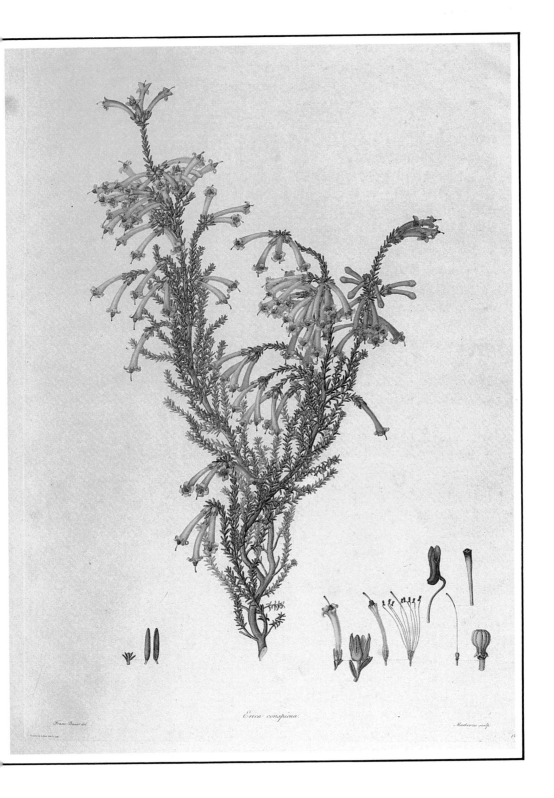

Erica conspicua.

Franc. Bauer del. | Mackenzie sculp.

12

Tab. XII.

J.D.H. del. Fitch lith.

Reeve, Benham, & Reeve, imp.

RHODODENDRON THOMSONI, Hook. fil.

Wilson's Gooseberry (*Actinidia chinensis*), a climber to 30 feet

Corylopsis veitchiana, the Winter Hazel bush with fragrant yellow flowers set off by red anthers; *Acer griseum*, a small maple with attractive peeling bark and horse-shoe 'keys' at seeding time; *Acer davidii* with green and white striped bark, green and yellow fruits, and red, yellow and purple leaves; *Schizophragma integrifolia*, the Climbing Hydrangea – and others too numerous to mention.

To get these, Wilson had to endure the undiminished horrors of Chinese travel: towns in which the main road ran along the top of a wall; where the east gate was closed by sewage; where there were inns haunted by mosquitoes, 'creeping things' and smells; inns where the business instinct was strong 'as I found when changing some silver,

Rhododendron thomsonii, lithograph by Walter Fitch from a drawing by Joseph Hooker. The plant was named after Dr Thomas Thomson, surgeon H.E.I.S., 'late of the Thibetan Mission'. Bush 6–12 feet high

and buying a goat' and rooms where there was vegetation under the bunks and in which dust descended from the ceiling each time the coolies sleeping in the loft above moved from one posture to another.

True, Wilson travelled in a sedan chair, but this was largely to build up prestige, and so secure good treatment for his party. He might have preferred to sleep in a tent but, as he put it, in a country where tents were unknown, and the people unusually

Beauty Bush (*Kolkwitzia amabilis*)

inquisitive about foreigners, it was better not to introduce innovations.

There was physical danger too. On one trip the whole company found themselves inching along a path consisting of some rotting planks tied to poles thrust into the side of a cliff.

There were places where Wilson's sedan chair had to be dismantled to get it across the rope bridge from one side of a river to the other. Wilson himself became an expert in using cable bridges which required him to hitch himself to a wooden saddle or traveller which slid at alarming speed down the suspension curve on the cable across the abyss and up the other side at least to a point where he could get his feet on the ground and haul himself up to the top. In such emergencies, Wilson's black spaniel dog normally travelled across blindfold and tied to a board.

Wilson got home to England for the first time in 1902, having sent home more than 35 cases of bulbs and roots and the seeds of 305 species.

He married that year, but set off again in 1903 – this time for another special flower wanted by Harry Veitch: *Meconopsis integrifolia*, the Lampshade Poppy with opulent yellow frilly blooms. It had already been discovered by Paul Guillaume Farges, (1844–1912) the botanist who collected for Vilmorin, the French nursery firm, but had since been lost. But Wilson, as was his habit, secured many more plants than he'd been asked to find. One of them was *Rheum alexandrae*, the rhubarb with yard-high spires decked with oval, plate-like bracts overlapping like fish-scales.

His best find on this trip was *Lilium regale*, a magnificent plant rising to six feet with fragrant white funnel-shaped flowers shaded on the back with purple, and coloured sulphur yellow and white within. It was not recognised as a separate species until 1912.

This second trip was an arduous one because the finest flowers, rhododendron shrubs and trees grew on mountains regarded as sacred and therefore not to be disturbed. Other plants, as Henry had discovered, were thought by the Chinese to have medicinal value and could not be collected.

But he unearthed, so to speak, a number of outstandingly beautiful roses, including *Rosa*

Lilium regale. This beautiful lily, which can grow to 6 feet in height, was another discovery of Wilson's

moyesii, with blood-red blooms, uncommonly few prickles and large carafe-shaped hips; *R. sinowilsoniii* (the official recognition of his specialist knowledge of China) and *R. willmottii* with pink flowers, straw-coloured thorns and orange hips.

It was on this trip that Wilson was in some peril while trying to bring his black spaniel dog down a wooden ladder hung on the vertical cliff face of Wa Shan mountain. The dog, whose nerves were less steady than Wilson's, had been blindfolded as usual, but struggled continuously and all but threw Wilson into the abyss below.

At the end of 1904, however, he was back in England and the following spring he took the kind of academic job he had originally fancied – as Botanical Assistant at the Imperial Institute.

Even then, however, there was little chance of settling down. His first trip had been to Ichang in central China. His next tour had taken him further west into Sikang Province which borders on Tibet. For his third tour, which was on behalf of the Arnold Arboretum and a few private subscribers, he returned to Sikang for there was now a growing demand for his *Lilium regale*.

On his third trip for which he left England in December 1906, he collected *Paeonia veitchii*, a magenta-flowered species; *Ribes laurifolium*, another of those Chinese plants, such as magnolia, wisteria, Witch Hazel, etc., which Wilson noted resembled those on the east coast of North America and confirmed his suspicions, since verified, that in the remote past Europe, Asia and north-east America had been joined together. This trip also yielded *Prunus mira*, the peach with the smooth stone; *Hydrangea sargentiana*, with deep green foliage and lilac flowers, and *Ceratostigma willmottianum*, a favourite border plant with funnel-shaped flowers of deepest blue which appear towards the end of August. His *Sorbaria arborea* is another popular small tree with pale green pinnate leaves and sprays of creamy flowers.

Above all, there was *Lonicera nitida*, the humble shrub with fragrant creamy flowers and violet semi-transparent bead-like fruits – greatly favoured for small boundary hedges.

Part of his success in the field was due to the fact that he seemed able to make friends with all sorts and conditions of men and to write with only the mildest reproach or disparagement of their failings. Thus of the Charungs, a tribe living along the Tachin river, he wrote 'Temporary marriages, so general in Tibet, are unknown among the Charungs. Nevertheless, the standard of morals in vogue among these people is a very low one. Hetairism precedes maternity. The pregnant damsel selects from among her lovers a husband who thus becomes the father of her child, her word in this matter being final. But divorce or legal separation after marriage are not practised'.

He had his own system for maintaining good relations with all comers. He made no attempt to speak Chinese or any other Asiatic language but dealt with all matters through an interpreter, thus laying to rest any suspicion that he could be a spy. He usually travelled with a large party of 25 or so, and found no difficulty in controlling them. Some he trained as collectors – and kept more or less permanent contact with them in between trips.

In this way he made sure that when seed was collected by his men it came from the right plant, even though there were no flowers to help identify it; he could be sure that they would select seed that was ripe enough to take, and that it would be methodically sorted and numbered, that it would be properly cleaned, dried and packed, and that it would therefore have the best possible chance of survival.

Wilson was also an extremely good judge of what

plants would be likely to do well in Europe and the United States, and he was careful to back up new introductions with the kind of information on soil, site, water requirements, which nurserymen and gardeners would need if the plants are to be successfully grown.

When he arrived home in 1909 after his third trip, Wilson was offered and accepted a post on the permanent staff of the Arnold Arboretum and, on behalf of the Arboretum, he made one more expedition to China – mainly for trees which, of course, were the Arboretum's overriding interest. He was also asked for *Lilium regale* for which there was still a tremendous demand on both sides of the Atlantic. And it was after arranging for 6–7,000 of these bulbs to be collected, packed, and shipped 'at silk rates' that Wilson came closest to losing his life.

He was returning from north Szechuan to his base at Cheng-tu, along a river gorge noted for the rockfalls which followed heavy rains. And there had been heavy rains. The dog was the first to scent, or perhaps catch the first sounds of, the avalanche of rocks and mud which suddenly descended on the party. An enormous boulder hurtled down just ahead like a shot across their bows. Wilson struggled out of his chair ready to take shelter under the cliff. A second boulder caught the chair and whirled it away into the river 300 feet below. A third broke Wilson's leg in two places below the knee leaving him lying helpless in the middle of the track. At that moment a mule convoy which had been travelling behind, overtook them. They could not be asked to turn back, or even to halt in such a dangerous spot. There was only one chance – to lay Wilson across the road and hope by a near-miracle that the mules – and there were forty of them – would step over him leaving him unharmed. He was in luck for not a single mule touched him though as Wilson afterwards wrote, the hoofs when seen from below looked extraordinarily large.

The heavy full-plate camera that Wilson always carried with him had been swept away with his chair and his hat, but the camera tripod remained, and of this they made a splint which they tied to the pole of a new chair on which Wilson spent the last three days of his journey to Cheng-tu. Not surprisingly, the leg became infected and it seemed as though the bones would never heal, and when he left China, Wilson was still on crutches. When he got back to Boston, the leg had to be broken and re-set, but in the end he was left with only a slight limp.

He did, however, make two further foreign trips in tour-de-luxe style, with his wife and daughter, Muriel (for whom he had already named a bamboo). In 1914 he went to Japan to secure the best of the Japanese cherries, and in 1917, he visited Japan and Korea which yielded *Viburnum carlesii*. In Japan he toured the island of Kyushu and discovered at Kurume a collection of 250 azaleas of a type then unknown to Europeans and Americans alike. The originals grew wild on the sacred mountain of Kirishima. This discovery was the achievement that gave him the greatest satisfaction of all.

In 1919 he was appointed Assistant Keeper of the Arboretum, with the agreeable task of fostering good relations between the Arboretum and other national and international botanical and horticultural institutes; in 1927 he succeeded Charles Sargent as Keeper. He had never taken out US citizenship, for he planned to live in Britain after retirement. But one autumn day when he was driving back with his wife from a visit to their now-married daughter, his car skidded on a drift of wet leaves and plunged 40 feet down an embankment. His wife was killed instantly and Wilson died before he reached hospital.

In almost every way Wilson was a contrast to the next explorer we shall now meet – namely Reginald

Farrer. Unlike Wilson, Farrer, born in 1880, came of a 'county' family. He was a cousin of Osbert Sitwell and his father had been High Sheriff of Yorkshire. And unlike Wilson, Farrer was self-assertive, outspoken and opinionated. He was born with a hare-lip and was obliged to undergo several only partially successful operations in an effort to correct it. Presumably because of this handicap he was not sent to school but was educated privately at home.

The Farrer estate was at Ingleborough in the West Riding, on limestone soil, and as early as three, Farrer had shown interest in the plants growing around the slopes of the Pennines and on that scarred and fissured Yorkshire tableland known as the Limestone Pavement. He even knew the whereabouts of the phantom Lady's Slipper Orchid, at that time still relatively common. At 14 he created his own natural rock garden with a moraine watered from below on the family estate, including in it some of the more suitable wild plants of the region such as the purple Opposite-Leaved Saxifrage and the Mountain Dryas.

He went on to Balliol College, Oxford, and after graduating, was sent on a world tour during which he was entranced by the mysticism of the Far East and was converted to Buddhism.

By this time, the surgeons' scars were hidden behind a luxurious moustache but some defects remained in his speech and his penetrating voice made them needlessly apparent. When on tour he was obliged to take with him a portable mincing machine to cope with the tougher sorts of Chinese chicken and goat. Never having had to submit to the rigorous discipline of a Victorian school, he remained uninhibited and unconventional both in manner and dress, but his love of flowers for their own sake and his determination to discover new species earned him widespread respect.

On his first trip to the Alps in 1903, he brought

back *Saxifraga cotyledon* (leaves in silvery green rosettes, reddish stalks and creamy starry flowers) and *Campanula bellardii* (later *cochlearifolia*), a re-introduced garden favourite which, with his flair for the right image, he compared to a fine cloud at night with the moon behind it.

His first book, *My Rock Garden*, was published in 1907 and he followed it up the next year with *Alpines and Bog Plants*. He returned to the Alps in 1910 and 1911, and searched the Dolomites in 1912 and the Alpes Maritimes in 1913. Ahead of his time, he showed himself to be a true conservationist by pleading with rock-gardeners not to disturb *Eritrichium nanum*, the silvery-leaved bright blue borage, which seldom survives transplantation from its mountain-top perch. These excursions led to two more books: *Among the Hills* and *The Dolomites*.

From 1910 to 1913 he joined forces with E.A. Bowles, whose garden at Myddelton House, Enfield, and the books he wrote about it, made him famous among the cognoscenti. His suggestion that seedlings are best watered by drops of water shaken from an old hairbrush is surely enough to endear him to almost any unpretentious amateur. Bowles was also responsible for Mrs Robb's Bonnet, the English nickname for *Euphorbia robbiae*. Mrs Mary Anne Robb of Liphook, Hants had brought back a plant of this lively spurge after attending a wedding in Istanbul in 1891, and had packed it in the hat box originally reserved for her best bonnet. Bowles made it a rule never to give up hope of raising a rare plant until he had tried it in three different sites, and his keenness, as Miles Hadfield recalls, was such as to lead him at the age of over 80 to wade into his water pond in a swimsuit to supervise the thinning of the lilies in it.

It was perhaps not surprising that Bowles should ask Farrer to write the introduction to his own book, *My Garden in Spring* published in 1914. The

Reginald Farrer (1880–1920)

sequel, however, was wildly improbable, for Farrer who detested artificiality of any kind, and particularly rock gardens of what he called the petrified porcupine variety, seized the opportunity to make a thinly veiled attack on the cherished four-and-a-half-acre rock garden, a scale model it was said of the Matterhorn, which Sir Frank Crisp, a wealthy company lawyer, had created over 10 years at Friar Park, Henley, using 7,000 tons of Yorkshire stone and 4,000 plants for the purpose. There was even a herd of cast iron chamois. Farrer saw this as an attempt 'to purchase the glories of the Alps at so much a yard with all the more contentment if the price be heavy' (Rousseau would have agreed). But Bowles was embarrassed, and Crisp who objected to Farrer's reference to 'tin chamoix' published an equally forceful counter-attack in a pamphlet, which was gleefully promoted by Farrer's critics. One of them, Ellen Willmott, went so far as to stand outside the entrance to the Chelsea Flower show, handing out copies from a bookie's satchel. No subsequent gardening scandal quite equalled this one.

But Farrer was not easily discouraged. In 1913 he had been shown a Primula with ash-grey leaves and bright mauve flowers, recently discovered in Kansu, north-west China, by William Purdom, a Kew-trained taciturn north countryman who had been collecting for Veitch near China's border with Mongolia.

Purdom had sent back several other winners, including *Buddleia alternifolia*, which produces lavender-coloured flowers arranged in rings round its arching branches; *Clematis macropetala*, known since 1692 but a welcome re-introduction; *Clematis tangutica* with grey-green leaves and deep yellow lantern-shaped flowers, first known here in 1898; and *Syringa microphylla*, a pink lilac.

Farrer was impressed by the possibility that

Kansu, the north China area towards the western part of the Great Wall, might have more to offer than Yunnan and Szechuan, the two southern states nearer to Tibet and India, which had already been extensively worked by collectors. Almost on the spur of the moment, he asked Purdom if he would like to come with him and organise an expedition to Kansu for no more than his expenses.

Farrer's enthusiasm was infectious, and Purdom accepted at once. The two set off soon afterwards by the Trans-Siberian railway for Peking, which they left in March 1914, carrying enough silver bullion to last them for two years. It did not buy them security once they had left Mien-chi-hsien, then the last railway station on the line from Peking to Kansu. A warlord known as the White Wolf, and his private army, were on the rampage. Local transport contractors were afraid to hire out their mules to Farrer, lest these animals be seen and commandeered by the invaders, and the Chinese mandarins were afraid to let Farrer's party travel in regions where they could not be protected, for, in the past, the disappearance of foreigners in China had led to protests and in some cases even retaliation, from the outside world.

Nevertheless persistence and patience allowed Farrer and Purdom to get their mules and to break away into the foothills of the mountains separating China from Mongolia. Good luck and speed of movement kept them out of trouble. They spent two summers prospecting and parted only in December 1915 when Purdom accepted a post in the Forestry Service of the Chinese government, while Farrer travelled home via Siberia, Finland, Sweden and Norway, evading enemy mines and submarines in the North Sea. News that war had broken out had reached them through missionaries only months after the event.

They reinforced a number of Purdom's earlier introductions including *Buddleia alternifolia*, *Clematis macropetala* and *C. tangutica*. But they also made many new discoveries – for example, *Viburnum fragrans*, since re-named *farreri* (though the ruler of the independent city state of Jo-ni, with whom Farrer had quarrelled, ate as many of the seeds as he could and threw away others in order to frustrate the collectors).

Other new species included *Leontopodium haplophylloides*, the Lemon-scented Edelweiss, established at home in 1915; *Potentilla fruticosa*; and *Omphalogramma farreri* – a mere six inches high but with deep purple flowers two inches long. Superficially it is more like a deep purple gloxinia or a giant pinguicula, though as Farrer rightly suspected, it is a relative of the primulas. *Meconopsis quintuplinervia*, the Harebell Poppy, a mere few inches high, with nodding purplish flowers was another Farrer discovery. In addition to several first-rate true alpine-type primulas, Farrer and Purdom sent back *Gaultheria trichophylla*, a minute 'alpine' with deep pink flowers appearing at the axils of the leaves, with blue berries to follow.

But Farrer's most treasured discovery was the gentian named after him. The flowers, light blue, four inches high, are striped on the outside with white and green. Farrer saw them in flower shortly before he was due to leave for home and could not wait to collect the seed, so he took the plants themselves in the hope that they would survive the rigours of the Trans-Siberian Railway. Not one did so. But later he found that, without him realising it, native collectors had already gathered the seeds for him and he had sent them mixed with those of another species to the Botanic Garden in Edinburgh, whose officials wrote to ask him for more details about this unidentified species.

The value of Farrer's introductions was greatly increased by his books about them. He was a talented travel-writer with an eye for arresting detail. But for him we might never have realised that the much maligned Chinese inns were for lower classes only, since the mandarins, when travelling, used special rest-houses; we might also have overlooked the fact that in Chinese inns, the mule is more important than the man – the charge for the night is based on the number of mules accommodated without regard to how many people were accompanying the beasts. But evidently the hotel trade was beginning to look up for, as Farrer reported, inns were now being established outside the walls of cities for travellers who arrived after the town gates had been shut for the night.

But for Farrer we might never have realised that the Chinese regarded milk as an unclean fluid taken from an animal or that, to a Tibetan, the copper jugs and cooking vats hanging on the walls of the kitchen – always the principal room of the house – were as valuable as a Romney oil painting to an Englishman. Farrer delighted in the Tibetan farms, each with its own chapel and flat roof for drying grain, with honey to come from hives made from tree-trunks sawn in two and hollowed out. He also had a gift for summing up the landscape in a few words. 'But oh, the utter dead immortal hopelessness of this pale, shallow land: so grisly and uniformly colourless in the grey ungenial brilliance' he writes of the plains to the north-west of Lanchow.

But it is when he came to write about flowers in his two Far East books *On the Eaves of the World* (1917), and *Rainbow Bridge* (1921), that his enthusiasm bubbled over and we are introduced to the blue *Lithospermum* 'imitating patches of fallen sky', *Buddleia alternifolia* 'sheer waterfalls of soft purple', gentians 'like green lights fallen from a rocket', *Oreocharis henryana* which 'sends up its little stems each of them unfurling a flight of two or three small thimbles of blossom in a subtly charming shade of bronzy rose, with suffusions of pink and cream' and 'solitary flowered Delphiniums with huge blossoms of richest Czar-violet, with black-tipped white eye, and a furry whisker of snow and gold to the purple lip'.

After the Kaiser's war was over, Farrer made one more journey to the Far East, arranged, after his fashion, in five minutes after a London tea-party. This time he went to Upper Burma with Euan Cox, who afterwards wrote an erudite book describing *Farrer's Last Journey*. Up country they foraged along many a mountain stream (with Farrer, using the field glasses, usually in a hurry to reach the opposite bank having spied something there that he thought might turn out to be promising). Some beautiful plants were found, but few were prepared to flourish away from Burma's moisture-laden climate. Cox had to return home at the year's end but Farrer decided to stay on and search along the Sino-Burmese frontier north of Myitkina. There he was in a land without game, or cultivated fields – where even the peasants, and there were few of them; starved. He had to endure six months of solid rain with intermittent fog, with only a leaky roof above for shelter. 'Here I sit in a poky little dark sad bungalow,' he wrote to Cox, 'I wonder if I shall emerge a saint or a philosopher or a gibbering lunatic.'

In October 1920, just as he was preparing to collect the bulk of the seed from the new plants he had discovered, he fell ill. His chief bearer made a four-day journey to Konglu and back in an effort to get medical aid but Farrer was soon beyond medical help and died, only 40 years old, on 17 October, probably from pneumonia.

His men prepared a coffin for him and carried back his body; they also brought away with them those possessions of his that they thought the most valuable – his tent, stores and equipment. Some seeds had already been sent home – *Rhododendron caloxanthum* with leafy shoots of a startling blue and canary yellow flowers opening from flower buds of apricot orange and vermilion; R. *tephropeplum* with bell-shaped pink blooms; *Nomocharis farreri* – a lily with tulip-shaped flowers spotted within, one *Primula sonchifolia*, with blue flowers and a mealy calyx.

But other seeds and specimens still being dried together with his records were never recovered.

Meanwhile another British – or more particularly Scottish – collector, whose expeditions in the Far East began before Farrer's and outlasted them, had been at work. George Forrest, born in 1873 in Falkirk, was something of a rolling stone. He worked first as shop assistant to a local pharmaceutical chemist. There he picked up some knowledge of drugs, and was sufficiently interested in the plants from which they were derived, to assemble his own herbarium of dried specimens. Then he went abroad to try his luck in Australia and South Africa without, however, greatly bettering himself. He returned to England in 1902 and accepted a post in the Edinburgh Botanical Garden with responsibility for looking after the herbarium. Two years later he was recommended by his employers to Arthur K. Bulley, a naturalist with the resources of a Liverpool cotton-broking firm behind him, and a desire to acclimatise foreign plants in his garden at Mickwell Brow, Neston, Cheshire, overlooking the Sands of Dee.

Bulley had originally relied for his plants on the good nature of missionaries, but eventually decided to send his own collector to western China to the area where four of the largest rivers of Asia, the Irrawaddy, the Salween, the Yangtze-Kiang and the Mekong flow through different gorges with only 100 miles between them.

It will be remembered that Farrer rejected this area because he believed it had already been largely worked out. It suited Forrest, however, and between 1904 and 1932, he made at least seven

George Forrest (1873–1932) and his dog

productive trips. But his first adventure would have been enough to put most men off for good.

While Forrest and his party of seventeen were staying as guests of Père Dubernard at the mission at Tseku, word came that a Tibetan force was on its way with orders to kill all foreigners – not merely the Chinese whom they had been fighting for years, but all foreigners, including Christians.

The Chinese authorities could offer no protection and the Tibetans carried two-edged swords, poison arrows, and were aided by outsize Tibetan mastiffs. The missionaries decided to abandon the mission and fly for their lives. But while one group of Tibetans harried the missionaries in the rear, a second advance group went ahead to cut off their retreat. Of their party of 80, 65 were killed – some quickly, some tortured to death. Forrest and one servant were the only members of his group of 18 to escape.

He did so by rolling 200 feet down a steep hillside when out of sight of both Tibetan gangs. For eight days he hid by day, fleeing by moonlight along the banks of the Mekong which was then in flood. He was almost without food. He had to take off his boots and bury them lest his tracks should betray him. His feet and hands were lacerated with thorns and his body caked with mud. Eventually the headman of a village, from whom he had seriously thought of demanding food at gun point, turned out to be friendly, and hid him at considerable risk to himself. He passed him on to another headman who guided him over a steep mountain range and through rhododendron thickets to safety.

He was not, however, unscathed, for on his way towards a village he trod on one of the sharpened wooden stakes with which the peasants protect their crops from raiders. It went through his foot and projected two inches above it.

When, at last, he reached the city of Talifu at the

end of some three weeks' foot-march, he had lost everything – photographs, dried specimens of 2,000 different plants and seeds of more than 80 different species. He had to borrow clothes from Mr G. Litton, the British Consul at Tengyueh who was to become a life-long friend.

In the seven expeditions that followed in 1910–11, 1912–14, 1917, 1918, 1921, 1924–5 and 1930–32, Forrest more than recovered the lost ground. He learned to speak Chinese, and got on extremely well with officials and farmers alike. All his expeditions were directed to the same area, that is in the upper reaches of the Mekong, Salween and Yangtze rivers near the Sino-Burmese border. To recount them in detail would be to weary the most patient reader. His introductions, too, can be more conveniently summarised under the types of plant in which he specialised rather than journey by journey. I say 'introductions' rather than 'discoveries' because some of his best species had already been found by Delavay in the 1880s and sent to Paris where, however, the seeds languished unplanted.

Among these were *Syringa yunnanensis*, *Trollius yunnanensis, Spiraea yunnanensis, Nomocharis pardanthina* and the dwarf blue *Meconopsis delavayi*. Primulas included *P. spicata*, an azure blue species; *P. serratifolia*, with deep orange flowers; *P. vialii*, more like a deep purplish blue Red Hot Poker than a primula; and *Primula malacoides*, with pale green foliage, ribbed and downy, and pendant lilac flowers – an outstanding success as a pot plant.

New Primulas owing nothing to Delavay include *P. aurantiaca* – coppery gold; *P. beesiana*, variously described as deep rose or reddish purple; *P. bulleyana*, another orange species; and *P. helodoxa* which sometimes grows four feet high and bears golden yellow flowers in whorls.

Forrest was particularly fortunate with rhododendrons. His best known successes were R. *im-*

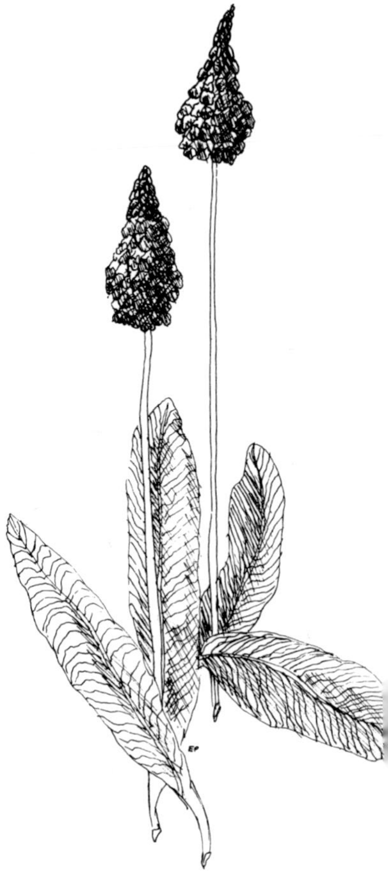

Primuli vialii, a Forrest re-discovery

peditum, a small shrub with pale mauve to light blue flowers; R. *radicans*, one of the smallest rhododendrons with single purple funnel-shaped blossoms at the end of the stalks; R. *forrestii*, another miniature species with bell-shaped crimson flowers; R. *haematodes*, a small shrub with brilliant red flowers; R. *hippophaeoides*, a medium shrub with bluish flowers and grey-green leaves rather like those of Sea Buckthorn; and R. *griersonianum*, a large shrub with geranium-scarlet blooms.

Forrest's *Camellia saluenensis*, with white or pinkish flowers and conspicuous orange anthers introduced in 1924, has led to many popular hybrids and we also owe him another winner without which many a garden would be the poorer – *Pieris forrestii*, as notable for its waxy bell-shaped flowers as for its brilliant red leaf shoots. His *Gentiana sino-ornata* is probably the species most often seen in gardens. His more unusual introductions included *Roscoea humeana*, with orchid-like flowers, and one petal standing up like a shoe-horn; and *Arisaema candidissimum*, like a Cuckoo-Pint with the hood veined green, and pointed trifoliate leaves.

With Forrest each expedition was to be his last, and five years went by after his 1925 sortie before he set out once more. It was to be a final clearing-up operation, and indeed it netted Forrest some 300 lbs weight of seed from between 400 and 500 species. There were many old favourites but some new plants as well among them: *Jasminum polyanthum* – a pinkish fragrant species which, though somewhat tender, is still cultivated in cool greenhouses.

In one of his last letters, Forrest wrote, 'If all goes well I shall have made a rather glorious and satisfactory finish to all my past years of labour'.

Early in the New Year of 1932, he was out shooting near his base camp at Tengyueh when he suddenly felt faint, cried out for help and fell dying to the ground. He was buried in a coffin draped with a Union Jack and a wreath of white roses from his Chinese servant at Tengyueh in a grave next to that of the consul, G. Litton, who had been his friend for nearly 30 years.

We are now well on into the twentieth century, but one other explorer, born in the Victorian era, remains to be mentioned here – Francis (Frank) Kingdon-Ward, originally spelt without a hyphen. Though he was the son of a Professor of Botany at Cambridge, Kingdon-Ward was as much if not more interested in exploration as in botany. For him it was as intriguing to discover the course of an uncharted river as it was to examine the plants growing along its banks, and he took greater pride in the awards he received from the Royal Geographical Society than in his most valuable plant introductions.

Except during the First World War when he served in the Indian Army as an Instructor on survival in mountain and jungle warfare, he was continuously exploring and his first botanical expedition was made for Arthur Bulley. Most of his collecting took place in south China in Yunnan and Sikang, the neighbouring province immediately to the north on the eastern borders of Tibet and Assam, and in Sikkim.

He believed in simplifying the problems of management by travelling light, and in consequence collected only modest quantities but he was a reliable and well-informed botanist and an experienced seed collector.

One of his most successful finds, discovered in 1913, was the yellow-flowered rhododendron, *R. wardii.* Two others came during his explorations of Sikkim and Tibet in 1924–5. The first was *Primula florindae*, the Giant Cowslip which grows up to six feet tall and produces fragrant pale yellow bell-shaped flowers. It was named after his first wife. The other was *Meconopsis betonicifolia.* This, as we have

Frank Kingdon-Ward
(1885–1958)

seen, had been discovered by Delavay but the credit for establishing it undoubtedly belongs to Kingdon-Ward.

On the same trip he found *Lilium mackliniae*, named after his second wife who went with him on five of his expeditions; appropriately it was a hardy species, with large purple tulip flowers and pointed petals, white within. He was also responsible for *Rhododendron permakoense*, a small evergreen species with mauve flowers; and *R. leucapsis*, another miniature with white flowers. His *Berberis hookeri* is still in general cultivation.

Kingdon-Ward was a prolific writer and produced at least ten travel books. He used to say that the thought of his next book helped him to overcome the feelings of loneliness and boredom which must attack all plant hunters at times.

Among his titles were *The Land of the Blue Poppy*, *Burma's Icy Mountains*, *In Farthest Burma*, *Plant-Hunter's Paradise* (also based on Burma); *Plant Hunting in the Wilds* (Tibet), *Mystery Rivers of Tibet* and *Assam Adventure* dedicated 'To my daughter Pleione'. His last expedition in 1956 was to Ceylon.

In 1958 he was in London in the midst of planning a new plant-hunting expedition when he died, suddenly, at the age of 73.

16 *A Profusion of Orchids*

Linnaeus, in his *Genera Plantarum* of 1753, listed eight genera of orchids and 69 species. Today there are – perhaps – 800 genera and 35,000 species of orchids – excluding hybrids. Orchid hunters have sought new plants in Venezuela, Colombia, Peru, Ecuador, Guatemala, Panama, Mexico, Honduras, Costa Rica, in Hawaii and the Philippines, in India and Assam, in Nepal, Bhutan, Sikkim, in Java, New Guinea and Borneo, in Madagascar, Sierra Leone and the Cape.

They seem to grow almost everywhere – in the cloud forests of Burma and Brazil, in marshes by the sea, on trees, on desert cacti – even underground, and in the case of *Calypso bulbosa*, coloured rose and brown with a yellow crest, at 68 degrees north, inside the Arctic Circle.

The Vanilla orchid was formerly singled out as being the only 'useful' member of the orchid family since it was the source of a popular flavouring. But since this is now produced synthetically, orchids now have to rely on beauty alone to earn them a living . . . a beauty which renders some of them as valuable as the finest porcelain.

And what could be more delicate than *Cymbidium ensifolium* with its fragrant greenish yellow flowers, so revered by the Chinese, or more startling than *Bulbophyllum barbigerum*, the fringed lip of which moves as if to utter an old man's blessing at the slightest zephyr . . . or more welcome than *Pleione pogonioides*, the Himalayan Crocus, as it emerges from its snowy blanket . . . or more attractive than *Vanda caerulea* . . . more intricate than the Venezuelan *Corianthes macanthra*, the Bucket Orchid with its advanced hydraulic system, or more appealing than Panama's *Peristeria elata*, the Dove Orchid perhaps five feet tall; or more bizarre than the *Catasetum barbatum* with its exaggerated whiskers, more arresting than the sobralias, reed-like and six foot or more in height? Orchids go to extremes. The flowers of *Pleurothallus* are a mere 2 mm in diameter; those of *Brassia* can be 90 times as large.

But even with all their good looks and arresting presence, the orchids often have a hard time of it, for their flower structure does not allow them to offer a meal of pollen to hungry insects and some orchids therefore can thrive only by growing in company with other plants with richer pollen that attracts insects to the neighbourhood. Other orchids go so far as to offer a substance which looks like pollen but turns out to be a floury imitation.

The degree to which orchids rely on mimicry for survival intrigues even the casual observer. For

Blue Vanda Orchid (*Vanda caerulea*), a native of northern India and Burma, its pale blue flowers can be 5 inches across

example, one of our own wild orchids, *Ophrys insectifera*, the Fly Orchid, carries flowers which so closely resemble the female of *Argogorytes mystaceus*, a small burrowing wasp, and its cousin the rarer *Argogorytes fargeii* that the male wasp endeavours to mate with the flower and thus transfers pollen from one plant to another. The deception is aided by the fact that the male wasp emerges a few days earlier than the female and the orchid flower tends to open just during that critical period when the male has no natural mate.

Many other instances of mimicry in orchids could be cited, and at first sight it might seem that such close resemblances could never have developed accidentally. But scientists identify mimicry as occurring whenever identical signals are sent by two different organisms – one the model, the other the mimic – to a common receiver which reacts to both signals as if they were equally advantangeous to it. They emphasise that it is the receiver and not the sender that is the more active partner in this kind of relationship, and in the case we have been considering it is not the flower that takes the initiative but the receiver of the message, in this case the self-deluding insect, which allows only those plants that stimulate its imagination to become fertilised.

In the early stages of its development, mimicry is of a fortuitous and tentative nature as for instance in the case of one caterpillar which looks more like a twig than the next and thereby escapes being eaten by a bird. Then, since survival depends on illusion, the members of each surviving generation of that species resemble more closely the twigs surrounding them but without any conscious effort on their part. And so, equally, with orchids.

Understandably, with so many species on the books, it has not been easy to sort orchids into logical and orderly groups. In most orchids the male and female organs are fused into a single column with only one anther distinguishable at the top. This provided a starting point for the early classifiers who found it possible to hive off the exceptions: *Cypripediums* (Lady's Slipper Orchids) which have two anthers and *Apostasieae* which have three from the other Tribes (the official botanical term) which had only one. But this was only a first step. New criteria were needed. The pollen sacs and how and where they were attached to the column were next analysed, and then the consistency of the pollen – whether it was waxy, powdery or granular. There

Siberian Lady's Slipper Orchid (*Cypripedium sibiricum*)

were also differences to be seen in the structure of the glands in the stigma.

Then there was the nature of the plant itself: whether its roots were in the ground or whether it was one of the epiphytic orchids which are attached to trees but whose roots are free standing and draw nourishment from the air, the rainwater and loose decaying vegetable matter. Finally there is the manner of growth. Some orchids form a new stem each year but in others the new growth takes place on the existing stem – a fundamental distinction.

No remains of fossilised orchids appear to have been discovered and it can only be assumed that the first of the family came into existence some time in the Tertiary Age, that is between 65 and say 2 million years ago. But it can be established that some of them are more 'advanced' than others.

Thus it is not too difficult to compare the structure of a genus such as *Cephalanthera* (some species of which grow wild in Britain) with plants of a similar nature such as Lilies. And other orchids such as *Oncidiums* can be compared with the *Cephalantheras*, but, in the case of the *Oncidium* specialisation has developed beyond the point where they can be compared directly with non-orchid species. Often similar refinements occurred independently in parallel in different parts of the orchid world.

By their behaviour the orchids themselves give some help to the botanist who wishes to classify them. Those that hybridise most easily are the most closely related.

As we have seen, the first tropical orchid to flower here was the pinkish flowered *Bletia verecunda*, a tuber of which was detached from a dried specimen brought back from the West Indies in 1731. More than 40 years later, Dr John Fothergill secured two orchid tubers from China, one of which, *Phaius grandiflorus*, flowered in the greenhouse of his niece. Still in the eighteenth century, *Epidendrum coc-*

bleatum, was being grown at Kew and in the early years of the nineteenth century Conrad Loddiges found it possible to specialise in orchid culture.

But most early orchid fanciers were handicapped by their ignorance of the requirements of the different species they were trying to cultivate – fresh air, moisture, plenty of light, and the right temperature – each in its appropriate season. The epiphytes which Sloane had discovered a century earlier were still considered in 1817 to be parasitic. Orchid tubers were plunged into hot beds filled with tanner's bark, a practice which led Sir Joseph Hooker to declare that England should be called the graveyard of tropical orchids. No orchids were grown here from seed until about the middle of the nineteenth century.

But enough survived to encourage growers to persevere. Some of the best of the early consignments came from Dr Roxburgh in Calcutta who provided *Vandas*, *Aerides* and *Dendrobiums*. There was a sensation in 1818. William Swainson, a visitor to Brazil, sent off a consignment of tropical treasures to Mr William Cattley of Barnet, packing them round with some unnamed plants bearing pseudobulbs but no flowers which would help to identify them.

Cattley cultivated these in his heated greenhouse in Suffolk and they flowered the same autumn – orchids with blooms five inches across with mauve petals and a trumpet-like lip with frilled edges, a purple base and a yellow throat. It was by far the most beautiful orchid then known and – more sensational – no more of its kind were found for the next 70 years.

Orchid collecting began to become fashionable in the early 1830s when the bachelor Duke of Devonshire, inspired by the sight of *Oncidium papilio* at an orchid show, started his collection at Chatsworth. Earl Fitzwilliam at Wentworth Woodhouse was another 'aristo' who set an example and his family name is commemorated in the flamboyant genus of orchids named *Miltonia*. Hugh Cuming descended on the Philippines in the 1830s and was the first to ship home live orchids successfully from there; four species are named after him. From then on until the end of the century, there was a gold rush of orchid prospectors.

Karl Theodor Hartweg spent nearly seven years in Mexico collecting for the Horticultural Society and achieved a triumph with *Epidendrum vitellinum*, the orange-red Dragon's Mouth Orchid which can be grown in a cool greenhouse. He found it 9,000 feet above sea level growing on the Totontepeque mountain ridge. One of his most valuable finds came after he had noticed an unusually fine bloom in the hat of a Quichole Indian; he followed the trail into the interior and found the original plant and half a dozen other new species.

Rosy-lipped Cattleya (*Cattleya labiata*), a native of Brazil, it grows on the trunks of trees. Its magnificent flowers measure 7 inches across

Thomas Lobb signed a three-year contract in 1843 to collect orchids in the Malaysia and Java area and sent home *Phalaenopsis amabilis*, the Moth Orchid with its broad white petals, and *Vanda tricolor*, the cowslip-scented orchid with cream or pale mauve petals spotted with brown and a rosy pink lip, and its variety *suavis* which is white, spotted with purple on the petals and lip. (By this time the competition was getting fierce, and Lobb took elaborate precautions to misinform rivals by sending misleading telegrams about his movements – no wonder even Alice M. Coats found him hard to follow – and sticking false labels of origin on his shipments.) Sir Hugh Low was also at work in the Borneo area on behalf of the family firm of Stuart Low & Co. of Clapton.

Nor did the craze for orchids die out as had happened with the tulip. The orchid nursery of Henry Sander, whose family firm became the best-known name in orchid growing, was set up in 1872. Its list of orchid hybrids, published in 1906, became the basis for the present *Register of Orchid Hybrids*, the management of which was taken over in 1961 by the Royal Horticultural Society.

In the early 1890s, Sanders had as many as 20 collectors scattered over South America, India, Africa and the Far East. Of these Benedict Roezl with an iron hook for a left hand (which he had lost while operating a machine of his own invention for processing hemp fibre) was probably the best known. Roezl who prospected in California and Patagonia as well as in Mexico, collected alarmingly large numbers of *Masdevillia* and *Miltonia* orchids – 100,000 tubers it is said from the volcano of Colima in south-west Mexico; and Albert Millican while collecting *Odontoglossums* and *Miltonia vexillaria* was equally ruthless, cutting down trees in order to procure his plants. One of his party was shot dead by a poisoned arrow from an Indian marksman.

Another famous orchid firm was founded in 1880 at Heaton, near Bradford, when Joseph Charlesworth left the wool business to do so. In 1906, a Charlesworth branch was opened in Haywards Heath and proved so successful that all the stock was moved there two years later.

Yet despite the profusion of collectors and of new discoveries – there remained at least two other lost species apart from *Cattleya labiata*. One of these was *Cypripedium curtisii*, a purple and white spotted Slipper Orchid, a very limited quantity of which had been collected by Charles Curtis for Veitch in Sumatra in 1883. No 'repeats' could be found and there was some uncertainty as to just where the originals had been found. It was not until the turn of the century that a Swedish collector named Ericsson sought refuge in a hut in Sumatra and saw a sketch of an orchid with the inscription 'C.C.'s contribution to the adornment of the house'. It was the missing orchid, and Ericsson was inspired to make an exhaustive search in the neighbourhood, though it was three weeks before he found any specimens.

Cypripedium fairieanum, coloured purple, violet, yellow and brown, with fringed petals, was lost for even longer – from 1855 to 1904.

James Bateman was one of the private patrons who stayed at home yet did much to encourage orchid hunting. He had been an orchid enthusiast from an early age and, while still at Magdalen College, Oxford, was obliged to write out half the Book of Psalms for having cut a tutorial in order to admire an orchid, *Renanthera coccinea*, which he had seen with his friend Thomas Fairbairn in the Oxford nursery.

Once freed of such handicaps, he sent his own collector to Demerara, and in 1831, engaged Mr G. Ure Skinner, a partner in the merchant trading firm of Klee, Skinner and Company of Guatemala, to procure specimens for him.

Among many splendid orchids, Skinner secured *Lycaste virginalis* (syn. *skinnerii*) with fragrant white wax-like petals, flushed with pink. It was afterwards chosen as the national emblem of Guatemala – the kind of honour which could have amounted to a death sentence if it had come to be worn in every patriot's buttonhole. But it has survived and is still cultivated.

Bateman produced a magnificent treatise, *The Orchidaceae of Mexico and Guatemala*. It contained 40 full folio size plates illustrated by three women artists – a Miss Drake, a Mrs Withers and Lady Grey of Groby. Each plate, it was said, cost £200 to produce and the complete book weighed 38 lbs – making it the outsize heavyweight of most libraries. The print was limited to 125 copies.

The hybridisation which has added greatly to the delight – and perplexities – of orchid fanciers began in the nineteenth century when John Dominy, working for the Veitch nursery, crossed *Calanthe masuca* with the pollen of *C. furcata* to give *Calanthe × dominii*. The cross pollination was performed in 1853, the seed collected in 1854, and the new plant, having the distinctive features of both parents, flowered in 1856.

'You will drive all botanists mad' commented Dr John Lindley of the Horticultural Society when he saw the result. But Dominy produced many other orchid hybrids and was followed at Veitch's by another outstanding hybridist, John Seden.

In the end it was Lindley who brought law and order into the world of orchids. As a young man of 23, he had been appointed Assistant Secretary to the Chiswick Garden of the Horticultural Society, and four years later was given additional responsibilities as Assistant Secretary to the Society itself. In 1829 and at the age of 30, Lindley was elected a Fellow of the Royal Society and appointed to be the first Professor of Botany in the University of London.

Four years later he organised the Society's first show under canvas at Chiswick. In 1841, the year in which he founded the *Gardener's Chronicle*, he was promoted to the post of Vice-Secretary and from 1858 Honorary Secretary.

Between 1830 and 1840, he issued his *Genera and Species of Orchidaceous Plants* published in instalments. It contained notes on all the 1980 species known at that time, and was followed up by a more detailed work, *Folia Orchidacea*, which although not completed, covered most of the more 'difficult' genera.

His *Sertum Orchidaceum* with finely coloured plates from Franz Bauer issued likewise in instalments, was completed in 1838.

It was unfortunate perhaps that in 1855 during Lindley's term of office, the Society was forced to raise money by selling off its own orchid collection. Its *Phalaenopsis amabilis*, said to be the finest specimen ever seen, went for £68.5*s*. *Dendrobium speciosum*, four-and-a-half feet in diameter and with 124 pseudo-bulbs went for £10. *Laelia* (now *Schomburgkia*) *superbiens*, 17 feet in circumference and still attached to the wood on which it had been found in Guatemala, went for £36.15*s*.

But the Society's reputation in this particular sector was more than restored by Sir Trevor Lawrence who became its President in 1885. Himself a noted collector, he organised a significant conference on Orchid Nomenclature which did much to reconcile the names the botanists proposed to orchids with those the average gardener was prepared to accept.

Orchid auctions were a feature of the late nineteenth and early twentieth century, the best known sales being held at Protheroe & Morris's premises reached through a narrow entrance near the Clock in Cheapside.

H. Rider Haggard, author of *King Solomon's Mines*,

who hoisted the Union Jack in Pretoria when Britain seized the Transvaal in 1877, was an orchid fancier and in his work *A Gardener's Year* published in 1904, he tells us of an auction he went to in June, 'a dear sale' at which 'a plant announced as "Odontoglossum crispum Raymond Crawshay, fine plant, two bulbs, one new growth" being one, I believe of the blotched varieties although I did not see the flower, fetched the trifling sum of two hundred and fifty guineas, whilst another Odontoglossum sold, I think, for one hundred and eighty guineas'.

It was the kind of sale attended no doubt by head gardeners from orchid fanciers, such as Lionel de Rothschild at Exbury and Lord Rothschild at Tring, Baron Schröder and Sir Jeremiah Colman, that gave orchids a bad name among amateurs who could afford only a few shillings for a bulb.

But more recent developments have raised hopes that 'orchids for the million' will no longer remain just a book title. Progress however has been slow. The first step forward came with the discovery in the 1840s that certain fungi described as *mycorrhiza*, from the Greek words for mushroom and root, are closely associated with the orchid roots. They have been detected in all species of orchids. But until the beginning of the twentieth century, all attempts to separate them from the orchid, or to discover what function they performed, failed. Then a young French botanist, Noel Bernard, learned how to extract and isolate the *mycorrhiza* and discovered that orchid seeds, the despair of nurserymen because so few germinated, would more readily spring to life if placed in a solution of starch containing *mycorrhiza*. Without *mycorrhiza* they remained inert. The importance of this discovery can be gauged by the fact that a single orchid is capable of producing two million seeds. Bernard's findings were published in various journals between 1904 and 1909 but were largely disregarded by the nurserymen who should have profited most from them.

Nevertheless Professor Hans Burgeff of Würzburg in Germany was able not only to confirm Bernard's experiments but to provide commercial orchid growers with standard solutions for seed germination.

The next problem, naturally, was to find out what it was that made germination possible only if *mycorrhiza* were present. The reason was to be sought in the fact that the orchid seed, unlike those of most other plants, is not provided with the nutritive tissue known as endosperm which surrounds the embryo in the seed of a flowering plant and provides it with a reserve of food until it can absorb nourishment through its roots and leaves.

From birth onwards, most wild orchids absorb nourishment in a pre-digested form provided by the *mycorrhiza*, which explained why in the experiments with starch solution, the orchid seeds germinated only if *mycorrhiza* were present.

Then in tests carried out between 1917 and 1922, an American scientist, Lewis Knudson, discovered that it was really sugar that orchid seeds needed to ensure germination and the value of the *mycorrhiza* to the orchid was its ability to convert starch (which was useless to the orchid) into sugar vital to its well-being. Knudson found that it was possible to induce most orchid seeds to germinate and grow by providing them with a sugar solution free from *mycorrhiza*. It amounted to a revolution in orchid growing since it was far easier to provide a solution of sugar for growing orchid seeds than a culture of *mycorrhiza*.

More recently, an even more revolutionary advance in orchid growing has been achieved by cultivating small pieces of tissue cut from the meristem – the growth section of the corm in the very early stage before the root and the leaf are distinguishable. Each cutting, if cultivated in nutrient solution, can develop into a fully grown plant.

The break-through was once again due to the efforts of a Frenchman, Dr Georges Morel, Director of the French National Institute of Agricultural Research at Versailles, who discovered in 1956 that meristem culture, which had already proved successful with strawberries, lilies, narcissus, carnations, chrysanthemums, dahlias and other species, could be applied to orchids. Though the results of his researches were published in the *American Orchid Society Bulletin* of July 1960, they remained unexploited until after he had pointed out four years later that if a protocorm were cut into four and each produced four protocorms in a month, it would be possible to produce more than four million of them within a year. And each would reproduce the exact image of the original plant (which is more than can be guaranteed in the case of many hybrid seedlings).

Skill and patience beyond that possessed by most amateurs is needed, but the way is now open to the professionals to provide the best and most dependable strains at a speed undreamt of in the past. We can only hope that the new trend will not lead towards a few standard 'best sellers' at the expense of the variety which is such an essential element in the fascination exerted by the orchid family.

17 *The Future Origins of Garden Plants*

Where shall we turn in future for new plants?

Travel has become easier, communications swifter, and precious seeds with a short life-span can now be kept alive in a deep freezer till it is possible to plant them. But the political difficulties of the kind that confronted earlier explorers such as Kaempfer, Fortune and Forrest have in no way vanished.

Large parts of the USSR are virtually closed off; China, including Tibet, is only just beginning to re-open; the Middle East and large areas of Africa and Latin America remain unsettled, and the conflict in Afghanistan could prove as great a threat as Rauwolf's terrible Turk or Farrer's White Wolves. There are other obstacles too.

The expenses of mounting a worthwhile expedition have increased sharply over the years. Few individuals can afford to finance even a small group of collectors and, if a syndicate is formed to share the cost, the organisation problems soon become formidable.

Two hundred years ago an expedition such as Captain Cook's, on which Banks travelled as official botanist, was part of the struggle for naval supremacy, and was expected to lead to discoveries of new plants of economic value. Botany, in short, was part of the spin-off of imperial progress.

Today the opportunities for new discoveries are more limited than formerly for, if all the land surface of the globe has not yet been fully explored, it has nevertheless been more or less effectively annexed. The concern of governments and that of private sponsors too is directed not so much towards discovering and exploiting new plants, as towards conserving those that are already in existence.

Nature reserves of all kinds – in deserts, mountains, swamps, jungles and pine forests, are protected not only because of the plants that grow there, but because an undisturbed habitat shelters wild animals of the kind that draw free-spending tourists. Some botanists, too, might be discouraged by the fact that the microscope and the test tube of the researcher seem to have become almost more important than the botanist's vasculum or the plastic bag in which his specimens are now collected. Yet, at heart, all gardeners are plant hunters – even if only at flower shows, or at the winter fireside, in the pages of flower catalogues, and it is safe to predict that plant hunting of a kind will always continue.

For example, in this century, the names of Frank Ludlow and George Sherriff are as indissolubly linked as those of Gilbert and Sullivan (for whom Ludlow had an undying admiration).

Between 1933 and 1947, Ludlow and Sherriff, who, throughout 20 years close acquaintanceship never came to use Christian names, undertook at least seven major expeditions, working gradually eastwards along the Himalayas in Tibet and Bhutan.

Ludlow was the more academic of the two. He had taught English and biology at Sind College, Karachi, and became headmaster of the school at Gyantse for élite Tibetans. In 1942 he was appointed British Resident at Lhasa. George ('Geordie') Sherriff, on the other hand was an artilleryman who had fought – and suffered from gas poisoning – in the First World War. But he made an almost complete recovery, and fought with distinction against the Tribes on the North West Frontier, and later in Assam. In 1943 he succeeded Ludlow in Lhasa.

Neither man found exploration in the twentieth century very much easier than it had been in

Hooker's day. There were leeches that crawled through the lace-holes of one's boots, bullocks that smashed precious flower-presses against tree-trunks, there were flies, there was mist, there was rain, and there was the sadzi-sadzi system of transport which meant that your team of baggage animals would carry you only as far as the next village, at which point the luggage had to be unloaded and transferred to a new team. Ludlow felt sure that most of the people who told him how much they would love to come flower hunting would turn for home before the expedition had left the last sizeable Tibetan town and Sherriff gave some confirmation to this view when he declared that curry was the solution to the traveller's needs in Tibet and added, 'If you don't like curry, then God help you'.

Most, but by no means all, of the discoveries by this team have been ascribed to Sherriff who is credited with 27 new primulas, 38 new saxifrages and 23 new gentians. He discovered *Meconopsis grandis*, the species with six-inch deep blue flowers and re-discovered *Meconopsis superba* which had not been seen since 1884.

His *Cyananthus sherriffii*, a bright blue rock-garden campanula, is still in cultivation, and when he finally retired to Kirriemuir, in eastern Scotland, he was successful in introducing that most striking plant, the sky blue *Corydalis cashmeriana*.

Lilium sherriffii, with tessellated yellow and brown flowers, was first spotted by Betty Sherriff on one of the expeditions which followed her marriage to Sherriff.

Sherriff was an excellent camera-man and was one of the first explorers to take colour photographs of his finds in their natural surroundings – despite the fact that the early colour film he was using in 1937 sometimes called for exposures lasting from 10 to 15 minutes. He developed his own films, usually overnight with equipment which he carried in the field.

Those who would like to travel, so to speak, as co-opted members of the Ludlow-Sherriff expedition should buy or borrow *A Quest of Flowers* by Harold R. Fletcher, which contains extracts of the diaries of the two men together with some of their original photographs both in colour and black and white.

Other post Second World War explorers in and around the Himalayas include L.H.J. Williams whose *Primula aureata* from Nepal flowered for the first time in this country in 1955. J.D.A. Stainton produced the red form of *Meconopsis regia*.

Oleg Polunin who collected with Williams and Sykes in 1952 found *Clematis phlebantha*, a new species with silvery leaves and white perianth.

Patrick M. Synge broke new ground, so to speak, when he went travelling among the giant senecios and other monstrous plants in the Mountains of the Moon in central Africa, and wrote an entertaining account of his journey.

Nearer home, Rear-Admiral Paul Furse, who retired from the Royal Navy in 1960, promptly took off in his Land Rover, the Rose of Persia, for the Middle East. With his wife Polly, he visited Turkey and Iran in 1962 and Turkey, Iran and Badakhshan – that part of Afghanistan nearest the Russian border – in 1964. A further expedition to Afghanistan followed in 1966. Furse, who died in 1978, was a good photographer and competent painter. He specialised in new tulips, Juno irises, fritillaries, and those recently popularised alpines, the dionysias. Brian Mathew, too, has specialised in fritillaries in Greece and Turkey and introduced *F. michailovskyi*, with dark purplish brown golden-tipped flowers, to Britain for the first time as well as a new crocus, *C. antalyensis* from Southern Anatolia.

A new garlic, *Allium mirum*, with a golf-ball head of white, green and mauve flowers was found by Per

Wendelbo and Ian Hedge during their expedition to Iran and Afghanistan in 1962.

Other visitors to Afghanistan in the 1970s included a joint expedition by Brigadier Brian Archibald, Christopher Grey-Wilson and Professor T.F. Hewer – though this by no means exhausts the list of Asiatic and Levantine searchers.

In Europe, Colonel Collingwood Ingram, nicknamed 'Cherry' Ingram because of his researches into the prunus family, is credited with *Cytisus ingramii*, bi-coloured with brown, a plant which he discovered in Spain in 1936, and with *Cistus palhinhaii* with solitary pure white flowers and dark green glossy leaves, which he found six years later growing on Cape St Vincent.

It would not be surprising if, at this point, someone were to ask, 'But do we really need so many new species?'

One answer to this would be that, as long as mankind is possessed by curiosity, and a desire for novelty, there will always be a demand for 'unusual' species. *Rosa rouletti*, a miniature rose only three to four inches high and hardy out of doors is one instance of highly unusual variety discovered by chance and developed into a plant now widely known and treasured by gardeners. It had been cultivated for generations as a window plant in the Swiss village of Mauborget overlooking the Lake of Neuchateal, and was noticed there by a Major Roulet of the Swiss Federal Army during the First World War when Switzerland, though neutral, was very much on the alert. Roulet was not able to revisit Mauborget until the war was over, and when he did so, he found that all the chalets where the rose had been grown had been pulled down except one. He secured what plants were left, and took them to the Henri Correvon nursery, one of the world's most famous centres for rock plants, near Geneva. There the rose was successfully propagated and became one of the world's favourites. Surely nothing would have been gained if Major Roulet had followed a laissez-faire policy of benign neglect?

Similarly, there was the case of the British nurseryman who looked over the hedge of a village doctor's garden and saw a drift of *Schizostylis coccinea*, the kaffir Lily, which, instead of scarlet flowers, had blooms of a clear pink. It was developed into the variety known as Mrs Blanche Hegarty, noted for its early flowering quality. Would it have been better if the hedge had grown too high to be seen over?

Where should we be if *Delonix regia*, the Flamboyant Tree, now reduced in the wild to a single colony in a limestone gorge in Madagascar, had been allowed to die out instead of being cultivated far and wide? And was it wrong to shoot the wild pigs on the Three Kings Island to the north of New Zealand in 1946 in order to save the creamy white trumpets of *Tecomanthe speciosa*?

Rather different arguments are advanced in favour of introducing new species which are not novelties, and do not differ very much from other similar ones already in cultivation. In this case, however, what matters is not novelty but vigour. For although we may regard the species we know as permanently established, they are mortal – like the traditional vines of France that were attacked in the last century by the scourge of the *phylloxera* aphis.

For the truth is that new species of virus evolve and are perfected in the same manner as in plants by the survival of the fittest, and in the case of the virus, such changes can take place far more quickly than the plant can develop new immunity. In fact only species which are already immune to the attacks of a new type of virus may be able to survive.

The American agricultural botanist, Harry V. Harlan, summed up the matter effectively in his book, *One man's life with Barley*, when he wrote, 'Tucked away in the hills of China or Nepal there may be a barley that could one day save the crop of Montana from a disease we have never seen. This barley may be gone tomorrow.'

But, apart from new species, explorers will be needed to bring back plants that are already known to be desirable but which have been lost, or have become uncomfortably scarce. 'Old' plants sent for in recent times include *Cyclamen alpinum* with bright carmine flowers bearing a purplish black spot at the base of the petals, which was introduced here as far back as 1892. This and *C. pseudoibericum* have been brought back lately from Turkey by Dr Peter Davis. The white-flowered *Camellia granthamiama*, discovered on the slopes of Shing Mung in the New Territories of Hong Kong in 1955, was at one time reduced to a single bush. Others were needed before it could come into general cultivation. The same goes for another Hong Kong species, *Camellia crapnelliana*, of which a single plant was found in 1903. No others were rediscovered till 1965, when an alert forester noted an unusual plant almost completely hidden in a hillside thicket.

Many other splendid plants formerly cultivated and lost for one reason or another, could be reintroduced as new species in the sense that no living gardeners would have previously seen them in cultivation.

Certainly the expertise – the knowledge for example, that some seeds will germinate only if left on the surface of the ground, whereas others need to be first frozen and then thawed – is more widely shared than ever before, and there would be fewer failures than in the past. Explorers who know how to write, now describe the plants as seen in their native haunts more fully, and their colour photographs, though often wanting in botanical detail, show the plants where they grow and are far more inspiring than any seed packet.

Today it is possible for amateurs who wish to

grow a particularly rare or uncommon plant to put a notice in *The Garden*, the journal of the Royal Horticultural Society, and from time to time, the results achieved in cultivating new discoveries are recorded there. There is thus every encouragement for plantsmen to persist with new plants.

But it does not do to be too complacent. Nurserymen today, with some praiseworthy exceptions, tend to concentrate on a few chosen families of plants instead of offering a wide selection of species for which the demand might be fitful, and the more commercially minded plantsmen tend to devote themselves mainly to those plants that look good and can be easily marketed in those small black plastic containers which make it unnecessary for a grower to pre-empt a large acreage of ground. Nurseries that specialise in flowers for cutting tend to go for a species that can be easily packed and will travel well, rather than for those of outstanding beauty. All this limits ones choice of plants.

Out of doors, there is a distinct leaning towards economy, and no signs of a successor to Miss Ellen Ann Willmott who kept a staff of 104 to tend the rose garden, the water garden, the palm garden and the orchid houses on her estate at Warley Place, near Brentford, Essex; a Swiss gardener, Jacob Maurer, was imported specially to watch over her alpines. Understandably there is a current demand for plants that are known to be hardy, easily maintained and free-flowering over a long period. Perennials are preferred to biennials or annuals – despite the 'instant flowers' appeal of the latter, and flowering shrubs are often preferred to herbaceous plants.

Indoors, the gardener's choice is often a second best. Thus as fuel becomes more expensive, the trend is away from the more striking stove plants and towards those that can be grown in a cool greenhouse and do not require automatic moisture or light control – or perhaps can even be grown in a corner of the living room. There is a surge towards miniaturisation. There are tower pots, that is pots fitted one on top of another, pillar-fashion so that, although they take up almost no floor space, a plant can be grown in each; there are Wardian cases reproduced in Victorian gothic style; there are coffee-table-size jardinières in which not only cacti but more spectacular plants can be grown; and there are bottle gardens. And when all is said and done the owner of a small garden, be it window ledge, a miniature Tufa rock garden or patio can afford to spend more on the plants grown in it, than if he had an acre or two.

There will be new hybrids, too, to tempt the gardener. Many of these will be derived from species that are already popular, and are supported by specialist societies as in the case of orchids, chrysanthemums, delphiniums, narcissi and the like, but there have been striking successes among the less generally cultivated species, such as the hemerocallis, now available in purple, maroon, brick red, and pink cultivars. Some new varieties will be achieved through pollen mutation induced by exposing the germ cells to X-rays or to ultra-violet radiation. Other improved hybrids will be launched with the help of colchicine, an extract from the colchicum plant, which inhibits the formation of new cell walls in the sex cells at the time when the chromosomes divide, so that each cell can have twice the normal number of chromosomes and thus develops more rapidly and vigorously.

Strenuous efforts are now being made, in the interests of both nurserymen and bewildered amateurs, to systematise the world of hybrids. National and international bodies, some with statutory backing, are now responsible for accepting (or refusing) the registrations and names of newly cultivated varieties of certain genera such as roses, and for providing protection for growers of approved cultivars of which details have been validly published. In Britain, the Seeds Act of 1964 entitles growers of such varieties to claim royalties on the sale of a new cultivar which has been duly approved. Application for protection of new varieties of certain plants, notably cymbidium, dahlia, delphinium, fuchsia, lilium, pelargonium, rhododendron and rosa, can be made to the Plant Variety Rights Office in Cambridge.

Yet hybridisation, despite all that we know about genetics, remains an uncertain art, and therefore costly to both grower and consumer. There is always a chance that some insect will manage to infiltrate and disrupt the breeding plans of a nursery so that a whole crop has to be destroyed. There is also an inherent risk that what scientists call 'inbreeding depression' will seriously affect a particular strain.

Or a hybrid may breed true, yet turn out to be especially vulnerable to some virus. The same risk can occur with successive generations of plants obtained from a single parent through cuttings or divisions, and might well occur with artificially induced mutation species especially if they were self-fertilising.

Not surprisingly, these potential hazards have led some gardeners to ponder how far it is to our advantage in the long run to rely so much on hybrids and cultivars as a source of future garden plants. For if, as we have seen, not even species which have weathered the centuries are immortal, how much less durable in all probability are hybrids?

It would theoretically be possible to establish public seed banks through which the seeds of the more traditional species would be distributed for growing in 'Species Only' gardens. But this might amount to merely putting back the clock. For the orchids, the lilies and other plants with vivid colours and fragrant scents that we love to cultivate, may not really be the advanced plants we might imagine, but complicated and potentially obsolescent species, since most of them depend on the existence of insects (or birds, bats, beetles or other animals) to pollinate them. The plants with a future are, we are told, the duller ones with catkins, which need only the wind to act as their pollinating agent. So a species flower garden, however pure in thought could be criticised as reactionary and artificial.

But then, as Rousseau pointed out, all gardeners are practitioners of the artificial. We condone unreality in our plants as well as in our gardens. We cultivate the extremes and the freaks. We cherish those varieties of plants that would be least able to protect themselves in the wild, including those that flower early before insects would be ready to pollinate them. We praise the rose without a thorn, and encourage the double flowers which, because they have more petals and fewer anthers, would have less chance of survival in the world at large, than their single-minded relatives.

Cyclamen pseudoibericum, recently brought back from Turkey by Dr Peter Davis

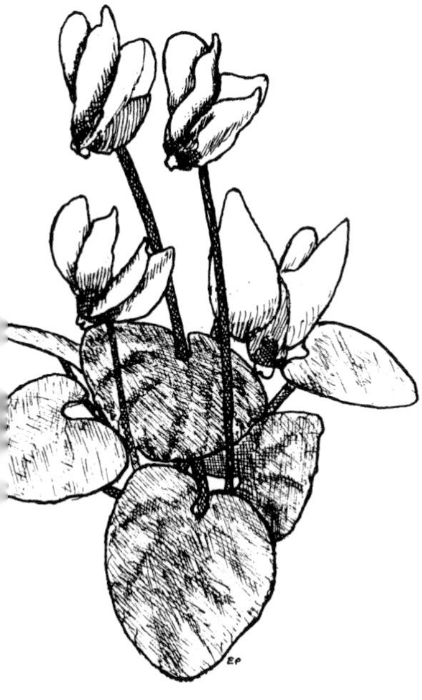

But let us not be discouraged about the plants to which our devotion has been pledged. The non-progressive flowering species whose origins have been the main concern of this book, may not be so obsolete after all, for their relationship with man could be regarded as akin to symbiosis, that is, a form of co-existence in which two different organisms living side by side, like *mycorrhiza* among the roots of the orchid, derive mutual benefit from their intimate association, and we can feel entitled to assume that, as long as certain flowering plants continue to fascinate gardeners, they will have protectors and promoters more effective than any number of birds, bats, flies or beetles. Indeed, in the long run, their future may be more assured than their past.

Bibliography

Reference books

No one investigating the history of garden plants can progress far without wanting to refer to the Royal Horticultural Society's *Dictionary of Gardening* published in four volumes (1956) with a Supplement (1969) by the Clarendon Press.

Those in search of colour can turn with benefit to the *Dictionary of Garden Plants in Colour* by Roy Hay and Patrick Synge and to the *Reader's Digest Encyclopaedia of Garden Plants and Flowers* edited by Roy Hay and K. Beckett, the latter with 2,500 colour photographs.

Select Bibliography

AITON, WILLIAM TOWNSEND, *Hortus Kewensis*, Longman, Hurst, Rees, Orme & Brown, 1810

ALLAN, MEA, *Darwin and his Flowers*, Faber & Faber, 1977

– *The Gardener's Book of Weeds*, Macdonald, 1978

– *The Hookers of Kew*, Michael Joseph, 1967

– *Plants that Changed our Gardens*, David & Charles, 1974

– *The Tradescants*, Michael Joseph, 1964

AMHERST, ALICIA M., *History of Gardening in England*, Bernard Quaritch, 1896

ANDERSON, A.W, *The Coming of the Flowers*, Williams & Norgate, 1950

ARBER, AGNES, *Herbals, their Origin and Evolution*, Cambridge University Press, 1953

ATTENBOROUGH, DAVID, *Life on Earth*, Collins/BBC, 1979

BACKHOUSE, JAMES, *A Narrative of a Visit to the Australian Colonies*, Hamilton Adams, 1843

BANKS, SIR JOSEPH, *Banks' Florilegium* (taken from the original engravings, hand coloured), Editions Alecto (34 parts), 1980–

– *Journal of the Rt. Hon Sir Joseph Banks* (ed. Sir Joseph Hooker), Macmillan, 1896

BLAIKIE, THOMAS, *Diary of a Scotch Gardener at the French Court*, George Routledge, 1931

BLUNT, WILFRID, *The Art of Botanical Illustration*, Collins, 1971
– *The Compleat Naturalist: A Life of Linnaeus*, Collins, 1971
– *Tulipomania*, Penguin, 1950
BOYLE, FREDERICK, *About Orchids*, Chapman & Hall, 1893
BOWLES, E.A., *My Garden in Spring*, T.C. & E.C. Jack, 1914
BRETSCHNEIDER, E., *History of European Botanical Discoveries in China*, Sampson, Low, Marston & Co., 1898
BRETT-JAMES, *Life of Peter Collinson*, Edgar Dunston & Co., 1925
BRIGGS, D. AND WALTERS, S.M., *Plant Variation and Evolution*, World University Library, 1969
BROWN, ROBERT, *Prodromus Florae Novae Hollandiae*, 1810
BURBIDGE, F.W., *Gardens of the Sun*, John Murray, 1880
CALMANN, GERTA, *Ehret, Flower-Painter Extraordinary*, Phaidon, 1977
CAMERON, H.C., *Sir Joseph Banks*, Angus & Robertson, 1966
CARRINGTON, RICHARD, *A Guide to Earth History*, Chatto & Windus, 1967
CATESBY, MARK, *Hortus Europae Americanus*, 1767
CHADWICK, GEORGE F., *The Works of Sir Joseph Paxton*, The Architectural Press, 1961
COATS, ALICE M., *The Quest for Plants*, Studio Vista, London, 1969
– *The Book of Flowers*, Phaidon, 1973
– *Flowers and their Histories*, Adam & Charles Black, 1968
COLES, WILLIAM, *Adam in Eden or Nature's Paradise*, Nathaniel Brooke, 1657
COWAN, J. MACQUEEN (ED.), *Journeys and Plant Introductions of George Forrest*, Oxford University Press for Royal Horticultural Society, 1952
COX, E.H.M., *Farrer's Last Journey*, Dulau, 1926
– *The Plant Introductions of Reginald Farrer*, New Flora & Silva, London, 1930
CRANE, M.B., AND LAWRENCE, W.J.C., *The Genetics of Garden Plants*, Macmillan, 1938
CROSSLEY, FREDERICK, *The English Abbey – Its Life and Work in the Middle Ages*, Batsford, 1949
CULPEPER, NICHOLAS, *Compleat Herbal*, W. Foulsham & Co., 1649
DARWIN, CHARLES, *Autobiography* (ed. Francis Darwin), Dover Publications (reprint), 1958

DENT, ALAN, *The World of Shakespeare: Plants*, Osprey, 1971

DICKINSON, J.C., *Monastic Life in Mediaeval England*, Adam & Charles Black, 1961

DILLINGHAM, WM. H., *A Tribute to the Memory of Peter Collinson*, Henry Longstreth, Philadelphia, 1853

DIMBLEBY, GEOFFREY, *Plants and Archaeology*, John Baker, 1967

DOUGLAS, DAVID, *Journal during his Travels in North America 1823–1827*, William Wesley, 1914

DOWDEN, ANNE O., *Shakespeare's Flowers*, Kestrel Books, 1969

DREWITT, F. DAWTREY, *The Romance of the Apothecaries Garden at Chelsea*, Cambridge University Press, 1928

EARNEST, ERNEST, *John and William Bartram*, University of Pennsylvania Press, 1940

EDMEADES, ROBERT, *The Gentleman and Lday's* [sic] *Gardener (Catalogue)*, Private printing, 1776

ELLACOMBE, HENRY N., *In a Gloucestershire Garden*, Edward Arnold, 1895

– *In my Vicarage Garden & Elsewhere*, John Lane, 1902

FARRER, REGINALD, *My Rock Garden*, Edward Arnold, 1907

– *On the Eaves of the World*, Edward Arnold, 1917

FLETCHER, HAROLD R., *The Story of the Royal Horticultural Society*, Oxford University Press for the Royal Horticultural Society, 1969

– *A Quest of Flowers*, Edinburgh University Press,

FORTUNE, ROBERT, *Visit to the Tea Districts of China and India*, John Murray, 1852

– *A Journey to the Capitals of Japan and China*, John Murray, 1863

– *Three Years' Wanderings in the Northern Provinces of China*, John Murray, 1847

– *A Residence among the Chinese*, John Murray, 1857

FOX, HELEN M. (TRANSL. & ED.), *Abbé David's Diary*, Harvard University Press, 1949

– *André le Nôtre*, Batsford, 1962

FOX, DR HINGSTON, *Dr. John Fothergill and his Friends*, Macmillan, 1919

FRICK, GEORGE FREDERICK, AND STEARNS, RAYMOND PHINEAS, *Mark Catesby*, University of Illinois Press, 1961

GAUNT, WILLIAM, *Chelsea*, Batsford, 1954

GENDERS, ROY, *Collecting Antique Plants*, Pelham Books, 1971

– *The Cottage Garden*, Pelham Books, 1969

GERARD, JOHN, *Herball or General Historie of Plantes*, John Norton, 1597

GORER, RICHARD, *The Flower Garden in England*, Batsford, 1975

– *The Development of Garden Flowers*, Eyre & Spottiswoode, 1970

– *The Growth of Gardens*, Faber & Faber, 1978

GREEN, DAVID, *Gardener to Queen Anne*, Oxford University Press, 1956

GUNTHER, R.T., *Early British Botanists & their Gardens*, Oxford University Press, 1922

– *Oxford Gardens – based on Daubeny's Popular Guide to the Physick Garden of Oxford*, Parker & Son, 1912

HADFIELD, MILES, *Gardening in Britain*, Hutchinson, 1960

HANMER, SIR THOMAS, *The Garden Book of Sir Thomas Hanmer* (1659), Gerald Howe, 1933

HARPER, FRANCIS, *The Travels of William Bartram*, Yale University Press, 1958

HARRIS, JOHN (ED.), *A Celebration of One Thousand Years of British Gardening*, Mitchell Beazley in association with New Perspectives Publishing Ltd., 1979

HARVEY, JOHN, *Early Gardening Catalogues*, Phillimore, 1972

– *Early Nurserymen*, Phillimore, 1974

HAWORTH-BOOTH, MICHAEL, *The Moutan or Tree Paeony*, Constable, 1963

HELLYER, ARTHUR, *The Shell Guide to Gardens*, Heinemann, 1977

HULTON, PAUL, AND SMITH, LAWRENCE, *Flowers in Art*, British Museum Publications, 1979

HULTON, PAUL, *The Work of Jacques le Moyne de Morgues*, British Museum Publications, 1977

HUTCHINSON, JOHN, *A Botanist in South Africa*, P.R. Gawthorn, 1946

HUXLEY, L., *The Life and Letters of Sir J.D. Hooker*, John Murray, 1918

INGWERSEN, WILL (ILL. CHARLES STITT), *Classic Garden Plants*, Hamlyn Publishing Group, 1975

INTERNATIONAL BUREAU FOR PLANT TAXONOMY & NOMENCLATURE, *International Code of Nomenclature of Cultivated Plants*, I.B.P.T.N., 1969 & 1980

JEKYLL, GERTRUDE, *Colour in the Flower Garden*, Country Life & George Newnes, 1908

– *Wall and Water Gardens*, Country Life & George Newnes, 1901

JOHNSON, A.T., & SMITH, H.A., *Plant Names Simplified*, Collingridge (London), Transatlantic Arts (NY), 1964

KAEMPFER, ENGELBERT (TR. J.G. SCHEUCHZER), *History of Japan (1690–1692)*, James MacLehose & Son, Glasgow, 1906

KING, RONALD, *The World of Kew*, Macmillan, 1976

KINGDON-WARD, FRANCIS, *Plant Hunting in the Wilds*, Figurehead, London, 1931

– *Assam Adventure*, Jonathan Cape, 1941

– *A Plant Hunter in Tibet*, Jonathan Cape, 1934

– *The Mystery Rivers of Tibet*, Seeley Service, 1923

LANGHAM, WILLIAM, *The Garden of Health*, Thomas Harper, 1579

LAWRENCE W.J.C., AND CRANE, M.B., *The Genetics of Garden Plants*, Macmillan, 1938

LEIGHTON, ANN, *American Gardens in the Eighteenth Century*, Houghton Mifflin, Boston, 1976

LEMMON, KENNETH, *The Golden Age of Plant Hunters*, Phoenix House, 1968

LOUDON, J.C., *The Encyclopaedia of Gardening*, Longman, Rees, Orme, Brown & Green, 1828

MCCLINTOCK, DAVID, *Companion to Flowers*, G. Bell & Sons, 1966

MASSINGHAM, BETTY, *Miss Jekyll*, Country Life, 1966

MATTHEWS, J.R., *The Origin and Distribution of the British Flora*, Hutchinson's University Library, 1955

MILLICAN, ALBERT, *The Adventures of an Orchid Hunter*, Cassell, 1891

MITCHELL, PETER, *European Flower Painters*, Adam & Charles Black, 1973

NORTH, C., *Plant Breeding and Genetics in Horticulture*, Macmillan Press, 1979

NORTH, MARIANNE, *A Vision of Eden* (abridged from her journals and autobiography by Graham Bateman), Webb & Bower in collaboration with The Royal Botanic Gardens, Kew, 1980

PARKINSON, JOHN, *Paradisi in Sole Paradisus Terrestris* (1629), Methuen (reprint), 1904

PENNINGTON, WINIFRED, *The History of British Vegetation*, English Universities Press, 1974

PRAEGER, ROBERT LLOYD, *The Botanist in Ireland*, Hodges Figgis & Co., Dublin, 1934

PRESTON, F.G., *The Greenhouse*, Ward Lock & Co., 1964

RAY, JOHN, *Historia Plantarum*, 1686–1704

– *A Collection of Curious Travels and Voyages* (tr. from High Dutch), Nicholas Staphorst, 1693

REINIKKA, MERLE A., *A History of the Orchid*, University of Miami Press, 1972

REPTON, HUMPHRY, *Fragments on Landscape Gardening*, 1816

– *Observations on the Theory and Practice of Landscape Gardening*, 1803

– *An Inquiry into the Changes of Taste in Landscape Gardening*, 1806

ROBINSON, WILLIAM, *The Wild Garden* (4th edition), John Murray, 1894

– *The English Flower Garden*, John Murray, 1956

ROHDE, ELEANOUR SINCLAIR, *Old English Gardening Books*, Martin Hopkinson, 1924

– *The Story of the Garden*, Medici Society, 1932

ROYAL HORTICULTURAL SOCIETY, *Wisley: The First Hundred Years*, Royal Horticultural Society, 1978

SALISBURY, SIR EDWARD, *Weeds and Aliens*, Collins, 1964

SCOTT-JAMES, ANNE (ILL. OSBERT LANCASTER), *The Pleasure Garden*, Penguin Books, 1979

SEEBOHM, M.E., *The Evolution of the English Farm*, E.P. Publishing Company, 1976

SIREN, OSVALD, *China and the Gardens of Europe in the Eighteenth Century*, The Ronald Press Co., New York, 1950

SMITH, H.A., AND JOHNSON, A.T., *Plant Names Simplified*, Collingridge (London), Transatlantic Arts (NY), 1964

SMITH, LAWRENCE & HULTON, PAUL, *Flowers in Art*, British Museum Publications, 1979

STATIONERY OFFICE, H.M., for the Dept. of Education and Science, *Taxonomy in Britain*, H.M.S.O., 1977

STEARN, WILLIAM T., *Botanical Latin – History, Grammar, Syntax, Terminology and Vocabulary*, David & Charles, 1973

STEARNS, RAYMOND PHINEAS, AND FRICK, G.F., *Mark Catesby*, University of Illinois Press, 1961

STERN, F.C., *Study of the Genus Paeonia*, Royal Horticultural Society, 1946

SUMMERHAYES, V.S., *Wild Orchids of Britain*, Collins, 1969

SWINNERTON, H.H., *Fossils*, Collins, 1970

SYNGE, PATRICK M., *Plants with Personality*, Lindsay Drummond, 1948

– *In Search of Flowers*, Michael Joseph, 1973

– *Lilies*, Batsford/R.H.S., 1980

– *Mountains of the Moon*, Lindsay Drummond, 1937

TREVELYAN, G.M., *English Social History*, Longmans Green (reprint), 1948

TROW-SMITH, ROBERT, *English Husbandry from the Earliest Times*, Faber & Faber, 1951

VEITCH, JAMES H., *Hortus Veitchii – the History of the Nurseries* (printed for private circulation), 1906

WALKER, D., AND WEST R.G. (EDS.), *Studies in the Vegetational History of the British Isles: Essays in Honour of Harry Godwin*, Cambridge University Press, 1970

WALTERS, S.M., AND BRIGGS, D., *Plant Variation and Evolution*, World University Library, 1969

WEST, R.G., AND WALKER, D., *Studies in the Vegetational History of the British Isles: Essays in Honour of Harry Godwin*, Cambridge University Press, 1970

WHITE, K.D., *Roman Farming*, Thames & Hudson, 1970

WILLSON, MISS E.J., *James Lee and the Vineyard Nursery, Hammersmith*, Hammersmith Local History Group, 1961

WILSON, ERNEST HENRY, *A Naturalist in Western China*, Methuen, 1913

– *Plant Hunting*, The Stratford Co., Boston, 1927

Index

Numbers in *italics* refer to illustrations